CHILDCRAFT

THE GROWING CHILD

Photographed in natural color especially for *Childcraft* by the Zylstra-Raymond Studios

THE GROWING CHILD

A happy environment, in which good books play a part, is the treasured inheritance of today's child.

CHILDCRAFT

IN · FOURTEEN · VOLUMES

VOLUME SEVEN

THE GROWING CHILD

INTRODUCTION BY
PATTY SMITH HILL, LL.D.
PROFESSOR OF EDUCATION, TEACHERS COLLEGE
COLUMBIA UNIVERSITY

THE QUARRIE CORPORATION
CHICAGO

CHILDCRAFT

CONTRIBUTORS

ALLEN, ELSA G., PH.D.
Instructor in Ornithology, Cornell University
BIRDS
GARDEN FLOWERS
WILD FLOWERS

BALL, RACHEL STUTSMAN, PH.D.
Formerly in charge of Instruction in the Psychology of Mental Tests and Head of Research in Psychology, Merrill-Palmer School, Detroit
MANNERS AND COURTESY

BANNON, LAURA
Supervisor of the Saturday School Junior Department, Art Institute of Chicago
ART SECTION OF VOLUME THIRTEEN

BLANKMEYER, RUTH M., M.A.
Supervisor of Art, Oak Park, Ill.
HANDWORK EXPERIENCE SECTION OF VOLUME THIRTEEN

BLOUGH, GLENN O., M.A.
Instructor in Science, Laboratory Schools, University of Chicago
SCIENCE IN VOLUME NINE
SCIENCE SECTION OF VOLUME FOURTEEN

BROWNELL, WILLIAM A., PH.D.
Professor of Educational Psychology, Duke University
ARITHMETIC

BRUBAKER, MIRIAM H., M.A.
Demonstration Teacher and College Instructor, National College of Education
THE KINDERGARTEN AND THE CHILD

CAMPBELL, ELISE H., M.A.
Instructor in Social Work, Wayne University
MANNERS AND COURTESY

CARPENTER, ROWENA SCHMIDT, M.A.
Assistant Chief, Foods and Nutrition Division, Bureau of Home Economics, United States Department of Agriculture
FOOD AND NUTRITION

COLEMAN, SATIS N., PH.D.
Music Investigator, Lincoln School, and Instructor, Teachers College, Columbia University
MUSIC SECTION OF VOLUME THIRTEEN

CROFOOT, IRENE B., B.S.
Kindergarten Instructor, Brookside School Cranbrook, Bloomfield Hills, Mich.
ART IN VOLUME NINE

CUTHBERT, MARGARET
Director, Women's Activities for National Broadcasting Company; formerly supervisor of Children's Sustaining Programs for NBC.
CHILDREN AND RADIO

DALGLIESH, ALICE, M.A.
Author; Editor; formerly Instructor in Children's Literature, Teachers College, Columbia University
STORYTELLING

DUSHKIN, DAVID
Graduate, École Normale in Paris; Director, Dushkin School of Music, Winnetka, Ill.
MAKING MUSICAL INSTRUMENTS

EDSON, NEWELL W., A.B.
Executive Secretary, Erie (Penn.) Social Hygiene Association
SEX IN THE YOUNG CHILD'S LIFE

FALK, ETHEL MABIE, PH.B.
Formerly Supervisor, Department of Curriculum and Method, Madison, Wis., Public Schools
LANGUAGE

FORMAN, HENRY JAMES, A.B.
Editor and Author
CHILDREN AND MOTION PICTURES

GAMBRILL, BESSIE LEE, PH.D.
Associate Professor of Elementary Education, Yale University
THE CHILD WHO IS DIFFERENT

GARDNER, ELLA, A.B.
Recreation Specialist, Extension Service, United States Department of Agriculture
INDOOR AND OUTDOOR GAMES

GOODENOUGH, FLORENCE L., PH.D.
Research Professor, Institute of Child Welfare, University of Minnesota
CHARACTER DEVELOPMENT

GRUENBERG, BENJAMIN C., PH.D.
Educator, Author, and Editor
CHILDREN AND MONEY

GRUENBERG, SIDONIE M.
Director, Child Study Association of America; Lecturer, Parent Education, New York University
CHILDREN AND MONEY

v

HARDY, MARJORIE, M.A.
Kindergarten-Primary Principal, Germantown Friends School, Philadelphia
READING

HARTWELL, SAMUEL W., M.D.
Professor of Psychiatry, University of Buffalo Medical School; Director, Buffalo Child Guidance Clinic
EMOTIONAL PROBLEMS OF CHILDREN

HEINIG, CHRISTINE M., M.A.
Principal, Kindergarten Training College, Melbourne, Australia; Educational Director, Australian Association for Preschool Child Development
THE NURSERY SCHOOL AND THE CHILD

HILDRETH, GERTRUDE, PH.D.
Psychologist, Lincoln School, Teachers College, Columbia University
AGE SCALE OF MENTAL DEVELOPMENT

HORN, ERNEST, PH.D.
Professor of Education and Director University Elementary School, State University of Iowa
SPELLING

JOËL, WALTHER, PH.D.
Instructor in Psychology, Los Angeles City College
PARENTS' RATING SCALE

LANGDON, GRACE, PH.D.
Specialist, Family Life Education, Education Division, Works Progress Administration
RIGHT AND WRONG FORMS OF AFFECTION

LEONARD, EDITH M., M.A.
Director Early Childhood Education, Santa Barbara State College, Santa Barbara, Calif.
COLOR HARMONY AND TASTE IN DRESS
COOKING AND SEWING
JOLLY ACTION JINGLES
CREATIVE PLAYS AND FESTIVALS
THINGS TO MAKE AT HOME

MADDOX, EDITH E., M.A.
Late Director of the Kindergarten and Instructor in Nursery School and Kindergarten Education, National College of Education
PARTIES AND HOLIDAYS

McCLOY, CHARLES H., PH.D.
Research Professor of Anthropometry and Physical Education, State University of Iowa
POSTURE

McKAY, IDA H., M.A.
Formerly Associate Professor of Speech, Michigan State Normal College, Ypsilanti
SPEECH DEFECTS

MILES, LILLIAN E.
Board of Education, San Bernardino, Calif.
COLOR HARMONY AND TASTE IN DRESS
COOKING AND SEWING
JOLLY ACTION JINGLES
CREATIVE PLAYS AND FESTIVALS
THINGS TO MAKE AT HOME

NELSON, FLORENCE
Writer; formerly Editor *Safety Education*
SAFETY IN THE HOME

OBERNDORFER, ANNE F.
Author; Lecturer on Music
MUSIC IN VOLUME NINE

PERSING, ELLIS C., M.S.
Assistant Professor of Elementary Science, School of Education, Western Reserve University; author of science readers for children
EXPERIMENTS IN ELEMENTARY SCIENCE
SKY AND WEATHER

PHILLIPS, MARY GEISLER, B.S.
Editor of College Bulletins, New York State College of Home Economics, Cornell University; author of nature books for children
DOMESTIC ANIMALS
INSECTS
SPIDERS AND THEIR KIN

PICKWELL, GAYLE, PH.D.
Professor of Zoology, San Jose State College, San Jose, Calif.
WILD FLOWERS (OF THE PACIFIC COAST)

REED, MARY M., PH.D.
Assistant Professor of Education, Teachers College, Columbia University
INDUSTRY SECTION OF VOLUME FOURTEEN
SOCIAL STUDIES

RICHARDSON, FRANK HOWARD, M.D.
Pediatrician, Children's Clinic, Black Mountain, N. C.; Vice-Dean, Southern Pediatric Seminar; formerly Consultant, Diseases of Children, New York State Department of Health
EDUCATION FOR PARENTHOOD

ROBERTS, MARGARET MANNING, M.S.
Kindergarten Director, Public Schools, Monrovia, Calif.
DRAMATIC PLAY

Rogers, James F., M.D., Dr.P.H.
Consultant in Hygiene, Office of Education, United States Department of the Interior
BETTER HEALTH

Scott, Carrie E., A.B.
Supervisor of Children's Work, Indianapolis Public Library
SUGGESTED BOOKS FOR OLDER CHILDREN

Scott, Clarice L., M.S.
Assistant Home Economics Specialist in Charge of Clothing, Division of Textiles and Clothing, Bureau of Home Economics, United States Department of Agriculture
CLOTHING

Scott, Esther W., M.A.
Teacher in Charge of Elementary Science and School Gardens, District of Columbia Public Schools
GARDENS

Simpson, Jean H., A.B.
Script Writer, Radio Council, Chicago Public Schools
HOBBIES

Stebbins, Fannie A., F.A.A.A.S.
Formerly Supervisor of Nature Study, Springfield, Mass., Public Schools
FROGS, TOADS, AND SALAMANDERS

Sternau, Helen G., A.B.
Author; Associate Editor, *Child Study,* magazine of the Child Study Association of America
WORK AND PLAY FOR THE PRESCHOOL CHILD

Teagarden, Florence M., Ph.D.
Professor of Psychology, University of Pittsburgh
CHILDREN AND THEIR HABITS

Tooze, Ruth A., A.B.
Special lecturer on selection of children's books, Northwestern University, Summer Session; owner, *The Book Box,* bookstore designed especially for children
A LIBRARY OF 300 TITLES

Troxell, Eleanor, M.A.
Supervisor, Early Elementary Grades, Kalamazoo, Mich., Public Schools
OBEDIENCE AND DISCIPLINE GUIDANCE

Vinal, William G., Ph.D.
Professor of Nature Education and Director Nature Guide School, Massachusetts State College
PETS AND THEIR CARE

Wagoner, Lovisa C., Ph.D.
Chairman Department of Child Development and Principal of the Children's School, Mills College, California
NORMAL RATES OF DEVELOPMENT

Wahlert, Jennie, M.A.
Principal, Jackson School, St. Louis, Mo.
HANDWRITING

Waring, Ethel B., Ph.D.
Professor in Home Economics, New York State College of Home Economics, Cornell University
RIGHT AND WRONG FORMS OF RESPECT

Webb, Hanor A., Ph.D.
Professor of the Teaching of Chemistry and General Science, George Peabody College for Teachers; Editor *Current Science*
TREES

Williams, Lou, B.S., M.S.
Geologist, Pure Oil Company; and author, handbooks for Girl Scouts
LOOKING AT THE STARS

Witmer, Eleanor M., M.A.
Librarian and Associate Professor of Education, Teachers College Library, Columbia University
LITERATURE

Wygant, Elsie A., B.S.
Formerly Instructor, Francis W. Parker School, Chicago
SCHOOLS OF TODAY

Zabriskie, Louise, R.N.
Author; Field Director, Maternity Center Association, New York City
BABY CARE
PLANNED CONVALESCENCE FOR MOTHER AND BABY

INTRODUCTION

D URING a serious family discussion of the future field of service of every member, each child was encouraged to express his or her individual preference. The oldest boy wished to prepare for medicine; one daughter chose art; another, nursing; and so on down the line to a little girl of six, who unblushingly announced, "Oh! I don't want to be anything. I just want to be a mother!"

There have always been certain superficial observers and thinkers who undervalue the ancient profession of motherhood. On the other hand, poets, musicians, and artists throughout the ages have had their creative genius inspired by their conception of motherhood. A few critical thinkers in every generation list parenthood among those professions demanding the highest order of intelligence, knowledge, wisdom, and skill. There are also the sentimentalists of all races who tearfully sing of "Mother, Home, and Heaven" without discriminating between those women who, from the beginning of time, have displayed a sort of unexplainable genius in meeting family problems on a high level of excellence and those women who have entered motherhood with no foresight or later consciousness of the serious responsibility which parenthood involves.

Today there is a widely spread and growing tendency to appreciate the fact that parenthood, like any other profession, occupation, business, or trade, has its own subject matter and techniques which must be earnestly sought and mastered to insure success. A generation or more ago the parents who realized this struggled singlehanded in their search for the knowledge and techniques necessary to successful family life. Dependable information regarding the nature and needs of childhood came into circulation slowly, reaching the teacher in the classroom long before it was placed at the disposal of parents. Today, young men and women entering upon the duties and responsibilities of parenthood are far more fortunate. For example, they now have available in CHILDCRAFT priceless knowledge regarding child care, which capable students of the subject have gathered from extensive research and which is here presented in a practical way.

Fortunately for little children, there has been a recent appeal for parents to *be,* as well as to *know* and *do,* the right thing for their children. You can fool some of the children all the time and all the children some of the time, but in the long run the hypocrisy of teaching and preaching one thing while living the contrary will not go far. Children gradually come to know ús as we *are—not as we want them to believe we are*. They are not only affected by what we know and do but by what we *feel* in our innermost hearts. Sincerity and genuineness are basic influences in all our contacts with children; they must believe in our integrity at any cost. This we breathe out (all unconsciously to ourselves) in our reactions to the personalities and events of daily living. Neither parents nor teachers can walk around children in their "moral slippers." Those who endeavor to embody the ideals they teach have discovered the best and most effective short cut in character education. To live daily with those who *are* honorable, just, generous, tolerant, and kind is a privilege of the highest order. No moral instruction can compare with the effectiveness of example. Froebel said to the mothers of his day:

> Believe that by the good that's in thy mind
> Thy child to good will early be inclined;
> By every noble thought with which thy heart is fired,
> The young child's soul will surely be inspired.

In planning CHILDCRAFT, the publishers, editors, advisers, and authors have worked together in the belief that education is a continuous process, including all those influences and activities which the child experiences every hour in the twenty-four, whether at work or at play, at home or at school, in the city or in the country. With this conception of education in mind the editors and advisers invited experts in the various aspects of child life to contribute articles setting forth their knowledge and experience. The wholehearted response of the authors makes it possible to recommend these volumes to conscientious parents. It is my sincere hope that CHILDCRAFT may go into many homes where eager, earnest parents are reaching out for assistance in the most important educational institution in modern civilization—the home.

PATTY SMITH HILL
Professor of Education
Teachers College, Columbia University

CONTENTS

		PAGE
EDUCATION FOR PARENTHOOD	Frank Howard Richardson	1
FOOD AND NUTRITION	Rowena Schmidt Carpenter	11
BETTER HEALTH	James F. Rogers	45
NORMAL RATES OF DEVELOPMENT	Lovisa C. Wagoner	72
BABY CARE	Louise Zabriskie	91
PLANNED CONVALESCENCE FOR MOTHER AND BABY	Louise Zabriskie	108
WORK AND PLAY FOR THE PRESCHOOL CHILD	Helen G. Sternau	112a
SEX IN THE YOUNG CHILD'S LIFE	Newell W. Edson	113
POSTURE	Charles H. McCloy	129
CLOTHING	Clarice L. Scott	140
COLOR HARMONY AND TASTE IN DRESS	Edith M. Leonard and Lillian E. Miles	164
SAFETY IN THE HOME	Florence Nelson	172
THE NURSERY SCHOOL AND THE CHILD	Christine M. Heinig	190
THE KINDERGARTEN AND THE CHILD	Miriam H. Brubaker	201

EDUCATION FOR PARENTHOOD

FRANK HOWARD RICHARDSON, M. D.

Parenthood is regarded from various points of view—as an obligation, a privilege, an opportunity, a joy, a duty, a blessing. Perhaps there are not enough people, however, who regard parenthood as a profession. The author is Director of the Children's (Summer) Clinic, Black Mountain, North Carolina, and was formerly Regional Consultant in Diseases of Children, New York State Department of Health. He is a frequent contributor to medical journals and women's magazines.

ATTEMPTING to practice a learned profession or a highly technical trade without adequate preparation is looked down upon by experts and laity. Every profession or trade has a name by which it characterizes those who refuse to enter by the usual route, and the names are not complimentary. "Quack doctor," "shyster lawyer," and "black-leg plumber" designate those who are inadequately prepared or who have low standards of practice. Everyone shrinks from the idea of subjecting loved ones to their inexpert ministrations.

Photo: H. Armstrong Roberts

Parenthood is a profession as well as a joyful duty.

There is another profession that many estimable people are attempting to practice, without even the insufficient preparation that the above-mentioned impostors usually have, and that is parenthood. In consequence, this profession is very frequently bungled. Common results are unhappy homes, spoiled children growing into bitter adulthood, and unfortunate marriages that could have been averted by thoughtful preparation and timely counsel. All these and a host of other quite unnecessary tragedies bear witness to the fact that a vast majority of young people undertake the highly specialized task of parenthood with no thought of its complexity or its responsibility.

People laugh at the utter ignorance of the cheerful idiot who, when asked if he could play the piano, grinned brightly and replied that he did not know whether he could or not, as he had never tried, but that he would be glad to make the attempt and see!

If an untrained person should attempt to treat a case of pneumonia, however, the laughter would cease, and the error would seem not ludicrous but tragic. So when young men and women enter matri-

I

mony in a similar spirit of blithe ignorance of what parenthood involves, it makes the judicious grieve, for they

Photo: Boy Scouts of America

Acting as Scoutmaster of a troop of Boy Scouts is one of the many experiences that help to prepare young men for parenthood. These boys belong to the Cubs, junior organization of the Boy Scouts.

realize what the years ahead are sure to bring.

PRACTICAL TRAINING

To be sure, there are many who get a valuable preparation for parenthood unintentionally and without the faintest idea that it *is* preparation. Older brothers or sisters in even a moderate-sized family cannot escape a training that is eminently valuable for future parenthood, though this thought may never occur to them as they face many of the

problems that will later arise in homes of their own. The only child, however, is deprived of this training.

There are other experiences of young men and women that help to prepare them for parenthood. The young fellow who acts as Scoutmaster of a troop of Boy Scouts, the young woman who teaches a club of girls in a settlement house, the church volunteer worker who spends one morning a week with a group of young seamstresses in a sewing circle, the teacher in day school or Sunday school who must constantly face problems of emotional control and mental training and discipline—each of these is unconsciously receiving splendid training for parenthood, though even an optimist would hesitate to call it adequate!

Thoughtful young men and women, who realize how valuable opportunities such as these really are, can greatly increase their value by consciously applying these experiences to anticipated difficulties of their own, making them serve as a sort of training school in preparation for future parenthood. Most of these young people, however, are not so far-sighted; so that these experiences are not made the most of and utilized as training for parenthood.

PLANNING FOR PARENTHOOD

Today, intelligent young people contemplating marriage look ahead to the problems of parenthood, even as far in advance as the early days of courtship, certainly by the beginning of the engagement. The time is past when it was considered highly indelicate for the young woman approaching marriage to hint even indirectly at the possibility of having children. Among sensible people, the situation is now exactly reversed; and we are shocked, not at such frankness, but rather at the downright ignorance of any young couple who refuses to take serious thought of possible parenthood.

For such changing conditions, society is beginning to make provisions, though they are inadequate at present. Several colleges provide courses in marriage for senior and graduate students, where definite, sound, constructive thought and attention are given to the problems of marriage and parenthood. Many high schools, colleges, and universities, as well as practically all normal schools, give definitely planned and well-thought-out courses in child psychology and child guidance. These are excellent preparation for parenthood.

Such courses of study are immensely helpful for those who are fortunate enough to have access to them. Unfortunately, however, they are not available at just the time when people are most in need of them, that is, when parenthood is definitely in view or when the first child has actually arrived. At such times parenthood is no longer a vague and delightful future possibility, but a very real and pressing present situation that has to be faced, well or badly, by young people who are almost submerged by its perplexities. Since that is the case, we shall have done with the discussion of advance preparation and see what is available for the mother in the home or the father in the office or store. Young

mothers and fathers want help. Where can they go for guidance and information, while still carrying on the business of life? How can inexperienced young parents fit themselves for the parenthood

Happy companionship with their children will reward parents who make a study of parenthood.

problems that are already confronting them?

BOOKS, PAMPHLETS, AND MAGAZINES

CHILDCRAFT in itself is an excellent study course for parent education. Much of the information parents need can be found within its covers, while an even more detailed treatment of some subjects is to be found by consulting the references that are listed. Parents will enjoy the task of hunting up the solutions of their problems in CHILDCRAFT, which is indexed with this use definitely in mind.

There are a number of inexpensive books, prepared by authorities on various phases of parenthood, that are very helpful to young parents. These books are usually classified under the various stages of parentage: (1) the prenatal period, (2) the first year of life, (3) the "runabout" age, (4) the preschool age, (5) the school age, and (6) the period of adolescence. All of these ages have been well handled in a simple, yet not an irritatingly patronizing, style by persons who are authorities in their subjects. One book for each age level may be chosen and should then be followed faithfully, though not slavishly. A list of some of the best known books of this kind is given in the Reading References at the end of this article. One may choose from the titles, or one's family physician may have a preference. This should be considered, as these books are to be used, not to supplant him, but to supplement his efforts.

Another source of information, though in much smaller compass, is found in the government, state, and city health departments and divisions of maternity and child health. Many of these departments issue pamphlets along various lines of child management and child development that are exceedingly helpful for parents who want to deal intelligently with their problems.

The United States Public Health Service, Washington, D. C., publishes bulletins and pamphlets upon many phases of health, both preventive and curative. These are never puzzling or technical; most of them are written by doctors who have an accurate conception of what their readers need and desire to know. A letter addressed to the Surgeon-General of the United States Public Health Service, Washington, D. C., asking for a list of the publications of that Service, will bring a selection of pamphlets that may be consulted by parents in search of help. Many of them are free, while a very nominal charge (five or ten cents) is made for others. Since these publications are part of the service of the government to its citizens, there need be no hesitancy about availing oneself of as many of them as one wants.

The Children's Bureau of the Department of Labor has many publications dealing with child health, as well as with nutrition, problems of management, child psychology, posture, and so on. Parents will find these pamphlets extremely practical. A card addressed to the Children's Bureau, Department of Labor, Washington, D. C., asking for a list of its publications always receives prompt attention.

Most of our state departments of health send out helpful publications, which may be had by the citizens of the state merely for the asking. Some states have departments of maternity and child welfare, many of which publish bulletins of their own and will send these regularly to those who request them. Those parents who do not get exactly what they want elsewhere may find it worth their while to write to their state or even to their city authorities, since many of the larger cities now supply their citizens with needed information in this important branch of citizenship.

Most of the women's magazines contain articles and departments of child welfare, child psychology, child guidance, infant welfare, and so on. It is unnecessary to catalogue these here; practically every one of the first-class magazines for women has departments in one or more of these subjects, conducted by physicians or psychologists attached to the magazine staff. In addition to these departments, both these and other nationally circulated magazines frequently present articles on various phases of parenthood and child management that are of great help to those who want to know more about this highly technical business of parenthood.

GROUP STUDY OF PARENTS' PROBLEMS

There are many problems that arise in home life, however, that seem to demand a more personal solution than any general book, pamphlet, or article, no matter how well written, can give. If it were not for this fact, the correspondence schools and bookstores would soon displace the regular institutions of learning. What, then, is available in the way of *personal* help for those who want parenthood education?

Probably the best way to come into contact with experts who can answer our questions and with parents who, from meeting similar difficulties, can encourage us by their sympathy, is to join some parent group already in existence in the community. If no such group is functioning, it should not be difficult to organize one. In any neighborhood where young married people live, there are many intelligent young men and women who would be only too

The importance of a wholesome home environment is realized by parents who conscientiously study the many problems of parenthood.

glad to join such a club or circle if its existence were made known to them. Gathering together a group of like-minded persons from among one's circle of friends and acquaintances is not a difficult task. The mere announcement that a number of people are getting together to study their common problems and to get help that they could not obtain individually will usually bring together as many as can conveniently function as a single group. As the individuals get used to working together, the membership may be allowed to expand, if so desired.

Starting a new organization in this way is possible; but, as a matter of fact, it is not usually necessary. Mothers'

Today is "open house" at school. Mothers are coming for a visit to observe the methods of the modern school. In these pleasant contacts, teachers and parents learn how they may co-operate to further the best interests of the children.

clubs are everywhere in existence, sponsored by church, school, settlement, or other welfare agency that brings people together. The fact that parents of infants are perhaps the readiest of all groups of parents to acknowledge their dependence upon others for help seems to make clubs for mothers of little babies the commonest of all aggregations of parents. Membership in such a club is immensely helpful. In these groups

fathers are, regrettably, more noticeable for their absence than for their presence; but there is no reason why these clubs or other agencies should not be widened in scope—as they have been in some outstanding instances—so as to include young fathers. There is a crying need for more masculine members in clubs for young parents.

In nearly all schools, both public and private, there are organizations of parents, frequently including both teachers and parents, which all mothers and fathers are invited to join. No parent who is alert to opportunities for improving his equipment for parenthood will have to be urged to become a member of such an organization and to assume the duties that go with membership.

There was a time when school authorities looked skeptically at the activities of parents who organized for the purpose of making the schools better. To be sure, in many instances there was very good reason for this attitude; for some parents in those early days were not wise enough to refrain from interfering in matters of school policy. Many of them even went so far as to use political influence to secure the appointment or removal of certain teachers, principals, superintendents, and members of the school board, often for reasons that were strictly personal. Naturally the school authorities resented this and opposed groups of parents who were guilty of this sort of interference.

Such misconceptions of the role of parent organizations no longer exist, and very seldom do school authorities now offer any opposition to the formation and active functioning of such groups. On the contrary, a school without an active parent-teacher organization is considered by educators today to be behind the times. It can readily be seen that there is no more practical means for teaching parents the needs of school children and for enlisting parental co-operation with the school than through the activities of such a group. Not only are parents brought in touch with the problems of the entire school, but they are given an excellent opportunity for finding out what difficulties their own children are meeting and of co-operating with teacher and principal for their correction.

Good speakers address these groups on topics of general interest to parents, and teachers often discuss their own urgent problems and ask for the co-operation of parents in solving them. In no better way can the problems of parenthood be studied than in the laboratory provided by an alert, wide-awake group of teachers associated with intelligent, interested parents.

THE STUDY OF MARRIAGE

In the above discussion the problems of child guidance, child psychology, and child health were mentioned as if they constituted the whole of the intricate business of being a parent. To be sure, they are an important part of the job, and without instruction and help along these lines parents may go far astray.

There are other aspects to parenthood, however, besides the management of children, important as that is, and parents need instruction in these other phases, too. We may briefly mention

some of them, together with the sources from which help may be obtained.

First of all, some knowledge of the

In this boy's happy smile there is every indication of complete well-being.

various phases of human nature and human activity that are involved in marriage is practically indispensable to successful parenthood. Only very recently, however, has any real help been available on this subject.

Some excellent books on the subject of marriage, with its various and diverse phases, have been written during the past few years. One of the most helpful writers along these lines is Ernest R. Groves, Professor of Sociology at the University of North Carolina, who originated the first college course in marriage. Professor Groves has written several excellent books, as well as many magazine articles, on the subject of marriage, some of which are listed in the Reading References at the end of this article. He has avoided the sentimental as well as the

Photos: H. Armstrong Roberts

Three generations in a well-adjusted and congenial home environment.

mock-scientific, which filled so many of the earlier books on marriage and sex; and he has not hesitated to tell the truth whenever plain speaking is necessary. At the same time he has avoided the objectionable overfrankness which characterizes some of the modern books on this subject. Professor Groves treats the subject of marriage like any other subject of human knowledge and human behavior that is studied by serious-minded people seeking sound advice.

Anything that helps young married people understand how the mind works should aid them in making the adjustments that are necessary in any marriage. Hence a few books on practical and applied psychology are helpful in educating oneself for parenthood. The father and mother who know how children in general think and feel are obviously much better equipped to understand the thoughts and feelings of their own youngsters than are parents who have no knowledge of psychology. For this reason, a few sound and easily understood textbooks on psychology are recommended in the Reading References.

HOMEMAKING

More tangible things than the working of the mind must be understood, however, if a home is to function as smoothly as it should and if first-class parenthood is to be practiced. For this reason it is sensible for the young wife to take one or more of the many practical courses in home economics, cooking, household decoration, and other related subjects that are offered by such organizations as the Young Women's Christian Association and the Young Women's Hebrew Association, as well as by many colleges and universities. Excellent textbooks and references will be found in the Reading References at the end of each article in CHILDCRAFT.

A favorite course in homemaking is one called a "brides'" course, in which every subject of study or discussion is planned to help a young housekeeper who is about to set up her own home.

As a part of the work in these courses, the young women visit art museums, private homes, and hotels; they study costs, buying, and planning; and they learn about budgeting in all its practical aspects. Fortunate, indeed, are the prospective husbands of these girls who are learning how to make a home what it can be made when a competent, intelligent, adequately educated home engineer is in charge.

THE IMPORTANCE OF TAKING ACTION

We have mentioned rather briefly some of the myriad ways in which earnest and conscientious young married people can educate themselves for the task that confronts them. No censure is either intended or implied in the statement that few parents enter their job well equipped for it. There is no reason, however, why they should *remain* inadequately prepared. The books suggested in the Reading References are decidedly practical and helpful. All of them may be easily understood by people of ordinary education who are intelligent enough to be interested in improving their preparation for parenthood.

It is not necessary to plan an elaborate course of reading or to set aside any definite period of each day to give to a study of parenthood. Adopting a time schedule is always wise, to be sure; but even those who hesitate to bind themselves to anything so rigid may become deeply interested in reading some of the things suggested or in practicing some of the activities outlined here.

After all, the most important thing is to begin doing *something* toward improving oneself, no matter how insignificant or trivial it may seem. The most difficult part of anything of this sort, especially to one who feels that school days are definitely past, is in making the start. Once a beginning is made, it is often harder to stop than to go on!

SUMMARY

We must be honest enough to face the fact that parenthood calls for a preparation that is not supplied by instinct, by maternal affection, or by a willingness to learn by experience. Except as chance gives some previous helpful experience, either in home life or in social contacts, most people enter parenthood with practically no training for it whatsoever. Aside from a very few colleges that offer courses in parenthood education, most of the training along this line is obtained after marriage by those who take the situation seriously enough to try to educate themselves.

For these parents, many sources of instruction are available and have been indicated in this article. The best ways of using books, magazines, parent-teacher study courses, and correspondence with specialists have been analyzed with a view to making it easy for the reader to avail herself of any or all of them. CHILDCRAFT itself is a practical, helpful, and easily accessible source of help for parents, since the material in this series was prepared by experts in each field.

There was a time when it was difficult for parents to obtain exact, skilled help in the solution of their problems. That time has passed. Those who want to improve their methods no longer have any excuse for failing to attain at least a moderate degree of efficiency in this highly technical trade—the learned profession of parenthood.

QUESTIONS

1. Should one wait until one has children before beginning to study the problems of parenthood?

2. How are many young people to receive a training for parenthood of which they are quite unaware?

3. What change has taken place in the way people look forward to having children? Is this desirable?

4. What formal preparation for parenthood is available?

5. Sum up the ways in which an intelligent, earnest father or mother can obtain valuable training in parenthood by using nothing but the monthly magazines. Could this source of instruction be made really personal? How?

6. Name six periods in the life of a child and give the name of a practical handbook for parent guidance.

7. What is an intensely practical way of learning about your child's difficulties during the school age?

8. Plan a practical procedure for a parent desiring to improve and willing to spend fifteen minutes a day; thirty minutes; an hour. Allocate this time in the way that would be most helpful for you.

READING REFERENCES

MARRIAGE

Bossard, James H., *Marriage and the Child* (University of Pennsylvania).

Groves, Ernest R., *Marriage* (Holt).

Groves, Ernest R. and Gladys, *Sex in Marriage* (Macaulay).

Overton, Grace S., *Love, Marriage and Parenthood* (Harper). A full view of married existence.

PRENATAL PERIOD

Maternity Center Association, N. Y., *Maternity Handbook* (Putnam). For pregnant mothers and expectant fathers.

Richardson, Frank H., *A Doctor's Letters to Expectant Parents* (Norton).

Van Blarcom, Carolyn C., *Getting Ready to Be a Mother* (Macmillan).

FIRST YEAR OF LIFE

Kenyon, Josephine, *Healthy Babies Are Happy Babies* (Little).

Richardson, Frank H., *Simplifying Motherhood* (Putnam). A handbook on the care of the baby during the first year.

Smith, Richard M., and Greene, Rosalind H., *The Baby's First Two Years* (Houghton).

RUNABOUT AGE AND SCHOOL AGE

Alschuler, Rose, ed., *Two to Six* (Morrow). Suggestions for parents of young children.

Bacmeister, Rhoda W., *Caring for the Runabout Child* (Dutton).

Blatz, W. E., and Bott, Helen, *Parents and the Pre-School Child* (Morrow).

Richardson, Frank H., *The Nervous Child and His Parents* (Putnam).

Sadler, William S. and Lena K., *Growing Out of Babyhood* (Funk).

ADOLESCENCE

Ellenwood, James L., *There's No Place like Home* (Scribner). Guiding adolescent boys and girls in their relations with each other.

Taylor, Katharine W., *Do Adolescents Need Parents?* (Appleton-Century).

Wile, Ira S., *The Challenge of Adolescence* (Greenberg).

PARENT EDUCATION

Baruch, D. W., *Parents and Children Go to School* (Scott, Foresman).

Lighty, Margaret, and Bowman, L. E., *Parenthood in a Democracy* (Parents' Institute).

Symonds, Percival M., *Psychology of Parent-Child Relationships* (Appleton-Century).

FOOD AND NUTRITION

Rowena Schmidt Carpenter

It is natural that we who are parents should want our children to attain their maximum growth and to enjoy the buoyant health that comes in part from eating the right foods. We must, then, know how to make wise choices from among the many food items that markets and gardens offer; we must know the kinds and amounts of food to provide for our children according to their age, sex, and activity; we must also know how to conserve food values in food preparation. The more facts we have, the better the choices we can make within the limits of the family budget. Mrs. Carpenter is a member of the staff of the Bureau of Home Economics, U. S. Department of Agriculture, and also Adviser on Nutrition to the Agricultural Marketing Administration on a nationwide basis. She is herself a mother, and understands from firsthand experience the problems involved in training children to eat foods that contribute to healthy development.

THE responsibility of selecting food for children is similar to the responsibility of a builder of houses —that is, in each case the choice of good materials is of greatest importance. Every good builder knows that the structure he builds will be no better than the materials he uses. He knows that it takes a solid foundation as well as strong beams to support a house for it to remain sound for many years. He knows, too, that in addition to the firm foundation and framework he must use only carefully chosen materials.

Parents, too, are builders, responsible for the choice of the materials that are helping to form their children's bodies.

Photo: U. S. Bureau of Home Economics

CHILDREN OF A PRIVATE KINDERGARTEN AT LUNCH

Their task as builders is not completed for many years. From the very beginning of a new life—from the period before birth until maturity—parents are the builders of their children's bodies. The prospective mother must eat wisely during the period of pregnancy, and likewise the nursing mother during the nursing period. A mother cannot afford to let personal likes and dislikes or unfounded prejudices govern her eating habits at these times, because what she eats is the baby's only source of building materials. She should drink milk and eat eggs, green and yellow vegetables, tomatoes or oranges, whole-grain or "enriched" bread and cereals, and simply cooked foods. She should take cod-liver oil during the winter and also in the summer if she cannot have plenty of sunshine. She must keep in mind that she is furnishing the substance for a living structure and that a variety of wholesome foods forms the building materials that go to make up this structure.

Just as a builder can do little to improve the foundation after the house itself is halfway built, so parents can do little to improve the fundamental physique of their child after growth is well under way. If the child receives poor bone- and tooth-building materials during the prenatal period or while he is an infant or a toddler, he is likely to have certain bone and tooth defects that can never be wholly corrected later.

On the other hand, many of the results of a faulty diet can be offset by improving the diet. Food has more effect on health and efficiency than any other single factor in hygiene. The analogy between the architect and the parent is, therefore, limited because food for the human structure provides more than building materials. It supplies the ma-

terials that provide fuel and lubrication for the proper functioning of the human engine, and in addition many other substances that play an important part in the control of the chemical processes that make life, growth, and good health possible.

Physicians and nutritionists have prepared descriptions of the well-nourished child that are helpful "specifications" for parents to use in checking the nutritional state of their children. A well-nourished child has a straight, strong body, well padded with firm flesh. His legs, ankles, and back are straight; his shoulder blades do not protrude. His weight is satisfactory for his height and build. His teeth are sound, and his hair is glossy and smooth, not brittle. His skin is clear, his lips are red, and his general color is good. The child who enjoys good nutrition has an alert expression and bright, clear eyes with no dark circles beneath. He is naturally active and has a good appetite for his meals.

A healthy child who has an abundance of the right kinds of food grows normally, and he is contented and well developed.

BASIC CLASSIFICATION OF FOODS

The right foods for children are milk, eggs, whole-grain cereals, foods prepared from whole-grain cereals or enriched flour, butter, green and yellow vegetables, tomatoes or oranges and other fruit, and (if necessary) cod-liver oil. Everything needed for a young child's nourishment can be supplied from this list. Meat, in moderation, can be added and simple sweets at the end of the meal. If parents

are wise, they will teach their children from babyhood to enjoy a variety of wholesome foods.

ESSENTIAL NUTRIENTS

Proteins, water, a number of chemical elements, and several vitamins, as well as fats and the carbohydrate foods, are essential components of a well-balanced diet for young and old alike. Some of these nutrients have been termed building materials and others regulating materials. Some are used largely as a source of energy. The present knowledge of nutrition indicates that a sharp dividing line between the building and the regulating functions of nutrients is too artificial to be useful. For purposes of this discussion, therefore, the functions of food will be considered under two main headings: (1) building and repairing the body and keeping it in good running order, and (2) supplying the materials for energy.

BODY BUILDING AND REPAIR
PROTEINS

Proteins are essential constituents of muscle as well as of other body tissues and fluids. They must be supplied in the diet in sufficient amounts to make up for the wear and tear on soft tissues as well as to build new tissues. Practically all the storage of protein in the body represents the growth of muscular and other tissues. For this reason protein needs should be met daily. When protein foods are eaten in excess of the amount used for growth and repair, the extra protein is broken down into simpler substances, some of which are used for body heat and energy and others are thrown off as waste products by the kidneys.

Many kinds of proteins are found in food. Some of them are better builders than others, and are called efficient, or complete, proteins. Food proteins from animal sources, as milk, cheese, eggs, lean meat, poultry, and fish, are especially efficient for body building and repair. The

plant or vegetable proteins of cereals, beans, and nuts are good supplements to those from animal sources.

Babies get most of the protein they need from milk; as egg and cereal are added to the baby's diet, additional pro-

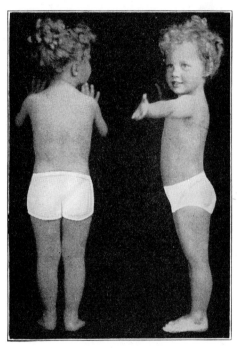

"A well-nourished child has a straight, strong body, well padded with firm flesh. The legs, ankles, and back are straight; the shoulder blades do not protrude."

tein is provided. As the child grows older, a little meat, poultry, fish, and cheese, and the seed vegetables, in addition to his milk, egg, and cereal quota, provide him with an abundant supply of proteins.

WATER

About two-thirds of the weight of the human body is water. It is needed in every living cell, and is an important component of blood, eye fluids, tears, mucus, digestive juices, milk, urine, and perspiration.

Water serves as a lubricant and protection for organs of the body. It helps to regulate breathing by keeping the air

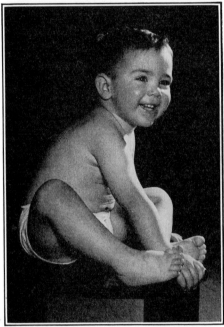

Photo: Freida Zylstra

A healthy child who has an abundance of the right kinds of food grows normally, and he is contented and well developed.

passages moist. It assists in the regulation of body temperature and the elimination of waste products by perspiration through the pores of the skin. Perspiring goes on constantly whether one is conscious of it or not. Water aids in digestion by dissolving food, and it encourages the elimination of waste products through the intestinal tract and the kidneys. In summer the loss of water through the kidneys is less and the loss through

perspiration is greater than in winter. However, children, because of their great activity, often perspire very freely even in winter. To take care of these various functions, water must be supplied in excess of the large amount required in the composition of the blood and other cells and body fluids.

The water used in cooking and that which occurs in milk and in the juices of fruits, vegetables, and meat help to fulfill the daily requirement. In addition, children should be encouraged to drink water—several glasses of it—at regular intervals every day.

Because of their limited stomach capacity, young children should not drink much water just before mealtime or during the early part of the meal lest it fill up space needed for other foods. Older children (and adults) may drink water if they wish at mealtime so long as they chew food properly and do not use water to flush the food into the stomach. Ice cold water is none too desirable (sometimes actually harmful), especially if gulped down when the body is overheated.

CHEMICAL ELEMENTS

A number of chemical elements occur in the composition of the body—in its fluids, bones, teeth, and soft tissues. Some of them aid in the digestion and absorption of food, keep the muscles in good tone, and help to control other important body processes. Since most of these elements are supplied in adequate amounts in a varied diet, it is not necessary to learn their names or to be concerned about them. Calcium, phosphorus, and iron, and in some sections of the country, iodine, may not occur in the diet in sufficient quantities unless special consideration is given to them in food selection.

Calcium and Phosphorus. Calcium and phosphorus are thought of as bone and tooth builders, since about 99 per cent of the calcium of the body and about 70 per cent of its phosphorus are contained in the bones and teeth. Rickets—that dreaded condition in children in which the growing bones do not calcify normally and therefore develop deformities —is prevented by proper amounts of calcium and phosphorus in the diet, together with vitamin D or sunlight.

Calcium and phosphorus are also important constituents of all soft tissues and body fluids; the brain and nerves require a small but essential amount of phosphorus. A very small amount of calcium is needed by the heart muscle to regulate its rhythmic beating. Calcium salts are also necessary for the coagulation, or clotting, of the blood, which prevents excessive bleeding in case of accident or in surgery.

For supplying calcium and phosphorus, no food is so good as milk. In fact, it is difficult for the growing child to get as much calcium as he needs unless he has an abundance of milk in some form every day. Other foods contain much smaller amounts of calcium than milk and cheese. Thin green leaves (such as spinach, beet tops, turnip tops, Swiss chard, kale, and green lettuce) and the cabbage family (green cabbage, Chinese cabbage, cauliflower, Brussels sprouts, and broccoli) are next best to milk as sources of calcium; also shelled beans, nuts, eggs, and unrefined sugars such as molasses, sorghum, and maple sirup.

Phosphorus is more easily supplied in the diet than is calcium, since all foods rich in calcium and some other foods as well provide this element abundantly. All cereal products that contain some of the outer coating or bran of the grain and the germ portion are rich in phosphorus.

Iron. Though needed in only small quantities, iron is of vital importance to health, since it is essential in the formation of hemoglobin, the red coloring matter of the blood. The function of hemoglobin is to carry oxygen from the lungs to all parts of the body. Without a constant and sufficient supply of iron, the number of red blood cells is diminished and a type of nutritional anemia may result. Traces of iron in the soft tissues may also take part in the oxidations continually going on there. The liver normally contains a larger proportion of iron than other soft tissues.

Iron is not so abundant in foods as calcium and phosphorus, but much less iron is needed. The chief sources are egg yolk, liver, kidney, brain, heart, lean muscle of meat, shellfish, thin green leaves, whole-grain cereals, enriched flour, dried fruits, dried beans and peas, and unrefined forms of sugar such as sorghum and molasses. Milk, valuable as it is for calcium, phosphorus, protein, and vitamins, contains only a small amount of iron, but in an easily assimilated form. Infants are born with a store of iron to tide them over the milk-feeding period, but modern practice adds egg yolk early to the diet to ensure the iron needs being filled.

All through the growing period, and in fact all through life, it is important to see that the diet includes some iron-rich foods for the making of red blood cells.

Iodine. Iodine is not always present in the diet in sufficient quantities, though it is essential for the formation of a highly important substance in the secretion of the thyroid gland. This substance (thyroxin) functions in the heat regulation of the body. A lack of iodine may cause enlargement of the thyroid gland—a condition known as simple goiter. Comparatively few cases of goiter, or thyroid enlargement, appear in sections of the country where the food contains the amount of iodine which the body requires. Sea salt and sea foods are rich in iodine. Sea salt and sea-salt dust, which is carried far inland by the wind, supply iodine to rain water, soil water, and soils. Some rocks also contain iodine, which is dissolved by rain. Plant crops absorb iodine from these various sources, and if one lives near such sources, the vegetables and fruits probably will contain enough of this element for his needs.

In the Great Lakes region and in much of the northwestern part of the United States, where mountains interfere with the spread of sea-salt dust, the food lacks iodine, and goiter is prevalent. Perhaps the cheapest and surest way to provide iodine in the diet in the goiter belt is to use iodized salt for about a month, twice a year, so that the body can accumulate a store of iodine.

It is especially important to protect expectant mothers and school children against goiter, in a region where it is prevalent, by using iodized salt. No danger results from its use unless the thyroid gland shows enlargement, in which case too much iodine might cause overstimulation of the gland. All cases of goiter, however, should be under the care of a physician.

VITAMINS

Vitamins are important substances that occur naturally in foods and are essential for growth, vigor, and the general well-being of the body. The different vitamins are distinct substances unrelated to one another and each has its own function to perform. They have one characteristic in common: Only a small amount of each is required for good nutrition. A serious deficiency disease will result from an actual lack of one of the vitamins. However, few persons in this country have diets actually lacking in the different vitamins so that clearly defined deficiency diseases rarely occur here. On the other hand, the results of a somewhat insufficient vitamin intake are far too prevalent in this land of plenty— plenty of variety of food and plenty of knowledge about nutritional needs.

A state of borderline nutrition lowers the body's resistance to disease, causes listlessness, lack of appetite, decreased efficiency, impaired growth, and sometimes marked underweight. Any one of these conditions may be in the nature of a warning that the diet is too low in some of the vitamins. Parents must heed such warnings lest a continued low intake of vitamins in their children's diet may open the way to rickets, pellagra, scurvy, beri-beri, xerophthalmia, and other nutritional deficiency diseases. Most children, even those not wisely fed, get some vitamins, but many do not get enough of all vitamins necessary to grow sturdy or to develop as perfectly as they might.

Foods rich in vitamins and minerals

THE PROTECTIVE FOODS SHOULD BE PROMINENT ON MARKET LISTS

Protective foods—so called because they protect health—are rich in vitamins and minerals. Some of them should be included every day in the child's diet. These foods are listed in the text below.

are called protective foods because of their relation to good health. The protective foods are whole milk, butter, eggs, leafy, green, and yellow vegetables, tomatoes, citrus fruits, some other fruits and vegetables, lean meat, especially the glandular organs, whole-grain and enriched cereal products. Cod-liver oil may well be added to this list for use by the mother during pregnancy and lactation (nursing); and for children during early years. Vitamin and mineral needs can be met by including protective foods in the diet every day.

The mother who likes to know the reason for everything she does will be in-terested in the following accounts of the separate functions of different vitamins essential for human nutrition and which foods are rich sources of each.

Vitamin A. This vitamin is necessary for growth, for sound tooth and bone structure, and for well-being at all ages. Vitamin A is responsible for the normal functioning of epithelial cells that form protective layers for body surfaces such as the skin, the lining of respiratory and digestive tracts, and the eyes. A long-continued lack of this vitamin causes a serious eye disease, xerophthalmia, which often results in blindness. An early sign of a diet low but not lacking in vitamin

A is the development of "nutritional night-blindness," or the inability to see normally in dim light. This condition can be detected by the use of a sensitive instrument known as the visual adaptometer.

Fortunately, the body can store a supply of vitamin A for a few weeks, so that an oversupply at one time will be of value later if for some reason the diet is low in this vitamin. From the beginning of the prenatal period throughout life every person should have this vitamin, but it is especially essential during all the years of growth.

Vitamin A is present in many animal and marine foods. This vitamin as such is never found in the plant kingdom, but plant foods having a deep yellow or green color are, in general, rich sources of certain pigments which are changed into vitamin A in the body. Fish-liver oils, fish roe, liver, egg yolk, butter, and cheese are excellent sources of vitamin A. All the green leaves, carrots, sweet potatoes, yellow squash, ripe tomatoes, green beans and peas, apricots, mangoes, papayas, prunes, and yellow peaches, are excellent sources of different pigments (carotenes and kryptoxanthin) which the body can convert into vitamin A. It is worth remembering that green leaves, yellow squash, and sweet potatoes are better sources than bleached leaves, white corn, and white potatoes.

To insure the protection that a sufficient quantity of vitamin A affords, children should have not only liberal amounts of whole milk, butter, eggs, and leafy, green, and yellow vegetables, but also cod-liver oil daily; at least they should have it during the winter months.

Thiamin (Vitamin B₁). Thiamin (also called aneurin) helps to maintain the appetite, keep good muscle tone, promote growth, and aid in the digestion and utilization of food, especially starches and other carbohydrates. Loss of appetite, listlessness, a sluggish digestive system, and nervous irritability result from a diet low in thiamin. An absolute lack of it causes muscular paralysis, called beri-beri. Thiamin is important in the diet during pregnancy, and it helps many nursing mothers to provide their infants with an abundant supply of good quality milk that contains this vitamin. Since thiamin cannot be stored to any extent, it must be constantly supplied in the infant's and child's diet.

Many foods contain a small amount of thiamin, and there are a few excellent sources—liver, kidney, chicken, lean pork, green peas, lima beans, the germ portion of wheat and rye, rice polishings, wheat-bran, entire-grain and enriched cereals, and mature seeds as dried beans and peas and peanuts. The richest sources of thiamin are, then, the seeds of grains and vegetables and a few kinds of meat. Many fruits and vegetables are good sources and many others contain a fair amount. Since cereal is one of the few foods on the thiamin-rich list that is introduced into the baby's diet early, it is important to choose a kind of cereal that contains the germ portion. The information on the package label is a guide to a suitable choice; if highly-refined cereals are used, it is well to purchase cereal germ in a sealed container at the drug store and add a little to the child's cereal just before it is served.

Thiamin (B₁) is more easily destroyed

by heat than vitamin A, and is also very soluble in water. Long cooking of the many succulent vegetables that contain appreciable quantities of thiamin is, therefore, undesirable. Its destruction is also increased in the presence of an alkaline substance like soda, and for this reason and because of the undesirable effect on flavor, green vegetables should not be cooked with soda to preserve the green color. The shortest possible cooking of green vegetables in the least possible amount of water, and the serving of cooking liquid, are good practices to protect thiamin content. Raw fruits and vegetables should be given as early as the child's digestive tract can handle them. (Thiamin in tablet form is now prescribed by physicians to correct certain conditions due to a serious deficiency of this vitamin.)

Ascorbic Acid (*Vitamin C*). A daily supply of ascorbic acid (also designated cevitamic acid) is essential for infants, children, and adults. It is a specific aid to good tooth nutrition. Bleeding gums, loose teeth, a painful stiffness of the joints, loss of appetite with fatigue and decrease in weight are symptoms that develop when the diet is extremely low or lacking in ascorbic acid. A severe condition of this kind has long been known as scurvy, which is rare in this country. Less acute evidence of these symptoms, or borderline cases of an ascorbic acid deficiency, occur when the diet contains some of this vitamin but not an adequate amount.

Oranges, grapefruit, lemons, tangerines, and the other citrus fruits, tomatoes (raw, cooked, or canned), or the juices of these fruits are excellent sources of ascorbic acid. Other excellent sources are leafy green vegetables, the cabbage family, turnips and rutabagas, liver and brain, and sprouted seeds. Many other fruits and vegetables provide considerable amounts, especially if served raw.

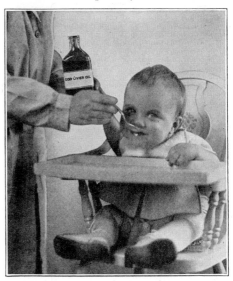

A baby soon learns to enjoy his cod-liver oil.

Ascorbic acid is soluble in water, and is also the most easily destroyed of the vitamins. Too long delay between the time of gathering from the garden and the time of cooking (as when shipped great distances or redistributed by several local dealers) causes many vegetables to lose a large percentage of their original ascorbic acid. However, storage or canning has little effect on this vitamin in acid foods such as tomatoes and the citrus fruits. The use of soda in making cream of tomato soup neutralizes the acid and makes the ascorbic acid content less stable.

Since vitamin C is not stored in the body, children should be given either to-

PROPER FOODS BUILD STRONG BODIES

Every child must have foods that build and repair his body and keep it in good running order, as well as those that supply energy. Only if he is supplied with these foods in the proper quantities will he develop a strong, well-proportioned, and attractive body.

mato juice, citrus fruit juice, or a raw leafy vegetable every day to provide a steady supply of this vitamin.

Vitamin D. The normal development of teeth and bones requires not only minerals (chiefly calcium and phosphorus) but also fat-soluble vitamin D. The presence of vitamin D improves the absorption of calcium and phosphorus from food and helps to regulate the deposit of these chemical elements in the bony structures. Adequate amounts of vitamin D also seem to reduce the occurrence of dental caries (tooth decay), especially in early childhood. This vitamin is also very important for the prevention of rickets, a disease which often results during childhood in severe deformities, particularly of the legs, chest, and head. Little is known about the function of vitamin D in adult life, except that pregnant and nursing women should receive

abundant quantities of this vitamin especially for the sake of their infants.

Only a few foods are good sources of vitamin D. Fish-liver oils are very rich in this vitamin; egg yolks are an excellent source if the hens have been on a diet high in vitamin D. Other eggs, salmon, sardines, and butter are also good sources. Liver, cream, whole milk, and oysters contain small amounts of vitamin D.

Vitamin D can be produced by ultraviolet rays (of direct sunlight or of ultraviolet lamps) acting on substances known as pro-vitamin D. These substances occur in a number of foods and also in the skin of human beings. Their presence in the skin explains the action of sunlight in preventing and curing rickets and in promoting general good nutrition. Since vitamin D can be stored in the body, the effects of exposure to direct sunlight in the summer carry over to some extent in the winter. However, under modern conditions of living, many children are not in the sunshine enough to depend wholly upon this source of vitamin D.

Some foods are exposed to the rays of ultraviolet lamps to increase their vitamin D content—a process called irradiation. Powdered or dry milk and also canned evaporated milk which have been treated in this way are labeled "irradiated" on the container, and are more effective in preventing rickets than fresh milk usually is. However, fresh milk that has been reinforced with vitamin D is also marketed by a number of city dairies. Even allowing for the fact that these vitamin D-enriched milks add materially to the vitamin D content of the child's diet, cod-liver oil may still be needed because it is rich in vitamin A as well.

Cod-liver oil and halibut-liver oil that have been considerably enriched in the amount of vitamin D they naturally contain, and viosterol and other substances rich in this vitamin, are widely advertised. While such preparations are often valuable for children under two years of age as a means of aiding bone and tooth development, they should be given only under the advice and direction of a physician. Too much vitamin D in concentrated form may cause calcium to be deposited too rapidly and in places where it does not belong. Besides, some preparations potent in vitamin D do not contain vitamin A. *Plain* cod-liver oil, egg yolk, butter fat, and vitamin-enriched milk are suitable and useful sources of vitamins A and D in infancy and childhood. *Plain* halibut-liver oil (often sold under the name haliver oil) which is a

highly concentrated source of these vitamins, might well be added to the approved list. Because of its natural concentration, much less is needed of it than of cod-liver oil. However, an advantage of *plain* cod-liver oil is that the usual daily quota provides enough fat to add some calories to the diet, and it is therefore considered a food fat rather than a medicine.

Vitamin E. This vitamin, also known as the antisterility vitamin, is related to the late stages of growth and to the reproductive processes in experimental animals. The only evidence so far of the need of human beings for this vitamin is based on a few studies in which women who had experienced repeated abortions (miscarriages) have carried babies to full term after concentrated preparations of vitamin E from wheat-germ oil were administered. This vitamin should, therefore, be considered in the diet of older girls reaching maturity. Green leaves, eggs, and the germ portion of cereals are important sources.

Riboflavin (Vitamin G or B₂). This vitamin is a yellow pigment widely distributed in plant and animal foods. It plays an important part in the oxidative processes of all living cells, and promotes growth and bodily vigor. Without sufficient riboflavin in the diet, growth is retarded, loss of weight occurs, and a definite type of skin disorder results. There is cracking of the skin at the angles of the mouth, nose, and ears, granulation at the edges of the eyelids, and swelling of the tongue. Other conditions may also be due to lack of riboflavin.

The best sources are green leaves, milk, cheese, eggs, lean meat, and the glandular organs such as liver, the germ portion of cereals, the seeds of plants such as peas, beans, and whole-grain cereals; yeast extract and dried brewer's yeast are also excellent sources.

Like thiamin (vitamin B_1), riboflavin is very soluble in water. Much of it may be lost if cooking liquid is discarded. It withstands heat much better than thiamin does; but like thiamin, riboflavin is destroyed when soda or some other alkaline substance is present.

Niacin (*Pellagra-Preventing Factor, formerly called Nicotinic Acid*). Pellagra is a disease common in localities where families live on diets of extremely limited variety. The early symptoms of pellagra are loss of appetite, loss of weight, and general weakness. The more acute symptoms are sore mouth, digestive disturbances, and nervous depression. Early symptoms are characteristic skin eruptions on the hands, arms, feet, and legs. Skin lesions due to a deficiency of niacin are now known to be different from those caused by a lack of riboflavin.

Pellagra may develop at any age and in families of any income level, though it is most prevalent in families of meager resources. While pellagra may prove to be due to more than a single deficiency, it now appears to be caused chiefly by a lack of niacin.

The best sources of this vitamin are fresh lean meat, chicken, liver, buttermilk, yeast, wheat germ, green peas, turnip greens, kale, collards, and tomato juice. A number of other vegetables, and milk, fish, and eggs contain fair amounts of niacin. (Niacin, or nicotinic acid, is now being given in capsule form to supplement diet deficiency. It should be prescribed by a physician and administered only under his direction.)

Vitamin K. This vitamin, also known as the coagulation vitamin, is beneficial to some persons who are subnormal in their blood-clotting time. It is of value in certain operations to insure prompt cessation of bleeding; surgeons, obstetricians, and dentists are experimenting with its use.

Bile (a secretion of the liver) seems to be essential for the absorption of vitamin K from the intestinal tract.

Green leaves are rich in this fat-soluble vitamin. An exceptionally rich source is the leaves of alfalfa, from which concentrated preparations of vitamin K have been made. Vitamin K is also present in egg yolk, tomatoes, and certain vegetable oils.

Other Vitamins. A number of other vitamins are now known to be present in natural foods, some of which have been isolated or greatly concentrated. Several are factors or members of what is sometimes termed the "vitamin B complex." Thiamin, riboflavin, and niacin are B vitamins whose functions in human nutrition are now well understood.

One of the newer vitamins, pyridoxine, or vitamin B_6, seems to be essential to human nutrition, although its exact function is not yet clear. Another member of the vitamin B family recently identified is pantothenic acid. Some investigators believe that pantothenic acid is capable of restoring graying human hair to its normal color; more experimental work is necessary before the effect, if any, on human hair can be established.

Certain unsaturated fatty acids (sometimes called vitamin F) are essential to good nutrition, though in the case of this factor, also, exact human requirements have not been determined. There is no scientific evidence to warrant the claim that these essential fatty acids, or vitamin F, are an aid to beauty when applied externally in skin creams.

Several other vitamins have been named, and their importance to growth and well-being of laboratory animals has been determined. In fact, notable strides are being made in the field of vitamin re-search constantly. Overenthusiastic writers interpret the findings of research, however, in terms that often make tentative results seem final and conclusive.

Until the role of any specific vitamin in human nutrition has been well established and announced in authoritative literature, it is sufficient for parents to be sure that the diet planned for children as well as adults provides the vitamins whose functions in relation to human well-being are clearly understood. At present, it is necessary to be concerned

MILK IS THE ALMOST-PERFECT FOOD

Milk contributes more to good nutrition than any other single food. It is enjoyed by young and old alike, and should be part of their daily diet.

only about vitamins A and D, ascorbic acid, thiamin, riboflavin, and niacin. If foods rich in these vitamins are provided as part of a well-balanced diet, persons in normal health will obtain at the same time what they need of vitamin E and vitamin K, and also of the more recently identified vitamins just discussed. If family members not in normal health need an extra amount of any of the vitamins, a physician should diagnose the need, and his advice should be followed.

MATERIALS THAT SUPPLY ENERGY

In addition to building the child's body, keeping it in good running order, and preventing deficiency diseases, food must supply fuel, the material for energy. All life processes use energy: the beating of the heart, breathing, muscle tension, and so on. Sitting up requires more energy than lying down; standing, walking, and running—each in turn increases the need for energy-yielding foods.

The fuel value of a food, or the amount of energy it provides, is measured in heat units called calories. Children require more energy materials in proportion to their weight than adults. The number of calories a child needs daily depends to a large extent upon his size as well as his activity. Boys, as a rule, need more energy foods than girls, because, in general, boys are more active than girls. As children increase in weight and become more active, their energy needs increase; and all children need extra food when they play out of doors, especially in cold weather. Regular gains in height and weight are one measure of sufficient calorie intake in children, though such gains

are not necessarily an indication that all the needs of good nutrition are being met.

FATS, SUGARS, AND STARCHES

All foods supply some energy, but fats and the carbohydrate foods (sugars and starches), or foods containing considerable fat, sugar, or starch, are mainly energy-yielding materials. Fats are a little more than twice as high in calories as carbohydrates or proteins. (Proteins, as explained earlier, may be used as a source of energy for the body if the protein intake is in excess of the day's need for this building material.)

When more fat is included in the diet than the body can oxidize or burn for fuel or energy, the excess is stored as fatty tissue, largely under the skin, between the muscle layers and around the internal organs. An excess is converted by the body into fat, and stored.

The storage of a certain amount of body fat, especially around such organs as the kidneys, is desirable, and during the years of growth and through adolescence, it is best to have some store of fat. Until the age of twenty or twenty-five, underweight is considered much less desirable than slight overweight. Body fat can be burned for energy if for some reason the food intake is not adequate, as in wasting illness. Therefore, if children are a little fatter or heavier than the average weight for their height, age, and body build, the parents have no reason to worry *provided* they are sure that sufficient protein, minerals, and vitamins are included in the diet.

Suitable energy foods for children are whole-grain breakfast cereals; whole-grain or enriched bread; butter, or oleo-margarine that has been fortified with vitamin A; potatoes and other starchy vegetables; bacon and a limited amount of fat meat; and simple sweets. Rich cakes, pastries, and rich gravies are not considered suitable for young children. Whatever form the energy items of the diet take, it is essential to include adequate amounts of protective foods.

FOODS CHILDREN SHOULD EAT

It is desirable to know all one can about proteins, calcium, iron, and the different vitamins, as well as energy-yielding materials. But when parents go to market or into the garden, they find no such names attached to the various foodstuffs. They must, therefore, have the facts about nutritive values related definitely to individual foods or groups of foods. The repetition is merely to help parents plan a child's diet more wisely.

MILK

Milk contributes more to good nutrition than any other single food. It has no equal as a builder of strong bones and sound teeth, first because of its high calcium content, and second because it also contains phosphorus and some vitamin D, both needed for the best utilization of calcium by the body. Milk is also rich in the vitamin riboflavin (G); considerable amounts of vitamins A and niacin (pellagra-preventing factor), and some thiamin (B_1). The proteins in milk make it a good body-building food; its fat and sugar provide energy.

So much for the nutritive values of whole milk. Skim milk has lost most of its vitamin A and vitamin D values and some of its fuel value in the removal of cream. It still provides the other three vitamins of whole milk and is still a rich source of calcium, phosphorus, and protein. A quart of skim milk when supplemented by one and one half ounces of butter provides the same nutritive content as a quart of whole fluid milk, sometimes at considerably less cost.

In general, children grow best when they have a quart of whole milk, or its equivalent in other forms, each day. The amount is more important than the form of milk. Canned evaporated milk diluted with an equal measure of water, or powdered, dry whole milk reconstituted with water, or skim milk supplemented with butter, may be used instead of fresh whole milk. No child should have less than a pint a day unless milk does not agree with him. In such cases, which are quite rare, a physician should arrange a special diet made up of foods that replace milk in nutritive value.

Milk is filling and, important as it is, should not be allowed to crowd out other necessary foods. If the drinking of milk at mealtime prevents the child from eating other food, it is wise to give milk toward the end of the meal or to reduce the amount temporarily. Drinking milk late in the meal rarely interferes seriously with a normal child's appetite.

Although nearly all children like milk, for variety part of their daily allowance may well be used in preparing other foods. In cold weather, for example, milk and vegetable soups, dilute cocoa, cereal cooked in milk, hot milk toast, and creamed dishes, as well as custards, puddings, and other milk desserts, are suitable; on hot days, milk sherbets, junkets, cool custards, and chilled milk flavored with fruit juice or vanilla. Cottage cheese and mild American cheese can be used as part of the child's milk quota.

Occasionally a child develops a prejudice against milk, and his milk quota should then be given to him entirely in milk dishes, at least for a time. Adding dry or powdered milk to such dishes and using fresh skim milk to dilute evaporated milk are practical ways of increasing the milk content without adding volume. Using undiluted evaporated milk or a concentrated fluid made of dry milk will also accomplish the same purpose. Cheese may also be used to some extent to supply the nutritive elements of milk.

EGGS, MEAT, AND FISH

Eggs and lean meat are good building foods because of the proteins they contain, and are especially valuable for their iron content and for several important vitamins. The calories they provide might almost be said to be thrown in for good measure, so well do the other values of these foods justify their price and the place they have in the diet.

Eggs, especially egg yolks, are rich in vitamin A, thiamin (B_1), riboflavin (G), niacin, and vitamin E, as well as in iron. They also contain vitamin K and small amounts of vitamin D. The vitamin content of the egg depends upon the feeding of the hen, and in the case of vitamin D, upon the hen's exposure to sunlight or ultraviolet rays.

Lean meat and poultry are rich in riboflavin, niacin, and iron. The lean of pork, either fresh or smoked, is a rich source of thiamin and differs from other muscle meats in this respect. The glandular organs, such as liver, kidney, and heart, are richer in vitamins and in iron than the flesh or muscle of the animal. Liver is such an excellent source of vitamin A, thiamin, riboflavin, and niacin, as well as of iron, that it may well appear in the family diet at least once a week.

Fish and seafood are, like eggs, meat, and poultry, good protein foods. Saltwater fish and seafood are valuable for their iodine content. Fish in general are rich in niacin, oysters in thiamin, and oily fish, such as salmon, sardines, and herring, contain vitamins A and D.

Eggs are the first of this group of protein foods to be added to the baby's diet, and the yolk of the egg because of its high iron content is given earlier in life than whole egg. Since egg yolk is a highly concentrated food that does not agree well with a few children, it should be given in small quantities at first. If a child seems to be allergic to egg (that is, develops a rash or other symptoms), a doctor's advice should be sought; egg is too important a food to be dropped from the diet list unless it is necessary to do so. Egg and other food allergies can often be overcome if they are recognized early and treated properly.

Beginning with a small amount of egg yolk in the second or third month of life, the portion is increased gradually so that by the end of the weaning period the child will be eating a whole egg at least four times a week. Throughout the preschool years children should have from four to seven eggs a week if the food budget allows. On those days when the young child does not have an egg, he should have a small portion of lean meat or liver. Oysters or fish may be given, occasionally, instead of meat for variety and to develop a taste for these foods with their own special values. When the child reaches school age, or even before, if he has sufficient appetite for milk and vegetables, he may have both egg and meat in his daily diet, with fish served instead of meat now and then.

Just as the milk used in preparing a child's food counts as part of his daily quota of milk, so do the eggs used in cooking children's desserts and other dishes take the place of poached, coddled, or scrambled eggs. Egg dishes solve the problem of supplying the food values of egg in cases of dislike.

CEREALS

Cereals and bread are important energy foods because of the large amount of starch they contain. They also provide plant protein, which is an inexpensive supplement to the animal proteins. Cereal products made from the entire grain contribute considerable amounts of essential minerals and vitamins to the diet.

This is true of many of the dark breads; some 100 per cent whole-wheat breads are now marketed. *Ordinary* white bread, which is made from highly milled or patent flour, however, has very little mineral or vitamin content. In 1941, recommendations of the Food and Nutrition Committee of the National Re-search Council for enriching white flour in certain vitamins and minerals were adopted, and Government standards for enriched flour and enriched bread were developed. To be labeled "enriched," white flour or white bread must contain specified amounts of two vitamins, thiamin and niacin, and also of the mineral, iron. Enriched flour and bread may also contain riboflavin, vitamin D, calcium, and phosphorus. Riboflavin in specified quantities will become a compulsory ingredient of enriched flour as soon as sufficient amounts of this vitamin are available. Whole-grain breads are still valuable because they contain the vitamins and minerals as supplied by nature. When whole-grain breads are not used, enriched white bread is much to be preferred to ordinary white bread, because of its protective value. Every meal for children may well include some kind of bread.

Commercially prepared breakfast cereals differ in the amount of minerals and vitamins they contain. The dark breakfast cereals usually contain some of the bran layer of the grain, which is rich in minerals and in thiamin. Some breakfast cereals also contain the germ portion and are therefore good sources of the vitamins thiamin, E, riboflavin, and nicotinic acid. In buying packaged cereals, read the label to learn what parts of the grain have been retained in the milling process. Pure cereal germ can be bought and added to refined cereals.

Cooked cereals are in general more suitable for children than most of the ready-to-serve varieties, though the latter may be used occasionally for variety, and

CHILDREN ARE HAPPY IF THEY ARE HEALTHY AND WELL NOURISHED

The alert, happy expressions of these children, no less than their well-developed bodies, show that they receive the right kinds of food.

some of them are whole-grain products. Again, it is important to read the label. Cleaned wheat grains, whole or cracked, are a very cheap and nutritious food. In spite of their large amount of indigestible roughage, when well cooked and thoroughly masticated, whole-wheat cereals agree with many children.

Macaroni, spaghetti, white or polished rice, and ordinary white bread consist largely of starch, and provide mainly energy materials. The food value of the first three is often reinforced by the addition of cheese, milk sauce, or tomatoes; and of the fourth, bread, by spreading it generously with butter. Brown or unpolished rice is, like other whole-grain cereals, rich in minerals and vitamins.

VEGETABLES AND FRUITS

Vegetables and fruits are valuable in supplying minerals and vitamins; they add variety and flavor to the meal. Every child should have at least two servings of vegetables—in addition to potatoes—each day.

The green vegetables, especially green leaves, are rich in iron, calcium, provitamin A, ascorbic acid (C), riboflavin (G), niacin, and vitamin K, and contribute considerably to the day's quota of thiamin (B_1). These food values are in spinach, green cabbage, Chinese cabbage, Swiss chard, kale, collards, Brussels sprouts, broccoli, green lettuce, endive, chicory, escarole, water cress, dandelion and mustard greens, lamb's quarters, and the tops of celery, beets, and turnips. Thin, green leaves, such as chard, collards, kale, spinach, and the many others just listed are richer in iron and calcium and in some of the vitamins than are bleached, thick leaves, such as winter cabbage and onion bulbs. All the so-called leaf vegetables, as well as tomatoes, green beans, green peas, carrots, asparagus, and cauliflower, are excellent supplements in food value to tubers, as potatoes; to white-root vegetables, as turnips; to cereals; and to dried legumes, as shelled peas and beans.

White potatoes, an old stand-by in the American diet, are a good food for children. Though a starchy vegetable valuable for energy, they contain considerable amounts of minerals and vitamins. In this way they differ from, and have a more important food value than, highly milled cereals, such as polished rice, and such cereal products as macaroni and spaghetti. Potatoes can be prepared in so many ways and have such a mild flavor that they may be used once a day without monotony; in low-cost meals, twice a day.

The method of cooking vegetables may have its influence on food value either up or down the scale: up, when nutrients are added in the form of milk or butter as seasoning; and down, because of the destruction of vitamin content if foods are overcooked, and the loss of soluble minerals and vitamins if cooking liquid is drained away.

The importance of bringing vegetables rapidly to the boil in the smallest possible amounts of water, cooking them only long enough to attain doneness, and serving them immediately, cannot be over-emphasized as a means of conserving vitamin values.

Long, slow cooking and keeping cooked foods warm for a long time greatly reduce the content of several vitamins, especially thiamin, ascorbic acid, and niacin in nonacid foods such as green vegetables. It is equally important to save vegetable juices, cooking liquids, or "pot liquor," call it what you may. Serve this liquid with the vegetables or save it to use in soups or gravies. Because ascorbic acid, thiamin, and niacin are readily destroyed in the presence of an alkaline substance, soda should not be added to vegetables in the cooking process, either to retain their color, as in the case of peas or string beans, or to soften the cellulose, as in dried beans.

Tomatoes, however, because of their natural acidity, retain their vitamin content when heated. For this reason, cooked or canned tomatoes are especially valuable as a source of ascorbic acid (vitamin C) when other vegetables and fruits are expensive or scarce. Tomatoes lend themselves to so many ways of preparation that they may well appear in the child's diet the year round. Children should also have one green-colored vegetable and one kind served raw every day.

Finely chopped cabbage or celery, grated raw carrots, chopped lettuce or water cress, and peeled tomatoes may be given raw to most young children. The raw, chopped vegetable, mixed with creamed butter or a mild salad dressing, may be made into sandwiches for at least one meal a day.

A variety of fruits, both raw and

cooked, is excellent for children. Beginning in infancy, children should be given the juice or the scraped or sieved pulp of raw, cooked, or canned fruit. The citrus fruits—oranges, grapefruit, tangerines, lemons, and various new kinds—and tomatoes are especially valuable as sources of ascorbic acid, though they also contain a little of some other vitamins and fair amounts of important minerals. At least twice as much tomato juice as orange juice should be used to obtain an equal amount of ascorbic acid, but tomatoes are also rich in vitamin A and are a better source of some other vitamins than are citrus fruits.

Bananas are a good vitamin and mineral food and, if ripe, are excellent for children. When the seeds of the banana are black and the skin has begun to darken, the pulp is mealy and can be easily chewed. For very young children, bananas may be baked or the raw pulp mashed. Apples, peaches, apricots, pears, plums, prunes, cherries, and raisins afford plenty of variety in children's menus. Two fruits a day (one raw) aid nutrition and simplify the dessert problem.

SWEETS

Sweets are concentrated fuel, or energy-giving foods, and supply calories in a form quickly used by the body. They add interest to the diet, but good judgment must be used in giving them to children. As a safeguard to the appetite, children should not be allowed to have sweets either between meals or early in the meal. Frequently children have so much sugar on cereals that the appetite is spoiled before an adequate breakfast is eaten. Sweets may be served in the form of a dessert or given as a special treat immediately after a meal. Even then, sweets are desirable for children only in limited quantities. When given in moderation, many sweets are considered wholesome for young children: raisins, dates, jelly, jam, preserves, honey, molasses, maple and corn sirup, many fruits (raw-ripe, cooked, canned or dried), simple candies, cake and cookies that are not too sweet or too rich, custards, simple puddings, ice cream, fruit sherbets, and other simple desserts.

FATS

Fats top the list of concentrated fuel foods, with twice as many calories weight for weight as carbohydrates or proteins. Butter and cod-liver oil are desirable fats for children because they furnish vitamins A and D. For some time a limited number of brands of vegetable margarines, or oleomargarines, have been fortified with vitamin A; the substance added also contains some vitamin D.

To prevent rickets, children need cod-liver oil every day until they are two years old, except when they are getting plenty of ultraviolet rays from the summer sun. Cod-liver oil continues to be desirable in winter throughout childhood because of its relation to growth, sound tooth and bone structure, and the normal functioning of epithelial cells.

Since all fats provide energy and most of them add flavor to the diet, various other kinds may well be given to children. Bacon fat, with its low melting point and its fine flavor, is a good food for children.

WATER, BEVERAGES, AND SOUPS

Children need plenty of water. Mothers should encourage the water-drinking habit by giving water or by reminding children to drink it at a definite time in the morning and afternoon. Four glassfuls a day are not too much.

Every food contains some water. Many beverages and soups are mostly water and contain little food value. This is not true of milk, milk soups, vegetable soups, and fruit juices which contain nourishing materials. Beverages and soups, however, are filling and must not be allowed to crowd solid foods out of the diet.

Tea and coffee are unsuitable for children because they are stimulating and are not nutritious. Chocolate and cocoa are probably the most popular milk beverages the year round by virtue of their agreeable flavor and because they may be served either hot or cold. Both cocoa and chocolate contain a mild stimulant, theobromine, and therefore they should not be used frequently or in large quantities in the diet of young children. When used occasionally and in a dilute form, cocoa (which is less rich in fat than chocolate) adds a pleasing variety to milk beverages and milk desserts.

FEEDING CHILDREN DAY BY DAY

THE VERY YOUNG CHILD

Modern practice in infant feeding recommends early supplements to milk whether the baby is breast or bottle fed. A bulletin, *Infant Care,* published by the United States Children's Bureau (see references), is of tremendous help to mothers in advising them about the amount and kind of foods to give and the age at which each should be introduced into the well baby's feeding schedule. Many families now turn the matter of infant feeding over to a pediatrician, and if professional advice has been sought, it should be followed in preference to general information of the kind given in bulletins or in this chapter.

In any case, it is customary to change the baby's diet gradually during the first year of life, both in consistency and in the variety of foods. The first supplements to milk are fruit juices, vegetable purées, egg yolk, and thin cereal gruel, and from the beginning of the teething period dry toast or zwieback are given.

By the time the baby is weaned or, according to the practice of some baby specialists, much earlier, the child begins to have thicker cereals, a greater variety of fruit and vegetable purées, soft-cooked eggs, more dry toast or zwieback, a little meat and sugar, and some butter, but no coarse, indigestible material. To remove the coarse particles from cereals, fruits, and vegetables, these foods are put through a sieve. It is not possible to say just how long beyond the weaning period this sieving is necessary, because children differ in their ability to digest coarse food without its irritating the intestinal tract. Solid foods should be introduced gradually, however, so as to get away from a liquid or semisolid diet as early as possible. It is important for children to learn to chew, both for the sake of their food habits in later childhood and

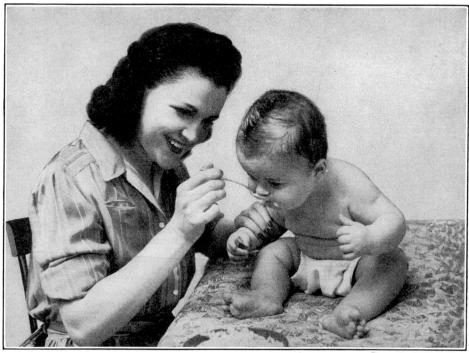

Photo: Harold M. Lambert

LEARNING TO EAT SEMISOLID FOOD

Before the baby is a year old, he has learned to eat semisolid foods from a spoon and to drink milk from a cup. New foods are introduced one at a time and in very small portions.

for the development of their teeth. Early childhood is the time to teach children to enjoy the flavor and the texture of a variety of wholesome foods. New foods should be introduced one at a time and in very small portions until the child becomes familiar with them and acquires a liking for them.

THE OLDER CHILD

As soon as the child has passed the sieved-food stage and has become adjusted to a coarser and more solid diet, his food habits begin to resemble those of the adult. By the age of two he has learned to eat with considerable independence. As the child progresses from babyhood to independent childhood and then to adolescence, he acquires full control of his eating tools. A greater variety of foods is suitable for him and his food may be prepared in a greater variety of ways.

The child's well-balanced diet supplies him with the essential building and regulating materials and with enough fuel foods to furnish energy for his constant and increasing activity. It is not necessary to supply all the elements of nutrition at every meal, but they should be supplied in the course of the day if possible. The following list will help you k up not only on the child's diet but t of the rest of the family, too:

For Every Child Every Day

MILK. ¾ to 1 quart (as a beverage or in oked foods; some cheese if desired).

TOMATOES, ORANGES, GRAPEFRUIT, GREEN CAB-AGE, OTHER GREENS. One or more servings (*especially* for vitamin C, ascorbic acid).

LEAFY, GREEN, OR YELLOW VEGETABLE. One or nore servings (*especially* for vitamin A and iron).

By the age of two, the normal child has learned to eat with considerable independence.

OTHER VEGETABLES OR FRUIT. Two or more servings (for minerals and vitamins).

EGGS. One if possible; at least three to four a week.

LEAN MEAT, POULTRY, FISH. One or more servings according to age of child; small serving at first, beginning in second year at least.

CEREALS AND BREADS. At every meal whole-grain or enriched bread; as activity increases, cereal and bread are needed in same meal.

FATS. Butter, or oleomargarine fortified in vitamin A, at every meal; other fats as activity increases with age.

SWEETS. Once or twice a day for dessert, after other foods have been eaten.

COD-LIVER OIL. Every day for young children; during winter months for older children.

WATER. Four or more glasses daily.

Suitable Amounts of Food

The amount of food children need depends upon their size, their activities, and to some extent upon the climate in which they live. Boys usually require more food than do girls, because they are generally larger and more active. Rapidly growing, energetic boys of teen age often require more food than their fathers. Children of the same age vary, too, in the amount of food they eat. The appetite of a healthy child is a good guide to the quantity of food he should eat, provided he has not had sweets or filling foods to give him a feeling of satisfaction early in the meal.

In early childhood, servings should be small because the capacity of the child is about one-half or one-third as great as that of the adult. The amount can easily be modified by experience. In presenting an unfamiliar food it is best to start with only a teaspoonful and increase the portion gradually. A serving of two or three level tablespoonfuls of a familiar, well-liked food is ample. The child may have more if he wants it after he has cleared his plate. Nothing is more discouraging to a little child than too much food on his plate; and nothing is more embarrassing to the adolescent boy than to be chided about the amount he eats. Growth and gain in weight are sure indications that the young child is eating a sufficient amount.

The meals suggested on the following pages are about average for the ages stated but should be used only as a general guide. By the time the child is of school age his own judgment and his mother's experience in feeding him help to determine the size of portions.

COMBINING FOODS IN MEALS

The slogan for every busy mother should be, "One menu for all." The family meal can easily be adjusted to the needs of the children if the menu consists

The two-year-old has small portions of the family dinner. To make eating easy for her, the baked potato and baked apple are removed from the skin and mashed, and the meat ball is divided into small pieces on her plate.

of wholesome food, simply prepared. Since the needs of young children are less than those of their parents, a rich or highly seasoned dish may be omitted from the youngster's plate and an extra portion of suitable food served, if desired, or the high seasonings or extra amount of fat or sugar desired by the adults may be added after portions have been taken out for the children. Modifications of this kind can be made in many meat dishes and also in vegetables and desserts. Giving young children vegetables without rich sauces, or serving them fruit when adults have rich cake or pie, is usually the only adjustment necessary. Simply pre-

pared dishes in which the natural h of the food is retained make the n wholesome meals for adults as well as children.

BREAKFAST

Breakfast for the young child usuall consists of fruit, cereal, toast with butte and milk. Serving different cereals an fruits and preparing the fruit in differen ways provide ample variety in the menu. Apples may be baked, stewed, made into sauce, or served raw. Ripe bananas, either baked or raw, are wholesome for children. The juice of an orange is refreshing for breakfast and enjoyable as a drink, and orange sections and slices are equally good. Stewed prunes or apples are improved in flavor by adding sliced lemon or orange during the cooking. Prunes and apricots may be cooked together and thus provide a change of fruit flavor.

A strip or two of bacon, cooked until crisp and drained of fat, may be served occasionally for variety. There is no objection to giving the young child egg now and then for breakfast on days when he is not having egg for dinner or supper. The older child has egg for breakfast frequently.

BREAKFAST SUGGESTIONS

Fruit (raw or cooked): oranges, grapefruit, stewed prunes, stewed apricots, apples, ripe bananas, peaches, or other fruits in season. (Seedy berries and figs should not be given to the very young child.)

Cereal with top milk. (Cooked cereals and those containing the germ portion are best.)

Egg or crisp bacon occasionally.

Toast with butter.

Milk to drink.

Dinner

The main meal for the family, which includes the principal protein dish of the day, may be served at noon or at night, according to convenience. Regardless of the time when the family has dinner, the child under school age should have his dinner in the middle of the day because he goes to bed so soon after his evening meal. If the family has a light meal at noon, it is not necessary to prepare a special dinner for the preschool child but merely to reheat and serve in appetizing style some of the family dinner that is left from the previous night.

A simple dinner, consisting of broiled meat ball, buttered string beans, baked potato, bread and butter, lettuce, milk, and baked apple, is suitable for the whole family and lends itself to the needs and food habits of children of different ages. The two-year-old has small portions. To make eating easy for her, the baked potato and baked apple are removed from the skin and mashed, and the meat ball is divided into small pieces on her plate. Many young children enjoy the flavor of potato and apple skins and digest them well if they are cut up and served with the food. For some children, however, even cooked or baked skins are irritating.

Six-year-olds need moderate-sized portions; nine-to-ten-year-olds require more generous servings of the building and fuel foods; rapid development and vigorous activity in adolescence still further increase children's food requirements:

Dinner, Menus for Children

Omelet
Creamed peas and carrots
Chopped lettuce sandwich

Milk
Fruit cup and gingerbr.

Broiled liver
Stuffed baked onion
Scalloped potato
Water cress sandwich
Milk
Sliced orange

Scrambled eggs
Creamed cabbage
Peanut butter and chopped celery
  sandwich
Milk
Chocolate cornstarch pudding

Moderate-sized portions of the family dinner are given to the six-year-old.

Broiled lamb chop
Baked Hubbard squash
Finely cut cabbage, with mayonnaise
Bread and butter
Milk
Baked prune whip

Meat and vegetable stew
Buttered peas
Toasted rolls
Milk
Pear, raw-ripe, stewed, or baked

Beef broiled on toast
Stewed tomatoes and celery
Toast

DINNER MENUS (CONTINUED)

Milk
Creamed rice with apricots

Casserole of chicken with rice or potatoes
Panned okra
Grated carrot sandwich
Milk
Ice cream

Photo: Freida Zylstra

The nine- or ten-year-old, with his hearty appetite,
requires very generous servings.

Liver and rice loaf
Carrots in parsley butter
Apple salad
Bread and butter
Milk
Quick blueberry pudding

Lamb or beef roast
Baked potato
Swiss chard, kale, or other greens
Bread and butter
Milk
Baked apple

Baked halibut
Summer squash
Sliced ripe tomatoes
Bread and butter
Milk
Tapioca cream or cookies

SUPPER (OR LUNCH)

It is more difficult to suggest menus for the third meal of the day (which may be supper or lunch) than for the other two meals because the habits of families vary so much at this meal. Children may eat lunch at school, either bringing it from home or buying it at the school cafeteria. In many homes where the mother does all the work, enough food is prepared for the main meal of the day to provide for supper or for lunch on the following day. The salad-and-sandwich type of meal, with a hot beverage or soup and attractive dishes made from leftovers, is a great timesaver in food preparation.

Dishes prepared for supper or lunch should include vegetables and fruits so as to make sure that the mineral and vitamin requirement for the day is covered. This is a necessary provision for all members of the family but is especially important for growing children. In low-cost meals, suppers must include more cereals than the menus given below suggest. Cereals are cheap foods, and whole-grain cereal products contain enough minerals and vitamins to make a satisfactory meal when served with whole milk and fruit or vegetables. Too light a meal in the evening is not advisable for children, because if they do not get enough food to satisfy and nourish them, hunger may cause them to awaken early in the morning.

Matching the supper menus given below with the dinner menus given above is not feasible, because it would require the preparation of a great many different vegetable dishes and desserts in one day. This is not practicable or desirable in the busy household. There is no reason why the dessert or any other dish may not be repeated if it is something that keeps well and is appetizing when served a second time. The object of the menus given here is to suggest a number of different dishes suitable for children. The dishes that are suggested may be used in various combinations, so long as the meals for each day contain all the food elements that are essential to growing children.

SUPPER OR LUNCH MENUS FOR CHILDREN

Baked potato and bacon
Fresh tomato and lettuce
Bread and butter
Milk
Fruit gelatin

Brown rice
Buttered kale
Milk
Stewed dried apricots
Oatmeal cooky or spongecake

Scalloped eggplant
Prune and cottage cheese salad
Bread and butter
Milk
Broiled peaches, fresh or canned

Creamed fish with vegetables
Buttered toast

Milk
Peach or apple tapioca

Cream of potato soup
Toasted rolls
Celery and cooked beet salad
Milk
Baked custard

Creamed hard-cooked egg
Buttered string beans
Bread and butter
Milk
Sliced ripe banana

Sieved Lima beans with bacon
Baked tomato
Bread and butter
Milk
Apple brown Betty or applesauce

Milk vegetable soup
Scalloped cabbage and apples
Buttered toast
Milk
Raisin cupcake

Scrambled eggs
Creamed spinach on toast squares
Bread and butter
Milk
Fruit and spongecake

Spaghetti with tomato sauce
Celery hearts
Bread and butter
Milk
Pineapple custard

FOOD PREPARATION

The importance of simplicity in preparing food for children has been stressed in an earlier section. No actual recipes are given in this article, but some of the bulletins listed in the Reading References (at the end of the article) contain many recipes suitable for children. A few general principles to be followed in preparing food for young children are given below.

MAIN DISHES

Young children are usually given poached, soft-cooked, or coddled eggs, but there is no reason why they should not also have eggs prepared in other ways. Children enjoy eggs scrambled or hard-cooked and served with white sauce, or made into omelets, and these dishes are good for them. Eggs, or mixtures containing a great deal of egg, must be cooked slowly at a low temperature so that they will be tender when done.

The meat given to young children should be tender and easy to chew. Tender cuts may be chosen, or the tougher cuts may be prepared to make them tender. Tender cuts are broiled or oven-roasted without moisture. Grinding meat in a food chopper or cutting it in small pieces, as in preparing stew and scalloped dishes, makes it easy for children to eat. Roast or steak should be cut in small pieces on the young child's plate.

Children should have liver about once a week because of its particular food value, but it requires special care in preparation. After the connective tissue is removed, the liver should be cooked at a moderate temperature to prevent toughening. To make it easy for young children to chew, it should then be cut fine or chopped, as in preparing scalloped liver or liver loaf.

Children are fond of combinations of rice (or vegetables) and meat and of creamed or scalloped meat, chicken, or fish. Such dishes provide excellent methods of using leftovers and of supplying young children with the small amount of protein which they need in addition to that of milk and egg.

Cheese is a wholesome food for children, containing all or most of the solids of milk, which are rich in nutritive value. Cottage cheese is made from skim milk and is a great favorite in many families, either served plain or seasoned as a salad or as a sandwich filling. Mild American cheese, which is made from whole milk, lends itself to even more uses. Because of its close, solid texture and the fat it contains, American cheese should not be served in chunks, for children are likely not to masticate it thoroughly. It can be grated or cut fine and used in sandwich fillings or between crackers. Melted at a low temperature in white sauce or tomato sauce, it makes an excellent dish to serve over toast squares, macaroni, or rice. Whenever cheese is heated, either in the oven or in a double boiler, it should cook slowly and with low heat so as not to toughen or "rubberize" it.

VEGETABLES AND FRUITS

A number of vegetables and fruits may be served raw, with all their natural flavor and food value retained. They are sometimes cooked to increase their palatability or digestibility for children or merely to add variety to the diet. In any method of preparation care should be taken to conserve as much of the food value as possible. The tendency in the past was to overcook vegetables. Long cooking at a high temperature destroys some of the valuable vitamins. Some methods of cooking remove the natural juices, which contain minerals and soluble vitamins and should therefore be retained. For this reason fruits and vegetables should be cooked in the smallest possible amount of moisture and only long enough to make them tender. The cooking liquid should be saved and served. Mild-flavored vegetables can be steamed or baked without added moisture or cooked in a small amount of milk or water which is served with them. Strongly flavored vegetables are often more palatable if cooked in a large amount of water to dilute their flavor; the cooking liquid from these vegetables can be used in soups or sauces. White or cream sauce for vegetables is made from a combination of milk and the vegetable juices extracted in cooking or drained from the can or jar.

Baking, casserole cooking, and scalloping are practical methods of preparing food because they retain all the nutritive value and flavor. Vegetables and fruits that have a heavy skin to hold the steam lend themselves especially well to baking. Sweet potatoes, potatoes, tomatoes, winter squash, eggplant, onions, apples, pears, and bananas are examples of such foods. Only simple seasonings are needed, such as a little butter and salt for the vegetables or a little sugar for the fruit if it is tart, though other materials are sometimes added to vary the flavor.

When the structure of the fruit or vegetable makes baking in the skin unsuitable, the casserole or baking dish, with some moisture added, is a good substitute. Turnips, celery, cauliflower, and cabbage are frequently scalloped. For variety, vegetables that can be baked whole, such as potatoes, onions, and eggplant, are sometimes pared, cut up, and scalloped.

Certain vegetables and fruits make pleasant combinations when cooked together. For example, apples may be scalloped with carrots, cabbage, or sweet potatoes. Other good combinations are stewed tomatoes and okra, tomatoes and finely cut celery, carrots and peas, celery and peas, and carrots and turnips. Some of these vegetables are especially good when creamed, either alone or in combination.

Vegetable, egg, and milk combinations make excellent main dishes for children. Corn pudding and carrot custard are familiar basic recipes that can be varied by using fresh asparagus, diced turnips, or any other vegetable that has enough flavor to give character to the dish.

DESSERTS

Raw, stewed, or baked fruits when served alone, in fruit-cup mixtures, or in stewed fruit combinations offer many possibilities for children's desserts. Fruit mixed with cereal and served with top milk or thin cream also makes a good dessert. Puddings made of rice, tapioca, or bread are often flavored with fruit. Cornstarch, rice, and bread puddings flavored with cocoa or caramel are popular with children. Cereal puddings of this kind and custards, milk sherbets, and simple ice creams provide a good means of including milk in the diet if there is

Children should be given eating equipment that is suitable in size.

difficulty in getting children to drink it. Eggs may be used in such desserts as tapioca cream, prune whip, rice and bread puddings, floating island, and a number of gelatin desserts. Milk or eggs used in preparing the child's food should be counted as a part of his day's allowance of those essentials.

BUILDING GOOD FOOD HABITS

Food habits are established early. They are a matter of training, not heredity. Help children, from the first, to develop

Photo: Harold M. Lambert

A regular schedule for meals encourages a good appetite and also helps the baby to form the proper eating habits.

a desire to eat the right foods. Let the child learn the taste of different foods from early babyhood, when he knows nothing else than to eat what is put before him.

DEAL WISELY WITH THE BABY

Remember that the baby has to get accustomed to food flavors, different temperatures of food, strange textures, and to unfamiliar eating equipment. Changing the baby's diet from liquid to semi-solid and finally to solid foods must be done step by step. Long before he gives up the bottle or the breast, teach the baby to take water, fruit juice, cereal gruel, and strained vegetables from a spoon and then from a cup. Make these gruels and purées gradually thicker in consistency until the child is prepared for the next step, which is eating mashed, scraped, or finely diced fruits and vegetables. Toast or zwieback causes the young baby to exercise his gums and teeth. In this way he gradually learns to chew and swallow foods of different texture and consistency, so that by the age of two years he has left baby foods behind him.

SET A GOOD EXAMPLE

By the time the child comes to the family table, see that he has a chance to benefit by good examples in eating. Children are observant. They are also great imitators and they want to be just like the adults they admire. Fussiness about food is often the result of imitation. Parents, sisters and brothers, grandparents, and even visitors share alike the responsibility of setting an example of polite acceptance of whatever food is placed on the table. If adults have prejudices which they are unwilling or unable to overcome, they can at least keep silent about them. Far too many adult comments, such as, "I don't like this," "I never could eat that," "Lettuce, spinach, and grass are all right for cows but none for me, please," give children the idea that it is smart to have food dislikes. The less said about food preferences and food quality, the fewer the reminders to eat; and the better the example set, the better the result with observant children.

Protect the Child's Appetite

The normal, rapidly growing child has a good appetite. He plays vigorously out of doors and sleeps long hours with fresh air in the room. He eats three meals a day, at regular hours, or more if he seems to need them. If he is unusually hungry because of his excessive activity, he is given sensible food at regular times as small, extra meals. These extra lunches are continued only so long as they do not interfere with the appetite for regular meals. There are never any sweet snacks or "piecing" for the child on a good diet schedule. Instead, his eating is wisely regulated so that he comes to the table eager for his meal and he eats with zest the food set before him.

Be Casual but Firm

The best way to deal with children is to give them well-prepared food and suitable eating equipment and then let them know that they are expected to eat. The young child often pays best attention to the job of eating if he is served alone at a small table.

Whether children eat with the family or alone, there should be no discipline at the meal hour nor any nagging, urging, or forcing children to eat. Refrain from harping on the "don'ts" and "can't-haves." Be casual but firm.

If, in spite of everything, the child persistently dawdles or refuses to eat, take his food away without discussion and remove him gently from the table, without making a scene. This is not punishment. It is the natural outcome of his behavior—he does not wish to eat, so he leaves the table and is given no food until the next meal. Absence of commotion when the food is removed and lack of concern on the part of the adults are effective procedures in this situation. Even if it takes more than two or three successive meals, there is much to be gained by holding out until the child eats willingly. If his appetite is poor because of fatigue, a slight upset, or beginning illness, it is better for him not to eat. If he is simply showing his power over his parents by worrying them into nagging him, he will learn that his eating is of less importance to them than he thought, and he will soon be ready to eat happily and without urging.

The parents' job in training in food habits is only half done when it is well begun. Much of the foundation is laid in early childhood, but new problems may develop at any time. Frequently the child is influenced by playmates who are allowed to pick and choose what they will eat or who are given money for sweets and sandwiches between meals. Furthermore, the appetite of even the best-trained child may be fickle at the time of puberty. Parents should, therefore, continue to supervise the child's eating as he is growing up. Good food habits make for good nutrition, and good nutrition is the basis for sound physical development.

Points Worth Remembering

1. Remember that what the child eats has a definite effect upon his growth and

development and also his fitness for life.

2. Be sure that his diet includes all the materials necessary for good bones, sound teeth, and all other needs.

If a child is unusually hungry because of his excessive activity, he may be given sensible food as an extra lunch, providing it does not interfere with his appetite for regular meals.

3. Begin, when the child is an infant, to teach him to like a wide variety of wholesome foods.

4. Stimulate the child's appetite by encouraging him in good health habits.

5. Serve him carefully planned and well-prepared meals at regular hours and allow no distractions during the meal.

6. Have the food attractive in color, odor, and flavor, so that it will tempt him.

7. Serve portions of suitable size so that the child can clear his plate without the feeling of being stuffed.

8. Take it for granted that he will eat happily everything that is served to him.

9. Let him feed himself and experience the joy of self-help.

10. Be consistent in responding to a child's pranks and ruses. Laughing at one time and punishing the next is never effective.

11. Remember that the table is a place for good comradeship and not for discipline and nagging.

12. Allow no differences of authority (between the parents or other adults) in deciding questions about the child's eating.

13. Refrain from discussing the child's eating habits in his hearing.

14. Remember that good food habits are the basis of good nutrition.

15. Watch the child's development closely and have periodic medical examinations, so that the child who is not growing normally or keeping healthy may have medical attention if he needs it.

SUMMARY

Parents have no greater responsibility to their children than to provide foods that will build and maintain healthy bodies, and to train children to enjoy a variety of wholesome foods. In marketing, remember that protective foods are valuable for vitamin and mineral content. The list of protective foods includes whole milk, butter, eggs, tomatoes, and citrus fruits, leafy, green, and yellow vegetables; entire-grain and enriched cereal products, and lean meat, especially grandular organs, have protective food values. While it is helpful and interesting to know what nutrients each food supplies, it is not necessary to tax the memory with details about food values if a wide variety of foods is included in the meals during the week. The mother who wishes to be sure that she is providing wisely for her child's nutrition will do well to refer frequently to the daily check list given previously in this article. (See page 33, in the first column.)

An ample number of inexpensive foods meet the needs of the growing body just as well as do the more expensive foods. Canned tomatoes are as valuable as fresh tomatoes, and either form may be used in place of citrus fruits by doubling the portion. Cracked wheat grains and oatmeal are even more nutritious than some of the expensive packaged breakfast foods. Whole-grain and enriched breads are richer in vitamins and minerals than refined, white, unenriched products. Cabbage, spinach, kale, green lettuce, turnips, carrots, onions, and potatoes are reasonable in price the year round in most places; they offer plenty of vegetable variety and supply everything that the more costly vegetables do. Dandelion greens, wild mustard, and the tops of turnips and beets are just as valuable as other green-leaf vegetables and their fine flavor makes them preferred in many families. Inexpensive cuts of meat have as much food value as expensive ones; the glandular organs, such as liver, kidney, and heart are especially rich in vitamins and minerals. Canned evaporated milk and powdered dry milk contain practically all the nutritive value of fresh milk, and in some localities the fresh milk costs much more than these concentrated kinds. There is no reason for children to be undernourished even in homes of low income.

Scientific studies have provided information on food values and nutritive needs. This information has been interpreted in popular terms, ready for application in the selection of the everyday diet. Now, as never before, children can and should be well fed. "Eat well, keep well. America needs you strong," is a timely slogan that may well be adopted in every home in the United States— adopted not only in word, but in daily practice; not only for the children, but for the whole family. Only as parents themselves learn by experience what it means to eat well for physical fitness, will they build a stronger America by seeing that their children eat the right food for growth and physical fitness.

QUESTIONS

1. What signs of good nutrition can a mother identify in her child?

2. Why is it so important to supply all nutritional needs during years of early growth?

3. Discuss the value of milk as a food.

4. Why is cod-liver oil needed in the diet?

5. What are the "protective foods"? What is the function of each?

6. What is the place of sweets in the child's diet?

7. How does the diet of the very young child differ from that of the older child?

8. How do the food needs of the adolescent child differ from those of his parents?

9. What is the value of a daily check list of foods for children? What should it include?

READING REFERENCES

BOOKS

Aldrich, Charles A., *Cultivating the Child's Appetite* (Macmillan).

Aldrich, Charles A. and Mary M., *Feeding Our Old-Fashioned Children* (Macmillan).

Bogert, L. Jean, *Nutrition and Physical Fitness* (Saunders).

Borsook, Henry, *Vitamins: What They Are and How They Can Benefit You* (Viking).

Gildersleeve, Elena, *Baby Epicure* (Dutton).

Hilles, Helen T., *Young Food* (Duell). Recipes and menus for children.

Holt, Luther E., *Care and Feeding of Children* (Appleton-Century).

Kugelmass, Newton, *Superior Children Through Modern Nutrition* (Dutton).

Lowenberg, Miriam E., *Your Child's Food* (McGraw).

McCollum, E. V., and Becker, J. E., *Food, Nutrition and Health* (McCollum).

1939 Yearbook of Agriculture, *Food and Life* (Government Printing Office).

Pattee, Alida F., *Vitamins and Minerals for Everyone* (Putnam).

Proceedings: National Nutrition Conference for Defense, May, 1941 (Government Printing Office).

Roberts, Lydia J., *Nutrition Work with Children* (University of Chicago).

Rose, Mary S., *The Foundations of Nutrition* (Macmillan).

Sense, Eleanora, *America's Nutrition Primer* (Barrows).

Sherman, H. C., and Lanford, C. S., *Essentials of Nutrition* (Macmillan).

Stanley, L., and Cline, J. A., *Foods: Their Selection and Preparation* (Ginn).

BULLETINS

From United States Department of Agriculture, Bureau of Home Economics, Washington, D. C. These bulletins are usually available without charge:

U.S.D.A. Circular No. 265C, *Conserving Food Value, Flavor, and Attractiveness in Cooking Vegetables.*

U.S.D.A. Leaflet No. 17, *Cooking Beef According to the Cut;* No. 28, *Lamb As You Like It;* No. 39, *Eggs at Any Meal;* No. 42, *Good Food Habits for Children;* No. 45, *Pork in Preferred Ways;* No. 49, *Ice Creams Frozen without Stirring;* No. 81, *Cooking Cured Pork;* No. 112, *Cooking American Varieties of Rice;* No. 113, *Honey and Some of Its Uses;* No. 166, *Soybeans for the Table;* No. 302, *Nuts and Ways To Use Them.*

U.S.D.A. Farmers' Bulletin No. 1674, *Food for Children;* No. 1705, *Milk for the Family;* No. 1757, *Diets To Fit the Family Income;* No. 1775, *Homemade Bread, Cake, and Pastry;* No. 1888, *Poultry Cooking.*

U.S.D.A. Miscellaneous Publication No. 216, *Meat Dishes at Low Cost;* No. 430, *Are We Well Fed?*

U.S.D.A. Unnumbered publications, *Aunt Sammy's Radio Recipes, Revised; Apple Recipes; Egg Dishes at Low Cost; Dried Fruits in Low Cost Meals ; Dried Beans and Peas in Low Cost Meals; Green Vegetables in Low Cost Meals; Three Market Lists for Low Cost Meals; Market Lists for Moderate-Cost and Liberal Meals.*

U. S. Department of Labor, Children's Bureau Publication No. 8, *Infant Care* (including information on infant feeding); No. 30, *The Child from One to Six, His Care and Training* (including information on the feeding of children and the proper servings at each age); No. 270, *The Road to Good Nutrition;* No. 8, *Breast Feeding;* No. 9, *Keeping the Well Baby Well;* No. 10, *Out of Babyhood into Childhood;* No. 14, *Well-Nourished Children* (prepared jointly with U.S.D.A. Bureau of Home Economics); No. 20, *Feeding Your Baby;* No. 24, *Your Children's Food and the Family Pocketbook.*

BETTER HEALTH

James F. Rogers, M.D.

Keeping healthy is not just a matter of keeping free from disease. Health is a positive rather than a negative attribute. The Chinese recognize this fact by their custom of paying a physician to keep them well and not paying him when they are ill. In this country people are recognizing more and more the importance of keeping in the best possible physical condition so as to prevent disease and to carry on their daily work in the most effective way. In this article the author gives parents practical advice for checking on, and maintaining, the health of their children. He is Special Consultant in Hygiene, Office of Education, United States Department of the Interior.

THERE are two ways of considering the health of the child. Many parents think that their children are healthy so long as they are free from colds, measles, or other acute and all too evident disturbances of their normal physical and mental condition. Such parents make no inquiry as to a child's state of health merely for the purpose of assurance or as a matter of routine duty.

The other way of looking at the matter is to think of the child as healthy when he is at his best for the purposes and demands of living. From this point of view, intelligent parents seek information about important aspects of health so that they may do everything possible to promote the physical well-being of their children.

Photo: H. Armstrong Roberts

"The health of the child is of the greatest importance, since it is the condition upon which his happiness and efficiency depend."

Parents who pay little attention to health matters so long as their children are apparently well (that is, when they are not ill) may regret their unintentional negligence. An attitude of inquiry and watchfulness in regard to a child's health, however, is not to be confused with the all too common habit of fussiness and over-anxiety.

INHERITANCE AND HEALTH

A child is healthy when he is at his best from the standpoint of his own individual make-up. No two persons are alike, and the health or best condition of one child cannot quite be the health or best condition of another, even of a brother or sister. All human beings are born different and remain different. Not all can be equally strong or equally enduring in body and mind, but each can seek to attain the best state of health possible under the existing conditions.

Too much must not be made of heredity; weaknesses or limitations cannot always be blamed upon the child's ancestors. On the other hand, the influence of heredity should be considered and the limitations of every individual must be respected. Many a child, as well as his parents, has been made miserable because more was expected of him than he could accomplish. Parents should try to steer a course between fatalism on the one hand and overanxiety for the child's well-being on the other.

The child is relatively old at birth. His rate of growth and the unfolding of his powers slow down with each day of his development. Before birth and in early infancy he is affected by factors beyond present knowledge or control, some of which may hinder his development or result in a defect or an impairment. When such is the case, these factors and their effect upon the child's health must be recognized.

Health—a Balancing Feat

Immanuel Kant, the philosopher, once remarked that for nearly eighty years he had kept himself in splendid health, "like a gymnastic artist balancing himself upon the slack rope of life without once swerving to the right or the left." He was never robust, and yet he kept himself at his best and accomplished a great work. Parents should endeavor to make the gymnastic feat of living as easy as possible for their children.

For any individual, health is a variable matter. People do not have the same condition of health—the same ability to function—at night when tired as in the morning when rested after sleeping. They do not have the same health on a hot, humid day as on a cool, dry day. People frequently are attacked by germs against which they are unprotected, and yet they can keep well and do their best work, day or night, summer or winter, if their bodies receive the best care which they know how to give them.

Growth and Development

It is characteristic of the child that he must grow and develop, but this simple fact is too often overlooked. The adult human body is always undergoing change—wearing and renewing itself constantly—but in the child there is not only renewal but growth of parts and increase in activity. This being the case, the child needs not only repair materials but also building materials in his daily food supply. The child needs more time for renewal and growth, more rest and sleep, than does the adult, and the evidence of this need—signs of fatigue—should never be disregarded. The most essential needs of the young child are *right feeding* and *abundant rest*. With regard to the latter, the child is not altogether helpless for, other conditions being right, he will go to sleep when he is tired.

This is not the case with the child's food supply, for in this particular he is utterly dependent. He has to take what is furnished him whether it is suitable to his growth and development or not. He fares very differently from the wild animals, which from birth are given the right sort of food. The condition of the teeth is said to be the most accurate test of good nutrition. The teeth of wild animals rarely show signs of deformity or decay. Children's teeth, however, all too frequently give evidence that poor building materials have been supplied. Parents are not to blame if the first tooth—over the appearance of which they become ecstatic—turns out to be a paste pearl or an imitation diamond instead of the real thing, for the human race has been, and still is, to a great extent, ignorant of how to grow good teeth. Much more is known today than was known a generation ago, however, and parents and doctors are making good use of this knowledge.

FOOD AND FEEDING

THE FIRST YEAR

As the infant grows, his food and feeding should be changed accordingly. If he is artificially fed, the milk will need to be made less dilute, the amount increased, and the feedings reduced in frequency. There must not be abrupt changes in either the quality or quantity of the child's food. The child should show a steady gain in weight and no symptoms of indigestion. Only general rules can be laid down, for each child is different from all others. A physician should be consulted for details. In the second six months the child should be encouraged to take foods other than milk. (See "Food and Nutrition," in this volume.)

If the child is breast-fed, within a few months or perhaps a few weeks he will require modified cow's milk one or more times a day in addition to the breast milk. Only very robust mothers have a sufficient supply of breast milk after six months, and it may fail to meet the child's requirements long before that time. Breast feeding should not be wholly abandoned, however, merely because the supply is not ample.

Weaning. Except in emergency, weaning should be done gradually. When the child has been used to a bottle one or more times a day, the complete substitution of cow's milk for mother's milk will probably not be difficult, but with children who have been entirely breast-fed for a long period there may be trouble. One should remember, however, that an infant is not likely to persist in a hunger strike. In *The Diseases of Infancy and Childhood,* Holt and Howland discuss the subject of weaning as follows:

The difficulties in weaning a child who up to nine or ten months has had no food but the breast are sometimes great. Much time and tact are necessary on the part of both physician and nurse in these cases. To try to teach older infants to take the bottle is unwise; feeding from cup or spoon is usually quite as easy. Continued coaxing of food is objectionable; forcing is much worse and prolongs the struggle. In our experience we have found the best way is to offer food at regular intervals and to take it away at once if refused. This is repeated every three or four hours. A variety of things may be offered—modified cow's milk, thick gruels, beef juice, broths, bread and milk, etc. The nature of the food seems to make very little difference. A strong-willed child will often hold out for twenty-four or thirty-six hours, and occasionally a very stubborn one is found who will do so for forty-eight hours. At the end of this time the pangs of hunger are generally so acute that he capitulates. Serious symptoms from withholding food in such circumstances we have never seen.

Weaning from the use of the bottle should be begun before the child is a year old. (See "Baby Care" in this volume.)

THE SECOND YEAR

In his earlier years the child's development proceeds at an even rate, without break, and therefore his feeding, although less difficult as he grows older,

"Since the child is imitative, she will copy the eating habits of her parents."

should be as carefully looked after in his thirteenth as in his eleventh month, in his twenty-fifth as in his twenty-third month.

The wild animal, like the human baby, starts life with milk as its only food but is entirely weaned within a few weeks after birth. The child has a far longer period of development than the wild animal, and throughout this period milk should form the basis of his diet. In his second year a pint and a half a day is none too much for most children.

Milk. It goes without saying that all milk should be produced and handled in as clean a way as possible. To make sure that it does not contain disease germs which might attack the child, milk should be pasteurized. This can be done in the home by heating the milk in a double boiler to 158° F., as registered by a dairy thermometer. The milk should then be removed from the stove and cooled rapidly. Both pasteurizing and boiling modify the food elements of milk to some extent, but these elements can be supplied by adding fruit juices to the diet. If the heating of the milk renders it unpleasant to the taste, it may be given to the child in soups, cocoa, or custards or served on cereals and desserts. Evaporated and dried milks are safe if the water used to dilute them is uncontaminated. Milk should never be served very cold, and for young or delicate children it should be warmed.

Fruit. After milk, fruit or fruit juices come next in importance, and fortunately these may be procured the year round.

Other Foods. An egg or an egg yolk each day is important as a source of iron, as are also beef juice and scraped meat. (Only a very small amount of egg should be tried at first, as this food causes trouble in some children and should not be forced upon them.) Vegetables such as mashed potatoes, carrots, green peas, and string beans—thoroughly cooked and sieved—are gradually added to the child's diet. Cereals which have been thoroughly cooked, and dry bread, toast, or zwieback may also be given the child during his second year.

GENERAL CONSIDERATIONS

There is no need for coffee or tea at any age; nor will the young child miss sugar if it is not customarily served on cereals and other foods. Puddings and custards often taste better with some sweetening, but the nutritionists warn, and with good reason, against the present-day excessive use of sugar. Between meals sugar in any form is taboo.

Water at the end of a meal and also between meals is desirable, especially in warm weather; but if the child drinks a great deal of milk his needs along this line will not be great, for milk is mostly water. If there is any tendency to constipation, the child may not be getting sufficient water.

Generally speaking, children will eat what they need of foods that are good for them provided there is a sufficient choice and if, from the start, they have not been unwisely fed. It does not pay to force any particular food on a child and his likes and dislikes deserve some consideration. Some dislikes can be overcome by offering the foods in a new and appetizing form or by giving very small helpings until more is requested. Cooked food should always be well cooked and, in the second year at least, served in such form as can be easily masticated. The food should not reach the stomach in chunks. The teeth are for chewing, and the old custom of giving the young child a piece of steak to gnaw or a bone to mumble is not a bad one provided the steak or bone is not small enough to be swallowed.

Parents are likely to be overanxious about the problem of feeding. If the child receives, at well-timed intervals, the right food in sufficient amount to satisfy his appetite, there is not likely to be trouble. If he does go "off his feed," the parent may be sure that there is some cause other than a fault of diet. If the child does not want to eat, do not urge him. Give him plenty of water if he will take it; and if he shows signs of being ill, put him to bed and call a physician.

Nutritionists recommend one or two teaspoonfuls of cod-liver oil for the child under two during the winter months. Holt and Howland suggest the following daily schedules:

AVERAGE DIET FOR ONE-YEAR-OLD CHILD

6:00 A.M. Milk, 7 to 8 ounces
10:00 A.M. Cereal, 4 tablespoonfuls
Milk, 7 to 8 ounces, some of it on cereal
One cracker or piece of toast
2:00 P.M. Vegetable or meat broth, 4 to 6 ounces, or 1 egg, or 2 tablespoonfuls of scraped or chopped meat
Green vegetable, 2 to 4 tablespoonfuls
Milk, 5 to 8 ounces (a smaller amount if broth is given)
6:00 P.M. Cereal, 4 tablespoonfuls
Milk, 7 to 8 ounces, some of it on cereal
One cracker or piece of toast
Cooked fruit, 1 or 2 tablespoonfuls

AVERAGE DIET FOR TWO-YEAR-OLD CHILD

7:00 to
8:00 A.M. Cooked cereal, 3 to 6 tablespoonfuls, with milk and a little sugar
Milk, 6 to 8 ounces
Dry bread, toast, zwieback, or cracker, plain or lightly buttered

10:00 A.M.   Juice of an orange (this may be given with one of the meals instead)

12:00 M. to
1:00 P.M.   Meat broth, vegetable soup, ground meat, or egg

White vegetables: potatoes, macaroni, spaghetti, rice, or hominy

Green vegetables: peas, beans, beets, spinach, asparagus, onions, carrots, squash (mashed or strained)

Cooked fruit or banana

Dried bread, zwieback, or toast, lightly buttered

A drink of milk or a cracker may be given in the middle of the afternoon provided this does not disturb the appetite at meal-times.

6:00 P.M.   Same as breakfast. In addition, soft-cooked egg, junket, custard, or some simple dessert may be given. A white vegetable (see above) may be substituted for the cereal; and soup, for the milk.

At the end of the second year the child should have a fairly efficient chewing apparatus. As soon as the first four molars have erupted, vegetables need no longer be put through a sieve and meats and other foods need to be less finely divided.

It is not possible to prescribe the exact quantities of food to be given. One must rely on the child's appetite, which is a satisfactory guide, particularly if the child feeds himself. . . . An attempt to standardize the child's intake is the cause of many feeding difficulties.

In *Feeding the Family,* Mary S. Rose gives the following plan for feeding a child aged one and a half to two years:

AVERAGE DIET FOR EIGHTEEN-MONTH-OLD
CHILD

7:00 A.M.   Orange juice, 2 to 3 tablespoonfuls

Strained cereal jelly, 2 to 3 tablespoonfuls

Top milk for cereal, 2 to 4 tablespoonfuls

Warm milk to drink, ¾ to 1 cup

Stale bread, dry toast, or plain zwieback, 1 to 2 slices

9:00 A.M.   Cod-liver oil, 1 to 2 teaspoonfuls

12:00 M.   Yolk of egg or 1 tablespoonful liver paste

Baked potato, 1 to 2 tablespoonfuls

Stale bread or dry toast, 1 or 2 slices

Sieved spinach or sieved green peas, 3 tablespoonfuls

Warm milk to drink, 1 cup

Cooked and sieved fruit pulp, 1 to 2 tablespoonfuls

3:00 P.M.   Warm milk, 1 cup

Hard cracker or stale bread

5:30 P.M.   Cereal jelly, 2 to 3 tablespoonfuls

Top milk, 2 to 4 tablespoonfuls

Stale bread, 1 or 2 slices

Cooked and sieved fruit pulp, 1 to 2 tablespoonfuls

Warm milk to drink, ⅞ cup

FROM THREE TO SIX YEARS

Besides milk, a small amount of thin cream can usually be given on cereals or milk toast. It may not agree, however, with some children. One or two cooked eggs (not fried) are good for most children. Finely chopped lamb, beefsteak, or roast beef; fresh, not too fat, fish; and the white meat of chicken are recommended. Other foods suitable for this age are mashed or baked potato, well-cooked string beans, carrots, peas, asparagus, celery, and spinach; thoroughly cooked cereals; stale bread and crackers, with butter added in the third year; cooked fruits, custards, rice pudding, and junket. Ice cream in not too large amount may be given. Oranges, stewed or baked apples or pears, and prunes, cooked until they are thoroughly soft, are stand-bys in the way of fruits.

The following schedule for feeding in the third and fourth years is given by Mary S. Rose in *Feeding the Family:*

AVERAGE DIET FOR THREE- AND FOUR-YEAR-OLD CHILDREN

7:00 A.M. Prune pulp or applesauce, 3 to 4 tablespoonfuls
Well-cooked cereal
Top milk, 2 to 4 tablespoonfuls
Milk to drink, 1 cup
Toast or dry bread, 1 to 3 slices

9:00 A.M. Cod-liver oil, 1 tablespoonful in 2 tablespoonfuls of orange juice

12:00 M. Eggs, soft cooked
Baked or mashed potato, 1 small
Sieved green vegetables, as spinach, asparagus tips, or peas, 2 to 4 tablespoonfuls
Milk to drink, ¾ to 1 cup
Buttered stale bread, 1 to 2 slices, or zwieback
Plain custard, junket, or cereal pudding, ¼ to ⅔ cup

3:00 P.M. Milk, 1 cup
Bread and butter, 1 slice, or whole-wheat cracker

5:30 P.M. Bread and milk, milk toast, cereal and milk, or baked potato
Cooked vegetable with bread and butter
Cooked fruit, as applesauce, stewed pears, steamed (and warm) mashed banana
Milk

Four meals should be sufficient for the average child and three may be enough.

Food should not be given between meals if it spoils the appetite for what is offered at the regular time.

EATING HABITS

Since the child is imitative he will copy the eating habits of his parents or other adults in the family. For this reason parents should make sure that they are setting a wise example by eating the proper foods and by eating in an unhurried manner. A depressing or a quarrelsome atmosphere at the table tends to interfere with digestion. With regard to discipline, a child should not be scolded because he does not manage his eating with the ease of an adult.

The child who sometimes plays with other children in their homes may have his food habits disturbed, but he is not likely to eat at any and all times if he gets what he wants and as much as he wants at home. An offer of candy will not often be refused, but if sweets are supplied at home in the form of a wholesome dessert the child is less likely to demand them between meals. As mealtime approaches, the child should be called from his play so that he can relax and rest a few minutes before eating.

FUNDAMENTALS OF CHILD HYGIENE

ELIMINATION

There should be regularity in getting rid of the unused waste from food as well as in the eating of food. Regularity in emptying the bowels should have been established in the early months of the child's life, but if it was not, it can be established at a later age. The child should be taken to the toilet soon after the first feeding and also just before bedtime. As he grows up these two times fit in best with the routine of life (which should not be disturbed oftener than is necessary) and elimination at one or both of these times is likely to become a habit. The child should, of course, be trained to tell his parent of his needs at other times. Patience and persistence will bring the desired habit formation.

The child's bowel movements should never be hard and dry or loose and unformed. In the former case he probably is getting too little water, and in the latter case he may be eating some food which is too coarse and irritating. Where these conditions cannot be corrected in a few days by a change in the diet or an increase in the amount of liquid taken, a physician should be consulted. The longer the child goes without an evacuation the more difficult it becomes. It should also be kept in mind that a bowel movement may occur but may be incomplete. In such cases gentle massage of the abdomen is helpful, but there are occasions when the use of a suppository, an enema of soap and water, or a laxative may be needed. It is best to use such measures, however, only upon the advice of a physician.

Full control of both the bladder and bowels is usually acquired by the third or fourth year. Many children, however, are not able to control their bladder at night until much later. In such cases a physician should be consulted, but the child should never be shamed or made to worry over the condition, which in itself is unpleasant enough for him.

SLEEP

A child will get as much sleep or rest as he requires if the proper conditions are provided. He must be well fed and he should not have the discomfort which comes from indigestion, for, though he may sleep, it is likely to be a troubled sleep. The room should be as free from disturbing noises as possible. His night clothes should be loose, and he should be neither too cold nor too hot. A child is much more likely to be too warm than too cold. No well child should sweat during sleep. Except in severe weather an abundance of fresh air should be admitted to the sleeping room, but direct drafts should be avoided. The amount of bedclothing should be adjusted to the temperature of the room. If the child throws or kicks his covers aside, one may be sure that he has more covering than he needs, and if it is replaced he is likely to throw it off in the night and become chilled. A delicate child needs more clothing than one who is robust.

Perhaps the ideal time for a child to go to sleep is when sleep overtakes him, but civilized life has to go largely by schedule. There should be a definite—and early—hour for going to bed at night, for although the child may be able to sleep during the day in his preschool years, at school age he will have to remain awake, and it will not be easy then to establish a new habit of going to bed early. The amount of sleep needed varies with the age and with the individual. Authorities differ as to the amount required at different ages. One statistician finds that children of two years average about thirteen hours; children from three to six years, eleven hours; children from seven to eleven years, ten hours. Another authority finds that children from two to three years of age sleep fourteen to sixteen hours; from three to five, eleven to fourteen hours. Children sleep about an hour less in summer than in winter.

The afternoon nap is a good thing for the preschool child. If the child is evidently tired he should, no matter at what age, rest for an hour or a half hour in the afternoon. It depends upon the individual. The very active child who is none too robust is definitely in need of such rest. Unless he can be persuaded to rest without being made cross, however, he is better left to his own inclination. Dr. Holt remarks that "sleeplessness is often caused by persistent activities of a fussy nurse or mother."

Going to bed at night is for the purpose of sleep and, while the parent should help to make the process as pleasant and tranquil as possible, he should not be wheedled into telling long bedtime stories or playing games. The earlier the child can gain a sense of self-sufficiency by going alone to bed and by preparing himself for rest, the better it will be for him.

TEMPERATURE

Aside from insufficient or improper food, the greatest dangers to the child's health are cold and excessive heat. Perhaps certain germs should be placed first, but extremes of temperature help—directly or indirectly—to make children more susceptible to attack by bacteria, especially to the germs which cause colds.

The temperature of rooms in which the child of two or more years lives should not rise above 70° nor fall much below 65° Fahrenheit. The bodily fires of the young child, after his first year or so, burn more intensely than those of the adult, especially when he is active. Whether awake or asleep the child should be so lightly clad that he does not sweat. He should also be evenly clad. There is no reason for exposing

the knees and there are good reasons for *not* exposing them. When the child goes out of doors in cold weather he should be comfortably clothed but not overclothed, and his extra clothing should be

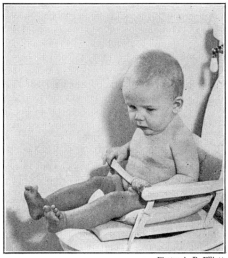

Photo: A. B. Elliott

Patience and persistence will bring the desired habit formation.

removed at once when he enters a warm room. Rubbers should be worn if the ground is wet, but should be removed immediately upon coming indoors.

SHOES

The feet should be carefully looked after. When the child is able to run about, he cannot with safety be allowed to go without shoes. Fortunately, children's shoes are now made more sensibly than formerly, and there is little excuse for purchasing shoes that are too tight or which have too narrow a toe. They should be snug enough to prevent the foot from sliding inside the shoe and long enough to extend beyond the toes when the child is standing. They should be as light and soft as possible, and certainly no heels are needed before school age. The child grows rapidly and, unless the parent can afford to buy new shoes often, it is wise to allow leeway in both width and length—a quarter of an inch for the width and three-quarters of an inch to an inch for the length.

GOOD AIR

Air is the most immediate need of the human being. No one can exist without air for even a few minutes. Everyone knows this; but there are many things about air that are still unknown. People do realize, however, that they need reasonably pure air indoors. Already mentioned is the need for comfortable temperatures. The amount of moisture in the air is another important consideration. Where there is excessive dampness, high temperatures are depressing and cold air is chilling. An excess of moisture is unlikely indoors, however; on the contrary, in homes heated with hot air, or overheated by any means, the air may become too dry for the health of the sensitive membranes of the nose and throat. Pans of water should be placed on the radiators or other devices should be used for adding moisture to the air. As much fresh air should be admitted as can be comfortably heated, but drafts should be prevented by the use of boards or air deflectors.

The gas escaping from leaking fixtures or the carbon monoxide gas from coal furnaces that do not work properly are very dangerous. Parents should therefore attend to these matters as a safety measure. (See "Safety in the Home," in this volume.)

SUNSHINE

In summer an infant one week old may be taken out of doors, but in other seasons the child should be at least a month old before he is taken out and he should become accustomed gradually, by short exposures, to temperatures below 70° F. There is no advantage, however, in having the child outdoors in very cold weather, and exposure to dampness and wind should be avoided. The child can be given fresh air indoors by wrapping him up and placing him in a room with open windows. The advantage of an out-of-door airing is in the exposure to certain healthful rays of the sun, which, in moderation, are very beneficial. These rays exist, however, in skyshine as well as in sunshine, and there is always danger in direct exposure to a hot sun. (See "Baby Care," in this volume.)

EXERCISE

The child begins to use his muscles before birth and he should be given ample opportunity for their exercise after birth. His clothing should not be confining to his arms or legs or to the movements of his chest. It is not sufficient to let the child lie in a narrow crib or basket and kick and squirm. From time to time he should be taken up and carried about and his position should be changed frequently. A thick comforter, covered with a sheet, should be laid on the floor (if it is not a cold, drafty floor) and the child should be allowed to tumble about. A bed that is not too soft is a good place for such tumbling, but there is the possibility that the child may wriggle to the edge and fall off.

In due time a baby makes an effort

to sit up and later to creep or hitch about. His development along this line should not be unduly hastened, but he may be given a little help in practicing these movements.

When the child is creeping or attempting to walk certain precautions for his safety should be taken. When he cannot be watched constantly he should be confined in a pen that is secure and of ample size, on the floor of which a comforter covered by a sheet is placed to provide safety and cleanliness. In such a pen a child can learn to stand and to move about while clinging to the frame.

The feats of standing alone and of walking, which are usually acquired by the age of one and a half years, should not be hastened by urging and by too much assistance, because their accomplishment merely adds to the possibility of falls and other accidents. Some persons recommend that the child be unhampered in his explorations about the house, but this advice disregards the many risks that the child encounters in his free moving about and in his investigation of objects that might be injurious. Such objects as the kitchen range, the gas stove, or other heating arrangement should be screened (window screens fastened together are a convenient device) so that they cannot be touched. Receptacles for hot water and containers of hot foods must be placed where they cannot be reached. The number of deaths and serious injuries every year from burns and scalds is astounding. These accidents too often result from carelessness and are the more tragic because of that fact. (See "Safety in the Home," in this volume.)

In the first two years of life the child is busy developing his machinery for getting about. This being accomplished, he proceeds to investigate the world about him. If he is out of doors the parent should be sure that he cannot escape into the street and that garden implements and other possible sources of injury are safely out of reach of his investigative fingers.

Whether indoors or out, the child will be occupied with something, and safe, clean, and simple playthings should be furnished him. Details with regard to playthings are given in "Dramatic Play" (Volume Eleven). Play reflects the natural inclination of the child, and if he takes to drawing or painting or reading rather than to bats and balls, he is perfectly normal. Parents must not expect their children to be interested in the same things that interested them. Something is wrong, however, with the child who does not want to play or who ceases to play.

When the weather is not too cold, windy, or wet the child should play out of doors—always in a safe place. In hot weather he should be sheltered from a scorching sun. (See "Indoor and Outdoor Games," in Volume Eleven.)

CARE OF THE SKIN

A child may be clean yet unhealthy, or unclean yet apparently healthy, but he will be more comfortable if he is clean. The habit of personal cleanliness, therefore, should be established early in life. The soap used should not be irritating to his skin, and the water should not be so cold as to chill him. After a warm bath the child should be sponged with cool water before being dressed. If the bath is given at bedtime, he should be put to bed at once. After bathing, the skin (especially the skin of the very young child) should be carefully dried, and if there are signs of

Photo: H. Armstrong Roberts

"There is no absolute standard of height or weight. . . . If the child is growing steadily, parents need not worry because of his size and build."

irritation the folds of the skin should be dusted with talcum. It is much easier to prevent than to cure diseases of the skin. (See "Baby Care," in this volume.)

Abnormal conditions of the skin often indicate some disease or ailment and should therefore never be ignored. Skin eruptions accompany many infectious diseases; they also occur in children who are suffering from nutritional defects or deficiencies.

It is impossible to keep a child's hands spotless. He will handle all kinds of things, dirty and clean, without discrimination. This handling is safe enough unless the child gets hold of something contaminated with disease germs. He should therefore be trained to keep his fingers out of his mouth, and he should be discouraged from putting objects in his mouth, particularly food which has been handled or mouthed by other children. The habit of washing the hands before eating should be established early in life.

RATE OF DEVELOPMENT

In the preceding pages the conditions which permit a child to develop healthfully have been discussed. The child should grow steadily in height and weight and should perform certain feats at certain ages. The chart below gives the height and weight for the average boy and girl. The figures in this chart, however, are merely the averages for normal children. There is no right height or right weight—that is, no absolute standard of height or weight—to which all children are expected to conform. If the child is tall and slender in his early months he is likely to remain so; conversely, if he is short and thick he will probably not change his relative proportions, at least not for some time. There are, of course, limits to normal heights, weights, and the relation of height to weight, but if the child is growing steadily, appears to be normal in every respect, and is developing his ability to do the physical and mental tasks that are normal for his age, parents need not worry because of his size and build. (See

"Normal Rates of Development," in this volume.)

Some children who are exceedingly delicate in early life are assisted to a hardy development through wise parental care. Others remain delicate regardless of what is done to effect improvement. Every child deserves care, but frail children need special care and attention. They should not be coddled, but special attention should be given to their feeding and clothing. They cannot stand prolonged exposure to very high or very low temperatures, and they tire more readily than do robust children. The underweight and delicate child should have a careful examination to see if he has any remediable organic defects, but attention should never be called to his thinness or to other physical peculiarities. He will get enough of this outside the family circle.

The ability to store up fat is a good thing, provided the fat is not excessive. The abnormally heavy child may require a change in diet, or his thyroid or other glands may not be functioning properly. In either case, he should be examined by a physician. Prescribed medication or correction of diet, or both, will usually effect improvement.

Professor Arnold Gesell finds that the average child of nine months can sit alone; at twelve months he can walk with help; at fifteen months he can stand and walk alone; at eighteen months he can climb on a chair or up the stairs; and at two years he can run. A great many healthy children require more time to learn these various feats, but if they are unusually slow in learning them it is well to inquire as to the cause. Improper hygiene or illness often accounts for retarded development.

PROTECTION AGAINST INFECTION

Throughout life the child will have to deal more or less with his arch enemies— disease germs. He is, however, partly or wholly protected by nature against some of them; by medical means he can be protected against certain others; and by care on the part of his parents he can escape still others.

DISEASES COMMON TO CHILDHOOD

Tuberculosis. Tuberculosis is not an inherited disease, but if there is a case of tuberculosis in the home the child may develop the disease if he comes in contact with the discharges from a tubercular person. Infectious material may be in the air which the child breathes or on

CHART OF HEIGHT AND WEIGHT

Age (in years)	BOY		GIRL	
	Height (in inches)	Weight (in pounds)	Height (in inches)	Weight (in pounds)
1	29.5	21.0	29.0	20.5
1½	32.0	24.5	31.4	24.0
2	34.0	27.3	33.4	26.5
3	37.5	32.5	37.0	31.5
4	40.5	36.8	40.0	35.3

objects which he handles. By placing contaminated objects in his mouth or by putting his hands in his mouth after handling such objects the child may become infected. There is additional danger if he is allowed to crawl on the floor

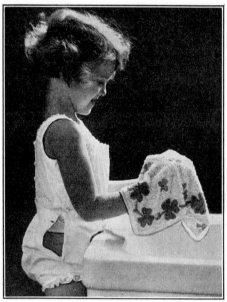

Photo: H. Armstrong Roberts

"The habit of washing should be established early in life."

in a home where tubercle germs are sprayed about by a coughing or sneezing patient. By proper care of the discharges from the infected person and by keeping the child from close contact, the danger of transmission of the disease is reduced to the minimum. It is not safe to permit a child to visit a home where a tubercular patient is known to live.

Tuberculosis may not exist in the home but it may appear in the barnyard or in the dairy from which the child's milk is purchased. In many states the dairy cows are regularly inspected and the

tuberculous animals are destroyed, but this is not required by law in every state. Where the child's milk is taken from the bulk mixture of a herd, the presence of one infected cow is not a serious danger because its contribution is greatly diluted. If, however, the milk comes from only one cow or from a herd numbering only a few animals, it is important to find out if the animals are regularly tested with tuberculin or if the milk is pasteurized. Tuberculosis in cattle is not quite the same as it is in human beings, but the bovine germ does attack children, especially in their bones and joints. Happily, as a result of preventive measures, tuberculosis of the bones and of other organs is now less common than formerly, but parents cannot afford to disregard existing dangers.

Smallpox. Those who are unacquainted with medical history have no conception of the dread in which smallpox was held before the discovery of a means of protection by vaccination. Only a little over a century ago it was customary to inoculate people with the disease itself—in what seemed a mild form—in order to escape the disease in a severe epidemic. Present-day vaccine is a protection against smallpox and rarely involves any danger if rightly used. Where vaccination is not practiced universally, smallpox appears with increasing frequency and severity, and for this reason it is wise to see that the child has protection at an early age. In many places vaccination is compulsory before the child can enter school. In communities affording such protection smallpox is rare indeed.

Diphtheria. That dread disease, diphtheria, loses its terror for the parents whose children are safeguarded by the use of toxoid. A physician should be consulted with regard to obtaining this means of protection. When a child who has not been so protected is exposed to diphtheria, he should immediately be given a dose (suited to his age) of diphtheria antitoxin. This treatment protects for only a short time and may need to be repeated if an epidemic continues or if diphtheria carriers (persons who, themselves immune, harbor the living germs in their noses or throats) are going about. In communities where many children have been protected with toxoid the number of cases of diphtheria steadily diminishes.

Scarlet Fever. Scarlet fever is another dreaded disease of early childhood. A serum is now available which protects the well child exposed to the disease; but, while the serum is of great importance during an epidemic, it has not yet been widely used as a preventive.

Measles, Mumps, and Whooping Cough. These three diseases—measles, mumps, and whooping cough—take a large toll of lives among young children (7,518 deaths resulted from whooping cough in a recent year); and those whom these diseases do not destroy, they often damage in eye, ear, or other organ. Science has been searching for a protective vaccination against these diseases, with the promise of success in the case of measles and whooping cough. The family physician should be consulted concerning progress in this field.

Tetanus. Lockjaw, or tetanus, is a very serious and all too common disease. It follows accidents from firearms, from stepping on rusty nails, and from other injuries in which dirt gets into a wound. A physician should be called at once whenever such an accident occurs, so that a protective serum can be given the child to prevent the development of tetanus.

SYMPTOMS OF THE COMMUNICABLE DISEASES

A child may not complain of a sore throat and yet be in the beginning stages of diphtheria. Similarly, the fact that he does not have a rash is no indication that he is not coming down with measles or scarlet fever or smallpox. Whooping cough is contracted long before the victim whoops.

Skin eruptions are by no means the first signs or symptoms of communicable diseases. The indicators of disease may be loss of appetite and possibly vomiting; weakness, fretfulness, listlessness, or drowsiness; a pale or a flushed face; sneezing, running nose, watering eyes, or complaints of a sore throat. These symptoms may mean the onset of a communicable disease, one of those which have been mentioned, or they may indicate some lesser ailment. In any event, they are warning signs and the child must be kept out of school and away from other children and should be carefully watched until his ailment has been definitely diagnosed.

FEVER

Changes of body temperature are likely to occur with slight cause in the very young child, but they do not occur *without* cause. Parents should own a thermometer and learn from a nurse or physician how to use it. If the temperature cannot safely be taken by mouth or if the child cannot breathe through his nose, the thermometer can be placed in the armpit and the arm held gently at the side for the desired length of time (twice the length of time necessary for taking the temperature by mouth). Before taking the temperature the parent should always make sure that the mercury is shaken to 98° or lower. After use the mercury should again be shaken down and the thermometer should be carefully washed with soap in cold or lukewarm (never hot) water.

Temperature taken in the armpit is roughly one degree lower than that taken by mouth or rectum. After the first few months of life the normal temperature by mouth varies between 98° and 99.5.° Occasionally, normal temperature as low as 97.5° or as high as 100° may exist, but such temperatures are uncommon in healthy children. It is well to learn your own child's usual, or normal, temperature.

Changes of temperature are to be taken more seriously as the child grows older, and by the time he has reached school age a rise of a degree will mean that the child is unwell from some cause. No matter what the signs of illness may be, the child should be put to bed. If he is cold or chilly a warm blanket or hot-water bottle (not too hot) should be used, but if he is already feverish he should not be overclothed. Plenty of water can be given, but food should not be urged. If the child desires food, fruit juice or milk will be sufficient. A physician should be consulted.

THE COMMON COLD

Colds are our most common ailments, regardless of age. With proper care, however, the child can escape colds up to four or five years of age. He can avoid them only if he is not overclothed, if the room is not overheated, if he is kept off cold floors and out of chilling drafts, and if due care is taken to avoid exposure to cold following a warm bath. He will need to be well fed and well rested and kept from contact with those who have colds.

If a child contracts a cold it is wise to put him to bed. His clothing should be warm but not too heavy. The air of the room should be cool, but there is no advantage in having it cold, and there is a great disadvantage if the youngster is overclothed and kicks the covers off. The object of this treatment is to keep the child at rest and comfortably warm until he shows evidence of being well on the way to recovery. His appetite or loss of appetite should be respected, but he should drink lots of water. His food should be confined chiefly to milk, and in his first year or eighteen months this may need to be diluted. Fruit juices and small quantities of cereals or custards will usually be acceptable to children who, when well, have these foods as items of their daily diet. If the bowels do not move as usual, an enema or a laxative should be given. If the child is taking much less food than normally, the time between movements may be longer.

A cold sometimes leads to bronchitis or pneumonia, and if the symptoms of a cold are at all severe a physician should be called.

Influenza occurs in all degrees of severity, and a mild attack resembles a cold. Early treatment of either a cold or influenza is practically the same; parents need not trouble themselves with differences of diagnosis, which even physicians find it difficult to make.

EAR TROUBLES

Of all the terrors of childhood, ear disease is one of the most treacherous. The parent may not know that it exists, for the very young child cannot explain where the trouble is. A child who cries and seems ill, without definite symptoms, should always be suspected of having disease of the middle ear, and a physician should be called. The child often has a high temperature and a rapid pulse. If the symptoms are definitely referred by the child to his ear, if he has earache, a physician (preferably an ear specialist) should be called without delay. An early puncture of the drumhead of the ear will give great relief from the pain and reduce the likelihood of an extension of the condition to the mastoid bone or farther. Heat applied to the region of the ear by means of a hot-water bag (not so hot as to burn) or a bag of salt (heated in the oven) will often afford temporary relief from the pain but will not cure the disease.

NOSE AND THROAT TROUBLES

Ear disease is likely to appear in the season of colds and usually has its beginning in the nose and throat, for there is a tube leading from that region to the ear and the germs causing colds and sore throats find their way along this tube. The problem of preventing ear disease, therefore, is the problem of preventing colds or other infections of the nose and throat. Where attacks of sore throat occur frequently, a physician should be consulted as to the condition of the tonsils, for their removal often reduces the tendency to infection. Adenoids are harmful, for they not only help to produce colds and ear disease, but they also interfere with the natural breathing of the child and may cause speech defects or deformity of the face. Adenoids and tonsils should always be removed if this is advised by the family physician.

RHEUMATISM

Complaints of pain or soreness of the joints or muscles should not be disregarded by the parent. Such pains are never "growing pains," for growth is not accompanied by pain. They indicate some infection or possibly rheumatism of the muscles or joints. Attacks of rheumatism and of heart disease often go together, and both may accompany tonsillitis. The child who complains of pain in his arms or legs should be put to bed and kept quiet and warm until he is rid of the condition.

MENTAL CONDITIONS AFFECTING HEALTH

Mind and body are one, and what affects one affects the other. It is said that a cross word will quicken the pulse of a sensitive horse and stop the digestive processes in an affectionate dog. The child's physical condition is not injured by lack of sympathy or by misunderstanding, but his mental nature may be sadly warped as a result of such treatment.

From an early age the child knows

when he is not doing the right thing; he should not be condoned for real disobedience, but justice should always be tempered with mercy and understanding.

A Cheerful Atmosphere. A cheerful atmosphere is beneficial both mentally and physically. While the child will come to be aware of domestic difficulties when they exist, he should not be subjected to emotional tension. The very existence of the child should be an incentive to adults to suppress any tendencies to quarrel or make scenes. Many parents are irritable and fretful with their children because of ill health or overwork, and sometimes these conditions are difficult to overcome. For the good of the family the parent will need to look after his own health and disposition as well as that of his child.

Sympathy and Understanding. Health of body and mind are promoted by sympathy and understanding. It is too often forgotten that the child has a mind of his own and that he does not find his greatest joy in life in meek service to the will or caprices of his elders. Only by trying to get his point of view and treating him with the same tact and diplomacy that the parent would use with adults, will he get his child's full cooperation and friendship. Never forget that the child is immature and cannot be expected to have adult reactions.

Self-Control and Consistency. A wise observer once remarked that parents are too often like the clown who appeared on the stage with a bundle of papers under each arm. When asked what was under his right arm, he replied, "They are orders." When asked what was under the other arm, he answered, "Counterorders." If a parent expects a child to be obedient, he should make definite decisions on any subject affecting the child's conduct. He should not immediately change his instructions if the child does not choose to obey. When the parent finds himself in the wrong, he should, of course, change his mind; but mere changeableness is not a desirable quality and it causes the child to lose his respect for the parent. Furthermore, the child is likely to imitate this quality of changeableness.

Variety. Variety is the spice of mental and physical life and for the young child it is also a means of education. Almost from the beginning he needs some variety of scene. He also needs some variety in playthings and, later, in playmates. Play has been called "the life of the child." He lives and he learns through play. It helps him to grow mentally and physically. Opportunity for play under safe and healthful conditions should be provided. (See Volume Eleven.)

LOOKING OVER THE HUMAN MECHANISM

Up to this point have been discussed the ways by which the child can be brought to his best and kept at his best by making the conditions to which he is exposed—either in the home or out of doors—what they ought to be. It is taken for granted that the bodily machinery of the child is as nearly perfect as possible, that he has no inherited physical defects, that he was not damaged before birth, and that he has escaped serious injury from disease. No matter what his age, he should be examined for physical defects or imperfections. If any are found, the parents should see what can be done to correct them without delay.

THE EYES

Clearness. The rounded, window-like front of the eyeball, surrounded by the white of the eye, should be as clear as the clearest and cleanest of glass. If this is not the case, if the window looks gray or whitish or if the black spot (the pupil) has a grayish or whitish appearance, something must have damaged the eye and the vision is not what it should be. A physician should be consulted.

Danger Signals. An inflammation of the eye or a discharge of water or pus are danger signals, frequently indicating a serious infection. Of course eyes become red from crying and from colds, but this refers now to something more severe. Such infections frequently accompany measles and other infectious diseases. Regardless of the cause, however, the eyes should have the best of care. A physician should be consulted and, in the meantime, the sore eyes should be cleansed every two hours with drops of a solution of boric acid (be sure the crystals are all dissolved) in luke-warm water. The application of cloths wrung from cold water will help to make the child comfortable until the parent is given further directions by the physician.

The Eyelids. Redness of the lids day after day or crusts on the lids are signs of eyestrain and should cause the parent to consult an eye specialist to see if the child needs glasses. These signs may be accompanied by sensitiveness to light or by complaints of pain, blurred vision, or headache. Such conditions are more likely to occur in the school child than in one of younger years.

Sties or painful swellings of the lids are not frequent in preschool children since such conditions are usually associated with eyestrain from close work. Sties may be due, in part, to poor general health. The frequent application of cloths wrung out of hot water helps to relieve the pain.

Cross-Eye. In his first months the child's two eyes may not always focus together, but by the age of one year this difficulty has usually been overcome. If only one eye is attracted to an object, while the other eye looks outward or inward or upward or downward, this latter eye is weaker and something is wrong with the muscles which control the eyes as a unit. This condition is called squint, or cross-eye, and should be corrected as early as possible. Otherwise the weaker and less-used eye will grow still weaker from lack of use. Some cases can be cured with special glasses, while others may need additional treatment. One of the eye muscles may need to be shortened or lengthened. The child who is treated early will not only see better but his appearance will be improved, which will please both the child and his parents.

Examination of the Eyes. Before a child enters school, his vision should be examined by an eye specialist.

THE EARS

A child who seems otherwise normal may not respond as expected to sounds which ordinarily attract a child's attention, such as the ringing of a bell (held where he does not see it). If he is deaf or hard of hearing, it is well to learn the fact so that if anything can be done to help him it may be done early.

One cause of poor hearing which may be remedied is a chronic discharge from the ear following acute disease. The parents cannot help but know of such a discharge, but they may not realize that the hearing is always affected by this condition. The running ear can always be helped, and usually cured, by proper treatment. Hearing improves more or less with the healing of the ear.

A child may have good hearing in one ear but not in the other. In the child of school age the ears can be tested separately by holding a watch close to the ear and then carrying it directly away toward the side a few inches at a time. The child then indicates when he can no longer hear the tick of the watch. The child should have his eyes closed, or a card should be held at the side of his head so that he cannot see the watch. One should also make sure that there is no other ticking object in the immediate neighborhood and that the child does not imagine that he hears the watch. The distance at which the tick should be heard may be determined by the parent by testing his own hearing (if it is normal).

The hearing of children is often damaged by such diseases as scarlet fever or measles, a possibility which should cause parents to be all the more cautious regarding needless exposure to infection.

THE NOSE AND THROAT

The nose may be stopped temporarily by a cold, but at other times there should be free passage of air. About one young child in twenty has adenoids (an obstructive growth in the nose). A child with such an obstruction not only cannot breathe well but he cannot sleep well or eat well; he is subject to frequent colds and to ear disease. Adenoids may also cause deformity of the face and chest. To find out whether or not he can breathe through his nose, ask the child to close his mouth tightly and try it, first showing him what you wish him to do. When adenoids are present they should be removed.

Sore throat is an all too common affection of childhood. In examining a little child the parent will be unable to locate the trouble without looking into the throat by opening the child's mouth and depressing his tongue with the handle of a spoon. With a child of three or four years and older a spoon or other tongue depressor is seldom needed. Merely ask the child to open his mouth wide and say a prolonged "Ah-h-h." He should stand or sit where a good light shines into his mouth. A flashlight is helpful in viewing the child's throat. In cases of sore throat the structures of the throat, including the tonsils, are red and swollen. The tonsils are the two rounded bodies which lie on either side of the throat just behind the curtain-like bands which descend from the soft palate at the rear of the roof of the mouth. The tonsils may be large or small, but in tonsillitis they often have yellowish spots where their natural crypts, or holes, are filled with material produced by the disease.

In diphtheria irregular spots or patches of gray substance often appear in the throat. No matter what their color or appearance, these spots or patches indicate an unhealthy condition and a physician should be consulted at once.

A foul breath may come from some diseased condition of the nose or mouth, but more often it is due to a disordered digestion and the cause should be investigated.

THE TEETH

As mentioned elsewhere, good teeth cannot be made from poor materials. Not all the causes of dental deformity and decay are known, but it *is* known that milk, fruit, and vegetables are the best builders of good teeth, and that candy (especially between meals) is particularly bad for teeth. A dentist is, of course, the person best equipped to find imperfections in teeth, and the child should become accustomed at an early age to visits to the dentist for examination. Any mother, however, can note marked irregularity in the teeth, especially of the second set.

If a child goes to the dentist early and regularly, much can be done to preserve the baby teeth for the usual time, and they deserve to be preserved if possible. The permanent teeth should have the best of care. The first of the permanent teeth are molars, which make their appearance about the sixth year directly behind the molars of the earlier set. These four new teeth are especially prone to decay. Therefore, the mother should

examine these and the other teeth every few weeks, between regular semi-annual visits to the dentist, for it is always easier to have small cavities filled than large ones. Parents make a great deal of fuss over the child's first teeth, but the first teeth of the second set are far more important. Gross irregularities or deformities of the permanent teeth should be treated as early as the dentist suggests, because in many cases much can be accomplished toward improving the child's appearance for life.

THE FACE AND LIPS

When considering the child's eyes, ears, nose, and mouth, his face and lips should not be overlooked. Not only should these parts be surveyed daily for evidence of the use of soap and water, but for any unusual flush or pallor, which may mean illness, or for dark circles under the eyes, which indicate fatigue. The lips are also telltale, for they may show by lack of color a poor quality of blood; or they may indicate by a bluish tinge some serious heart trouble.

Any eruption on the face is abnormal. If unaccompanied by general symptoms it will mean some form of skin disease due to a parasite or to faulty diet. Such skin diseases as impetigo or ringworm are frequently contracted at school and may be passed on by the school child to younger members of the household.

THE NECK

Swollen glands on the side of the neck are readily felt, and sometimes seen, as a chain of rounded lumps. They usually have their origin in decayed teeth, adenoids, or infected tonsils. The glands enlarge because they are overworked in trying to protect the rest of the body from the poisons which drain from these diseased structures. The glands usually diminish to their customary small size when the diseased organs are removed or cured. Sometimes, however, the glands are tubercular.

The thyroid gland, which lies at the front of the neck, often becomes enlarged and is then known as a goiter. Goiters are much more common in some sections of the country than in others, a condition which is apparently due to lack of iodine in the water or food. (See "Food and Nutrition," in this volume.) While a goiter may not always affect health, a physician should be consulted about the child who is afflicted in this way.

THE BACK

Every stockman is proud of the good points of his horses and cattle. Likewise, every parent should be proud of the beauty of his child's body and should look him over for his good and bad points.

Whether the child's back is perfect or not, the parent should be able to tell when something is wrong. There should be no marked difference from a normal appearance, such as projecting lumps on the spine. Furthermore, the child should not have to hold his backbone stiffly as if he were afraid to bend it. These two conditions indicate that there is something seriously wrong, especially if the child complains of pain in his body or limbs.

When viewed from behind, the spine should deviate very little from the vertical when the child stands with both feet together. If the spine deviates greatly or if one shoulder is much higher than the other, a physician should be consulted.

In the thin child the shoulder blades may be prominent, but in a child who is not overfatigued these bones should be held back sufficiently to prevent round shoulders. When viewed from the side, children differ widely in their posture. If the child tends to droop from his normal attitude, if his head and shoulders are farther forward than usual, he is overtired or ill. (See "Posture," in this volume.)

THE CHEST

Every child should be able to take a deep breath without pain, and both sides of his chest should expand equally. The child should not become breathless on slight exertion, such as going upstairs, when the adult or normal child would not show this reaction. Rapid breathing in a child who is otherwise apparently well usually indicates a leaking heart, and he may need to be kept from strenuous exercise. A physician will make recommendations as to the amount of exercise such a child may safely indulge in.

THE ABDOMEN

The child's abdomen should show no protrusions. A lump or swelling at the navel or in the groin is not natural and probably indicates a rupture, or hernia. This condition is not uncommon, but it should receive the attention of a physician.

ABNORMALITIES

Deformities. A child should be examined for deformities or irregularities and asymmetry, not only of the trunk but of the limbs. Children are frequently born with a deformity, such as clubfoot. The earlier these conditions are treated the more easily they are corrected. In many cases the treatment can be carried out by the parent.

Infantile paralysis has been all too frequent in recent years. There is no known way of preventing an attack of this disease except by keeping the child from contact with other children during an epidemic. A great deal can be done to bring about improvement if paralysis has occurred, and the parent should follow the physician's directions carefully and persistently.

Speech Defects. Many children have defects of speech, such as lisping or stammering. Some of these defects are due to physical conditions (such as tongue-tie) or to faults in the palate. Besides physical treatment, the child will need special training in speech.

The child who stammers or stutters has a nervous defect which is not easy to correct but which it is often possible to cure. Many children stammer more or less when they are learning to talk, for their desire for expression runs ahead of their ability. By the time the child is five years old he should talk naturally and distinctly. The stammering child should be treated with the utmost sympathy by his parents and others in the household and should also have the best of help in overcoming his defect. (See "Speech Defects," in Volume Eight.)

Nervousness. One could fill pages with definitions and descriptions of the nervous child without adding materially to the average person's conception of the meaning of the term. Everyone has some understanding of what the term signifies. Nervous people are those who accomplish things in the world, their very restlessness being a constant urge to activity. The nervous child needs to be curbed as much as possible, but wisely. He needs more sleep and rest than other children do, and he should have plenty of easily digested food. Any physical disability which tends to exhaust him, such as eyestrain, should be removed.

Nervousness on the part of the father or mother, or both, makes the child more nervous than he would otherwise be. Therefore treatment may need to begin with better control on the part of the parents. An atmosphere of calm in the home will help greatly in overcoming a child's nervousness.

SCHOOL DAYS

Should the child be sent to school at the age of five or six or seven or later? Some of those who have studied the problem would not have the child enter school until he is eight or even ten. The vast majority of children, however, who are in normal physical condition should enter school along with their fellows at the prescribed age. If a child is sickly and delicate it may be well to keep him at home until he is stronger.

The matter of going to school should not be discussed before the child other than to give him the impression that school days are happy days—which they should be and usually are. If the child does not go to and from school in a bus or other conveyance, he should be sent in care of an older child who can be relied on for safe conduct. The child himself should receive early training in caution and in safety procedures, but great care must be taken with very young children in view of the enormous accident rate.

THE SCHOOL AND HEALTH

The modern school is, as a rule, a healthful place. Educators have made health one of their main objectives and, while it is not always possible to attain that objective, they are striving in that direction. Much depends on the co-operation of the home. Parents must see that the school building is comfortable and is furnished with sanitary equipment and efficient janitorial service. They must co-operate with the school health service in protecting the children against communicable diseases. Most important of all, they must help the child to practice the health facts which he is taught in school.

MORNING PREPARATION FOR SCHOOL

"Early to bed and early to rise is the way to be healthy and wealthy and wise." The child is not likely to get the best results from the time spent at school if he is hauled, half asleep, from his bed for a very hurried or meager breakfast and then rushed to school. Already mentioned is the need for plenty of sleep and for an early bedtime in order to establish the proper health habits. The child should be up in time to wash his face, clean his teeth, comb his hair, clean his fingernails, and carefully dress himself before breakfast. He should eat deliberately, visit the toilet after breakfast, and still have plenty of time to reach school.

PROPER CLOTHING FOR SCHOOL

In September the child does not need a special type of clothing, but he should not be so finely clad that he cannot play comfortably with his fellows. Throughout the year he should be protected against wet weather by a good pair of rubbers and a raincoat or an umbrella. In some schools children are asked to keep a pair of stockings at school so that a change can be made if their feet get wet in coming to school. Wet shoes and stockings are not much of a menace when the child is active, but in a warm, dry room the rapid evaporation of water from wet shoes chills the feet and leads to colds or more serious illnesses. Rubbers, galoshes, or zippers should not be worn in school or in the home.

Outer clothing should be suitable for the weather, but the indoor clothing worn at school should not be heavier than that ordinarily worn at home. Schools are usually overheated rather than underheated, and many children are overclothed in school. Sweaters and all other cold-weather garments should be removed by the child when in the schoolroom or when engaged in active play. He should be trained to put them on immediately after vigorous play, however, if he remains where it is cold or windy. (See "Clothing," in this volume.)

FEEDING THE SCHOOL CHILD

The school child is, or should be, hungry at mealtimes, and hungry children need more food for their size than do adults. He should begin the day with a good breakfast of fruit, cereal, egg (or a slice of bacon), toast, and milk. The milk should not be too cold. Hot milk (flavored with cocoa if preferred) is excellent in cold weather.

If the child stays at school for the noon lunch the parent should see that he chooses what is suitable. If his eating habits have been well formed there will be no difficulty along this line. If the lunch is brought from home it should be a nourishing one. (See "Food and Nutrition," in this volume.)

The child who shows signs or symptoms of a communicable disease (including a cold) should not be allowed to go to school until it is evident that he has no serious illness. No child with a fever should be sent to school. If an ailing child is sent home the parent should be thankful that the school is so considerate.

DISEASES CONTRACTED AT SCHOOL

In spite of all precautions taken at school, communicable diseases are often contracted there. As mentioned elsewhere, there is no need for the child to contract smallpox or diphtheria. The possibility of his acquiring skin diseases, such as impetigo, the itch (scabies), and ringworm, or a vermin-infested head is quite common. Some of these afflictions —especially lice—are no respecters of persons. If a mother receives notice from the school that George or Lucy has a skin disease she need not be astonished or feel that she is forever disgraced. If daily inspection of the child is the practice at home, however, the mother herself will be the first to make such a discovery.

THE SCHOOL HEALTH SERVICE

In many modern schools children are examined by physician, dentist, nurse, or teacher at the beginning of the year (sometimes before school opens) for such defects of eyes, ears, teeth, and so on, as have already been mentioned. Often the mother is invited to be present at this examination and the child's general health and health habits are discussed. Sometimes a note is sent from the school principal or other official telling the parents what the examination revealed about the child's health. It is expected, of course, that the parent will consult the family physician or dentist in regard to these findings. If the parents have followed the suggestions made previously in this article the child will ordinarily be in good health when he goes to school. If all parents gave their children adequate care there would be no need for medical and dental inspection in schools.

HEALTH EDUCATION

Schools endeavor to instruct children in the daily practices which make for health, such as cleanliness, rest, and proper eating habits, which children will acquire at home if the parents are giving attention to these essentials of hygiene. The child, of course, cannot very well carry out what he learns at school if conditions in the home are not conducive to proper health habits. There must be intelligent direction and co-operation on the part of parents—a fact which is obvious from the preceding pages.

HOME STUDY

As a rule there is little need for home study—in the usual sense of the term—

during the child's first three or four years in school, but most children like to talk about their schoolwork at home. Parents should show interest and enthusiasm in what the child is doing and should keep in close touch with the school. The teacher is very greatly interested in the progress of the pupil and welcomes an equal interest and understanding on the part of parents. The school life of the child should never be a source of worry and anxiety to him. Any difficulties which arise can usually be adjusted between parent and teacher in friendly conference.

The child should have a special place for his books and the other materials he uses at home—a table or desk of suitable size and height. He should have a comfortable chair, and if this must be of adult dimensions, the child will need a stool or box on which to rest his feet. He should have adequate light which does not shine in his eyes but comes from above or over his shoulder (preferably the left). If the child prepares lessons at home, he should be required to get them done early enough so that he will have ample time to prepare for bed and go at the usual hour.

SUMMARY

The health of the child is of the greatest importance, since it is the condition upon which happiness and efficiency depend.

The newborn child is the most helpless of beings; therefore his start in life depends upon the knowledge and care bestowed by his parents.

Proper feeding is one of the essentials of health. The child must have all the food elements necessary for growth if he is to develop properly. Furthermore, his feeding must be adjusted to his age and individual characteristics, since no two children are exactly alike. General rules must be modified to fit the individual.

Besides proper feeding the infant needs abundant rest and the opportunity to exercise his eyes and ears and limbs. He should have good air to breathe and should be comfortably housed and clothed. He should be kept clean and given frequent baths in the sunshine.

From the day of his birth the child is beset with his life-long enemies—the germs of disease. He can be protected from these to a large degree and some diseases can be prevented entirely.

Many children have imperfections of eyes, ears, heart, limb, or some other member or organ, and these should be noted early and corrected if possible.

When the child goes to school, new health problems arise. Everything should be done to make school a happy and healthful experience. The teachers are as desirous of such results as are the parents.

Children of all ages need a healthy emotional atmosphere in the home. Parents should understand fully the conditions which make for mental health as well as those which have to do with physical health.

QUESTIONS

1. What is health?
2. What foods are of first importance?
3. Why does the child need relatively more food than an adult?
4. What is the relation between the kind of food and the quality of the teeth?
5. Why is sleep so important to the child?
6. How does light affect the health of the child? Is there danger from direct sunlight in summer?
7. Is there a right height and a right weight for the child?
8. Against what diseases can the child be protected? How can he be protected?
9. Should he be shielded from all infectious diseases so far as possible?
10. How is the condition of the throat related to ear troubles?
11. How does the emotional atmosphere of the home affect the child?
12. Why should cross-eye be treated as early as possible?
13. Why should the school child go to bed early?
14. Should outer wraps and overshoes be worn indoors?

READING REFERENCES

BOOKS

Alschuler, Rose H. (editor), *Two to Six* (Morrow).

Cameron, Hector C., *The Nervous Child* (Oxford).

Dwyer, Hugh L., *Your Child in Health and in Sickness* (Knopf).

Kenyon, Josephine, *Healthy Babies Are Happy Babies* (Little).

Langdon, Grace, *Home Guidance for Young Children* (Day).

Norlin, Elinor E., *Everyday Nursing for the Everyday Home* (Macmillan).

Rose, Mary S., *Feeding the Family* (Macmillan).

Sherbon, Florence B., *Child: His Origin, Development and Care* (McGraw).

PAMPHLETS

American Medical Association, *Keeping Your Baby Well.*

Carpenter, Rowena Schmidt, *Good Food Habits for Children* (U. S. Department of Agriculture, Leaflet No. 4).

Gillett, Lucy H., *Diet for the School Child* (U. S. Department of the Interior, Office of Education, Health Education Series No. 2).

Murray and Eliot, *The Child from One to Six, His Care and Training* (U. S. Department of Labor, Children's Bureau, Publication No. 30).

Shaw, Henry, *The Healthy Child* (Funk).

Sherman, Henry C., *The Problem of Sweets for Children* (American Public Health Association, New York).

U. S. Department of Labor, Children's Bureau, *Backyard Playgrounds.*

NORMAL RATES OF DEVELOPMENT

Lovisa C. Wagoner

Height and weight are two important measuring sticks of health during childhood. Physicians, psychologists, and others who have worked with children have also found certain definite abilities, making their appearance at approximately the same age in all normal children, which can be used as a standard for determining whether or not a child is progressing as he should. The author is Chairman of the Department of Child Development, School of Education, Mills College, California. She has had a number of years' experience with children of preschool age, and is the author of *The Development of Learning in Young Children*.

THERE is an ancient nursery rhyme that deals with the growth of Mistress Mary's garden. Included in that garden's growing are "pretty maids all in a row." Far back in time stretches an interest in the growth of children. Many a doorjamb in humble home and in royal palace is marked to show successive heights of the children who have lived there. With increased precision of technique, measurements have become increasingly accurate and have been made in greater variety.

In the developing individual, growth of structure and of function are so intimately related that it is often impossible to separate the two. In the youngest children development is measured or estimated in terms of responses. As language is acquired, it is possible to gather information as to the child's grasps of relationships and of ideas.

Is the child all right? Is his body perfect? Such questions are uppermost in the mind, if not on the lips, of every parent of a newborn baby. Day by day growth is eagerly watched and every sign of growing intelligence noted attentively. Inevitably each parent compares his own child with other children to judge whether he is developing as he should. Such casual standards must in the nature of the case be inexact. If the important question, "How bright is my baby?" is to be intelligently answered, some reliable schedule of development is needed.

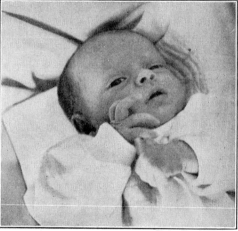

Photo: Donald M. Snow

" 'Is the child all right?' is probably in the mind, if not on the lips, of every parent of a newborn baby."

To be trustworthy a schedule or scale of development must be based on continued observation of many children. As a matter of fact, such information is steadily being gathered so that the significance of the manner of responding to parents and of reacting to objects is more and more apparent. This article is intended to help each parent to compare and to decide for himself what may be expected of his own child.

Every parent knows that each of his own children is a person in his own right, is unique, and that each shows some individualities in development. He knows also that he himself is not exactly like his brothers and sisters. Since babies do not come in standard sizes—and, fortunately, are never identical—each child's development will, to some extent, be unlike that of every other child. There are times when a baby seems to be developing slowly and other times when development goes along more rapidly. Then again there may seem to be pauses during which little or no development occurs.

During certain periods a child may be consolidating his gains. Again, sickness, accident, or the upsets that are inevitable in family life may temporarily retard a baby's growth. The younger he is, the more far-reaching the effects of adverse conditions. Yet babies, fortunately, are remarkably durable; nature provides a margin of safety great enough to take care of most mishaps.

The growth impulse that characterizes all normal individuals, ensures progress toward maturity. Obviously growth cannot take place in all directions at the same time. The point of emphasis of most rapid growth changes so that the needs of the developing organism are anticipated. The upper part of the body develops earlier; those body parts that are essential to survival develop first; heart, lungs, liver; head rather than trunk; arms before legs. Then those that provide for a more extended radius of activity grow more rapidly. In addition, seasonal variations in growth appear. In summer and early autumn the baby grows in height; in winter he increases in weight.

The orderly progress of development should be kept in mind. One stage of growth follows another in much the same order in all children. While there are individual variations, comparison of children reveals the fact that growth and development are neither haphazard nor undirected but follow a systematic sequence. Each stage is important in and of itself and as a basis of preparation for the next. Orderly as the course of development is, it may not run smoothly. At times the baby seems to be at a standstill; at other times he seems to have slipped backward; but looking back over a period of months, the mother can see that progress has been made.

It must never be assumed, however, that growth proceeds identically in different children. The margin of safety mentioned above permits considerable variation in the age as well as in the manner of development of body and of responses. This variation within the normal range permits a certain elasticity in the interpretation of standards or criteria of growth.

Occasionally babies are born who will

never develop normally, but these are the exception rather than the rule. Good physical care, opportunity for exercise, affection, and as much freedom as is practicable—these things will help to bring about normal development.

In order to give a child the training that is best for him, it is important to know what children should be able to do at various ages. Such queries do not imply that all children are exactly alike. Each child is unique and differs in many ways from any other child who ever was born. Underneath the differences, however, are definite likenesses and similarities. It is the likenesses which make it possible for human beings to live and work together.

A person who knows only a few Chinese, and knows them only casually, finds it difficult to distinguish one from another because apparently they all look alike. Strangers see family resemblances that escape the members of the family itself. Sisters who think themselves completely different may be embarrassed when acquaintances confuse one with the other. Just as there is a certain "doggy" quality that characterizes all dogs—large, small, long-haired, or short-haired—so there is a catlike quality that marks all cats, even kittens. In somewhat the same fashion there are human traits that all persons possess merely because they are human beings.

Such homely proverbial phrases as "chip off the old block" or "the very spit and image" indicate that family likenesses are expected. Such likenesses are not limited to resemblances to the parents. A grandmother, cousin, great-

aunt, or even a more distant relative may be the one whom the child resembles. In one of his novels Joseph Hergesheimer describes the Black Pennys who appeared generation after generation in a certain family.

Because these fundamental likenesses do exist, it is possible to state with some definiteness what may be expected of a child. Knowing what a given child probably is able to do, parents can understand more clearly what he should be learning and how to go about teaching him. They can find out the sort of playthings he should have and the kinds of things that will probably interest him. Children seem to have a good deal of ability in choosing for themselves the playthings that are best suited to their needs, but adults must carefully select the opportunities and materials that are offered a child. No one expects a child who is just learning to walk and is barely able to hold himself upright to enjoy a walking board that is raised several inches from the ground. On the other hand, the child who walks freely enjoys testing his skill with such a board. Bulkheads offer an almost irresistible temptation to children and most adults remember the pleasure they had in successfully walking the rails of the railroad track.

RECORDS AND NORMS

From time immemorial parents have kept records of their children's development. In ancient Greek and Latin manuscripts interesting observations regarding children are found. In one such account a Grecian woman attributes all her child's faults to his father. The

Scriptures tell of the Child who waxed and grew strong and found favor in the eyes of God and man.

In the nineteenth century certain distinguished physiologists kept careful records of the age at which their own children sat up, smiled, walked, and talked. Charles Darwin also kept such records of the development of his oldest son, although he did not publish them until thirty years afterward. Baby books are filled with these interesting records. To be of any value, such individual records must be supplemented by observations of large numbers of children. In the twentieth century records have been kept of the development of many children and these records are even more valuable than individual ones because they were all made under the same conditions. Gradually enough of these careful records have been accumulated so that norms are established.

A norm is a statement of what may be expected of a normal or average child. This simply means that the majority of children who have been studied behave in the way that is described. It does not mean that *every* baby will. Because children differ, these norms have to provide for what is called the "range of variation." If this difference is too great, if the child is too different from the majority of children, he is spoken of as either subnormal or superior. In other words, some children are precocious in their development and some are slow. The extremes are described as genius or idiot. This article, however, considers only the great majority of children, those called normal, usual, or average. (See the next volume for "The Child Who Is Different.")

For the average child these standards or norms serve as a sort of check sheet against which progress of a particular individual can be estimated. If the discrepancy seems too great, it is well to talk the matter over with an experienced pediatrician or child psychologist. These specialists have seen and worked with enough children to be able to estimate progress achieved and to interpret standards. It is never wise to trust the word of neighbors and relatives nor to be satisfied with comparing one's own children with his cousins or with the children who live next door.

Differences Due to Inheritance

Inheritance sets the limits of development beyond which the individual cannot go. The possibilities of development may be interfered with by accident, disease, or other limitations of the environment. Parents are interested in making sure that each of their children develops to the fullest of his possibilities. Complete development is furthered by fortunate conditions and consequently home, school, and community work together to provide, in so far as possible, the best conditions for each particular child.

Physical differences among families are reflected in differences among children. The children of tall parents are likely to be tall but not quite so tall as their parents. The children of small-boned individuals tend to be delicately built. Temperament seems to be closely related to the physiological structure. A child's

Photo: Camera Guild-Monkemeyer

A NORMAL, HAPPY CHILDHOOD IS THE RIGHT OF EVERY HUMAN BEING

The best way to further children's normal development is to surround them with wholesome conditions of life and to enjoy them because they are themselves.

vigor or vitality is in part a matter of the inherited or family strain and in part a matter of the conditions under which he has developed. All these factors contribute to variability; they join in making each person different from every other person.

In deciding what to expect of a particular child it is important to remember his actual age, especially in the case of babies. According to Dr. Arnold Gesell, of Yale University, the actual age of a child should be figured from conception rather than from birth, since the prema-ture child is actually younger than the child born at term.

While the premature infant is handicapped because he is less fully developed at birth, he does respond to the increased stimulation of the environment and does tend to lessen his handicap and to catch up with his brother who was born at term. Just when this will happen depends upon the degree of prematurity. In order to facilitate this catching up, the child born before term must have a protective environment and the special care he needs.

Rate of Physical Growth

In considering the normal rate of development remember that, while the child is increasing in size, his growing bodily structures are becoming more and more capable of making use of the world in which he finds himself. In other words, the child is both growing and developing.

The heart of the newborn child beats much more rapidly than does that of the adult. The pulse rate is 130 to 150 per minute as contrasted with 60 to 72 in the adult. His respiration rate is 35 to 45 per minute while the adult rate is 16 to 18. Variation is the most conspicuous characteristic of the infant heartbeat and rate of respiration.

The head of the newborn is tremendous, the trunk is long and tends to be barrel shaped, and the arms and legs are short. In bodily proportions the baby differs markedly from the adult. If the adult's head were greater in breadth than his shoulders, if his head were one quarter the length of his whole body, and if his legs represented another fourth of his height, he would be a grotesque creature indeed—a figure of fun or of pathos, as one happened to look at it.

It has been said that the minerals in the human body could be bought in the open market for seventy-five cents. When one realizes that the body of the fetus is 95.5 per cent water, the newborn's 74.7 per cent and the adult's 58.5 per cent, one understands this apparently absurd statement.

The legs of a baby are bent and the soles of the feet face one another. The large liver demands an abdomen large in proportion to the rest of the body. The softness of the skin, the flexibility of bones so largely cartilaginous, the slow reactions of the pupils of the eyes to light —all these contribute to the picture of the newborn child. Infant and adult are alike in the number and the nature of organs, muscles, and bones, and in the chemical elements present. They differ as to size of the various parts, both absolute and relative, and in the amount of the chemical constituents.

Leonardo da Vinci was the first artist who understood the anatomy of the child well enough to draw the body in its true proportions. The children in the paintings of earlier artists seem queer because they are drawn like little men and women.

Not so long ago children were regarded as miniature adults so far as their treatment in illness was involved; doses were scaled downward, to be sure, but there was little other change. Pediatrics is a comparatively young branch of medicine. In many parts of the world today children dress exactly like their fathers and mothers. As a matter of fact, children's clothes are a fairly recent fashion, even in America; family portraits show clearly that this is a modern change.

This notion that children are miniature adults was even more obvious in the management and training of boys and girls. Even yet it has not altogether disappeared from our thinking and our attitude toward children. In his book, *Children and Puritanism,* Sandford Fleming has described the little men and women who carried adult responsibilities at tender years and who were expected to

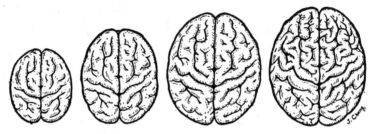

At birth the brain has acquired more than a quarter of its adult size; by eighteen months, more than half; and by six years, nine-tenths. At the right is shown an adult's brain.

behave with the discretion of adults and to have the emotional responses of adults.

Just as structure and function in the child differ from those of the adult, so does the behavior of the child differ from adult behavior. It is not to be expected nor would it be desirable that a child should act like a tiny adult. Activity, growth, and development are intimately related; behavior suitable at one age ceases to be acceptable as the child grows older. The child is constantly progressing toward maturity, and while childhood is not an end in itself, its value as progress toward maturity does not cancel its importance at every stage of development. The activities of the child also progress toward maturity; behavior once suitable ceases to be acceptable as the child develops. Upon this almost kaleidoscopic change depends the perfection of adult functioning. It is easy to accept the statement that changes in behavior are manifestations of development, but it is not always easy to understand that activity (so often inconvenient) is progressing toward maturity. It is easy also to lose sight of the continuity of growth.

The rate of growth is most rapid at the beginning of life; thus infancy is extremely important in the development of the child. As life goes on, the rate decreases. During the first three months of prenatal life the fertilized ovum (which is a single cell less than one seven-hundredth of an inch in diameter) grows into a body containing practically all the important structures found in an adult. Another illustration of this tremendous rate of growth is shown by the fact that from fertilization until birth the human ovum increases from less than a millimeter in diameter to about 530 millimeters and from .0000005 of a gram in weight to 2,500 grams or more. During the years of childhood the body multiplies its birth weight about twenty times. According to some authorities, long babies grow into tall adults. Birth weight, however, gives less indication of what the adult weight will be.

Growth conforms to what is called the law of developmental direction, which means that the head and trunk develop first and the extremities later. In other words, growth proceeds from head to foot. The primary importance of the brain and nervous system in the development of the individual is brought out by Scammon's statement that at birth the brain has acquired more than a quarter of its adult size; by eighteen months it has acquired over half; and by six years, nine-tenths.

After birth, growth is most rapid during the first two years, gradually decreasing from the exceedingly rapid rate of the first months. From two to ten years of age the rate is slow but constant. Between the ages of ten and seventeen or eighteen there comes another period of rapid growth, when arms grow out of sleeves and muscles are not quite equal to managing the bones that have become suddenly long. Usually before the age of twenty this awkwardness disappears and growth proceeds at a slower rate, giving muscles a chance to catch up with bones.

Each organ or part of the body grows according to its own particular fashion or rate. Lungs, blood, and skeleton grow at approximately the same rate as the body as a whole. Heart, liver, and spleen have done much of their growing before birth, increasing from ten- to fifteenfold between birth and maturity. The nervous system and sense organs have accomplished so much of their growth before birth that they increase only fourfold in all the postnatal life.

The increasing repertoire of a child's responses may be compared with standards of normal development. At the risk of being tedious, it must be said again that a child's conformity to these standards is seldom exact and that any given baby may be slower or faster in his development and still be a normal baby. It should be remembered that illness or other unfortunate conditions may interfere with the baby's development. The best way to further his development is to surround him with wholesome conditions of life and to enjoy him because he is himself; he does not need to be exactly like any other baby. In so far as possible, parents should plan a child's surroundings so that they will call forth desirable behavior. Always remember that no matter how much a child resembles someone else, he really is *himself*.

What May Be Expected of the Child

The responses and activities that may be expected at each age level give a more or less definite picture of a child at that particular level.[*]

PRENATAL DEVELOPMENT

Before the baby is born he has had a good many experiences and during the nine months of prenatal life he has been developing as well as growing. These prenatal experiences are important because they are steps in the journey toward maturity. Certain impressions from the outside world reach him, and his own body functions have their particular type of activity. He responds to his own limited and uniform environment, which does provide sensory stimulation. Though limited in comparison with the greater opportunities into which birth ushers the child, these very experiences make later learning possible.

Information about the responses of the fetus is gathered in several ways, but first of all from the reports of the mother, who is naturally very sensitive to the movements of the child. By means of a

---

[*] The material on children's responses has been drawn from authoritative scientific reports.

stethoscope the physician can listen to the fetal heartbeat. Other careful recording devices are used to gather more information about actual activities of the fetus. Children born prematurely and fetuses removed by Caesarean section—and therefore not subjected to the strain of the birth process—are additional sources of information with regard to the stages of development.

The fact that the infant is mature enough to function as an independent person some time before the completion of the usual period of gestation protects it against the hazards of premature birth. Dr. Gesell says that nature apparently hastens to perfect those functions most vital for postnatal life and thus provide against the contingency of premature birth.

Children born during the sixth month of pregnancy have some chance of survival. The infant delivered prematurely at six months is able to cry, and a fetus born at the beginning of the seventh month shows the usual responses of a full-term child. In summarizing, it can be said that during the prenatal period movements of the head, trunk, arms, and legs occur and the fetus is sensitive to touch, temperature, movement, and pain.

Some responses which prepare the fetus for the outside world are listed below.

Photo: Vivian Rodvogin

At about nine months the normal baby should begin to creep.

RESPONSES OF THE NEWBORN BABY

The baby at birth may cry, sneeze, and yawn; at the age of seven days he may

STAGES OF PRENATAL DEVELOPMENT	AGE OF APPEARANCE
Activity of heart detected	3rd week
Fetal movement actually occurs	5th–6th week
Temporary teeth begin to form	7th week
Slow movements of arms and legs	7th week
Peristaltic movements possible	7th week
Mouth movements	3rd month
Heartbeats can be detected by doctor	15th–16th week
Calcification of crowns of temporary teeth begins	17th week
Movements perceptible to mother (quickening)	17th–18th week
Movements of thorax, regarded as respiratory	5th month
Hiccup	5th month
Fetal heartbeats at rate of 130–160 per minute	5th month, until term
Crowns of permanent teeth begin to calcify	8th month

hiccup. At birth he is able to turn his head or even raise it and is also able to kick, sometimes alternating his legs rhythmically. Sucking, swallowing, and other movements of the tongue, cheek, and lip, all of which are needed in feeding, are possible for the newborn. Crying is usually accompanied by a rhythmic kicking. If supported properly, many babies make walking or prancing steps.

During the first days after birth the newborn infant is adapting himself to what probably is the greatest change of his whole existence. His environment heretofore has been a changeless, constant one in which he has been fed with no effort on his part. He has not been subjected to the variety in texture nor to the handling which are inevitable after birth. Sounds, vibrations, changes in temperature now surround him.

During the prenatal period the respiratory, digestive, and excretory systems act hardly at all because these functions are taken care of by the placenta. At birth, however, these systems begin to act in the manner that will characterize the rest of the individual's life. The process of breathing in itself would make his present activity vary from that of prenatal life.

As soon as the child has suckled for the first time, his own digestive apparatus begins working. The alimentary canal of the baby plays a dominant role in his activity, for when hunger contractions occur he is more active. Every mother is familiar with the restlessness of the hungry baby and the subsequent quiet after nursing. She also knows that a baby is very active early in the morning, but she may not know that he is likely to be quiet around noon. A baby spends most of his time sleeping. In fact, according to Pratt and Nelson (in *The Behavior of the Newborn Infant*), during the first two weeks after birth the infant is awake only a limited amount of the time. During the day the sleep is broken about every two hours.

What sort of person is this newborn? He is not very efficient in the regulation of his own body heat, partly because the surface area of his body is so great in

Responses of Newborn Baby	Age of Appearance
Turns head to free nose, when face down	At birth
Sensitive to intensity of light	At birth
(If held horizontally will turn the eyes toward a faint light.)	
Sensitive to taste substances	At birth
(This is shown by facial expression, changes in sucking responses, circulation, and respiration.)	
Cries (first use of organs of speech)	At birth
Waves arms and legs, wriggles, stretches	At birth
Spreads and closes hands	At birth
Sneezes, hiccoughs, yawns, swallows	At birth
Comparatively insensitive to pain	At birth
The hand grasps an object that touches its palm	At birth
Makes fleeting attempts to catch sight of moving or bright objects	First week
Blinks at a sound	First two weeks
Focuses his eyes on his mother's hands or face	Two–three weeks
Holds chin up when lying face down	Three weeks

comparison to its bulk and partly because the necessary nervous centers are not yet fully developed. When cold, a baby may help to increase his heat production by shivering or crying. In terms of unit weight, the metabolism of the newborn

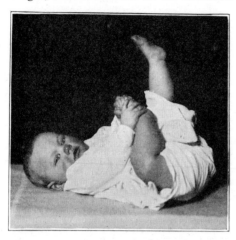

The six-months-old baby likes to play with his toes and can put his big toe in his mouth.

is two and a half times that of the adult. When crying, a baby's metabolism may be three times as great as when sleeping quietly. A child's blood pressure increases as he grows older.

The amount of energy a baby uses up is very great; in proportion to his size it is about two and one-half times that of the mother. Crying further increases the proportional difference; when he is asleep he expends perhaps one-third as much energy as when he cries. Hungry babies cry and so do thirsty ones.

The whole body of the newborn baby responds to light stimulation. Not only do the pupils of the eyes contract or dilate, but other movements are made as well. As every mother knows, the move-

ments of eyelids and eyeballs are not symmetrical. Sudden, sharp, loud sounds call forth more of a response than gentle sounds. Each type of sound stimulation calls forth a response of its own. The baby may seem deaf at first because the canal between the surface of the face and the middle ear is not yet filled with air or because the auditory cavities are filled with mucus or for some other temporary cause.

RESPONSES AT ONE MONTH

The baby looks at his mother's face.
His eyes follow a moving light.
When held against the shoulder he lifts his head.
If he lies on his stomach he lifts his chin.
He makes crawling movements when he lies prone on a flat surface.
Pays attention to sound.
Looks at a moving object.
Stares at a window.
He has different cries for discomfort, pain, and hunger.
He will hold a ring (a large wooden one) which is placed in his hand.

RESPONSES AT TWO MONTHS

The baby looks at his mother's face; his eyes are open more widely; his expression seems to show more interest than the one-month baby.
He frequently brings his hand to his mouth.
His eyes follow a moving person.
He turns his eyes toward a bright light.
He turns his head in response to a speaking voice and reacts to changing tones of voice.

He holds his head erect.

If placed on his stomach he can hold his chest up.

In the bath he kicks his feet and reacts with pushing leg movements.

He expresses feelings of comfort and discomfort.

Between two and six months of age babies babble in reply when talked to.

Singing tones develop.

The baby coos.

He smiles at his mother.

He may stop crying for a moment at the sound of a comforting voice.

RESPONSES AT THREE MONTHS

He recognizes his mother and father.

He looks toward the source of a sound.

His eyes follow a moving pencil.

He fingers one hand with the other and feels objects (active touch).

The muscles of eyes, head, and neck are well controlled.

He props himself on his elbows.

He turns his head in different directions.

He holds both head and shoulders erect when he is lying prone.

The baby holds a rattle for a minute or two.

He reaches for the dangling ring.

The thumb no longer lies across the palm but is held parallel with the fingers.

He expresses pleasure vocally.

He returns a glance, smiling or cooing.

Some babies laugh out loud.

He babbles even when alone.

A comforting voice usually serves to stop his crying.

Music quiets him.

He gives a variety of grunts, clicks, and gurgles.

Such syllables as "ma," "ba," "goo," "hauh," and "aah" are uttered.

RESPONSES AT FOUR MONTHS

His eyes now begin to see details.

He turns his head to follow a moving person with his eyes.

Photo: Loder

The two-year-old likes to play in the sand.

His eyes follow objects moved up and down, sideways, or in a circle.

He promptly turns his head toward the source of a sound.

When carried he holds his head steady.

His hands are no longer always clenched but frequently are open.

He plays with his hands and looks at them with interest.

When in his bath, he splashes with his hand.

He grasps an object he sees.

The baby recognizes his bottle.

When an adult stops playing with him the baby expresses displeasure.

He smiles at another child.

He laughs out loud.

By the time a child is two and a half he enjoys using paints and brush.

He is but little affected by strange persons.

He wants to play at feeding time.

RESPONSES AT FIVE MONTHS

He turns his head when he hears a voice.

His eyes follow what his hands are doing.

He holds his bottle.

He will smile at another child.

He can pick up a rattle he has dropped.

He rolls from side to back.

If supported he sits up; if supporting hands are withdrawn he sits for a brief moment.

He sits up on his mother's lap.

When his hand touches a small object he picks it up.

He can pick up a cup.

Familiar adults are welcomed.

He discriminates between people he knows and strangers.

He expresses both interest and displeasure.

He resents opposition or interference.

He smiles and waves his hands when he sees his bottle but protests when it is removed.

He reflects friendly or angry facial expressions.

He repeats syllables such as "awooh-awah" or "lul-lul-lah."

RESPONSES AT SIX MONTHS

His eyes follow a toy when it drops.

He rolls from back to stomach or from stomach to back.

He sits for a moment without support and can sit alone in his high chair.

He can pick up a small object deftly.

For a moment he holds two cubes, one in either hand.

He reaches persistently for something just too far away for him to touch.

He bangs with his spoon or pats the table in play.

He can use the handle to pick up a cup.

He pushes with his feet, plays with his toes, puts his toe in his mouth.

He enjoys playing with his toes.

He will hold out his arms to be taken up.

He recognizes familiar people.

He coos to music.

Most babies of six months laugh out loud.

He shows that he knows the difference between friendly and angry talking.

RESPONSES AT SEVEN MONTHS

He can sit alone for a minute.

He smiles at his image in the mirror.

He looks momentarily for a spoon that has fallen.

He shows that he recognizes his mother when she reappears.

Often he cries and draws away when danger approaches.

He smiles and reaches toward another baby.

He expresses his satisfaction vocally.

He is interested in such sounds as the banging of toys or the ringing of bells.

RESPONSES AT EIGHT MONTHS

He puts his bottle back into his mouth.

He lifts a cup that is upside down, by the handle.

He stands with help.

He yells to attract the attention of adults.

He plays peekaboo or pat-a-cake.

He is interested in throwing.

He enjoys making sounds in play.

RESPONSES AT NINE MONTHS

He sits alone.

He crawls on hands and knees.

He stands with support and is able to let himself down again so that he sits on the floor.

He makes stepping movements.

He may creep or "hitch" across the floor.

Music calls forth rhythmic movements.

He uses thumb and finger to pick up small objects.

He can reach for, pick up and hold small objects.

He drops and tries to throw his toys again and again.

He can hold his cup.

He listens with interest to familiar words.

He waves bye-bye.

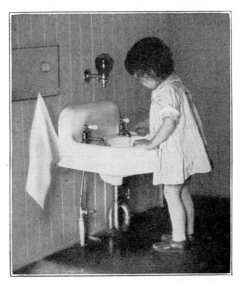

A three-year-old child should be able to wash her hands without help.

He makes various sounds, including squeals of delight, grunts of pain or disgust, shouts to call attention, scolding sounds, and the inflection of questions.

He jabbers to persons and repeats syllables like "da-da."

He talks without words, using the inflection and intonation of adult speech.

RESPONSES AT TEN MONTHS

The baby plays with his image in the mirror, pats it, laughs and leans toward it.

He pulls the stopper out of the bathtub.

He recognizes his own name.

He repeats actions he sees, such as ringing a bell.

He makes the movements he sees another child making.

He scoots backward.

He can point with his index finger.

It is no longer easy to take his toys away from him.

RESPONSES AT ELEVEN MONTHS

He walks when led.

He jabbers to persons and at his playthings.

He repeats sounds like "um-wow" and "puh-puh."

He understands the meaning of certain sentences and will obey simple commands, such as that to hold up his bottle.

He is pleased when a person who has left the room suddenly reappears.

He can stamp his foot.

He understands, "No, no!"

When laughed at, he repeats what he was doing.

He will turn from his toys toward a child.

If another child takes his toy he cries.

He craves the attention of another child.

RESPONSES AT ONE YEAR

He walks with help.

He walks backward.

He will turn his head in order to keep his eyes on a person moving to the rear.

When standing he can lower himself to a sitting position.

He holds a cup and drinks from it.

He invents words to express his wants.

He can open simple boxes.

He uses two words besides "mama" and "dada" and will repeat three or four.

He takes off his shoes and stockings by himself.

If asked, he will stop playing with his food or tugging at his clothes.

He can tap a small bell.

RESPONSES AT FIFTEEN MONTHS

He walks alone.

He scribbles of his own accord.

He uses a spoon.

He can co-operate in dressing and undressing himself.

His jabbering in sentence form is more fluent.

He enjoys looking at pictures.

He can throw a ball.

When another baby laughs or smiles he does also.

He is likely to interfere with other children.

He can follow simple directions, like "Bring that," "Leave it alone!"

RESPONSES AT EIGHTEEN MONTHS

He can climb stairs, climb over an obstacle, or get up on a chair.

He can slide or back down a few steps.

He walks freely.

He scribbles vigorously.

He tries to put his shoes on.

He uses a spoon, spilling very little.

He can throw a ball into a box.

If asked, he can point to his eyes, nose, or hair.

He understands simple questions.

He enjoys looking at pictures.

He likes to turn the pages of a book or a magazine.

He can give you the name of certain objects, such as a ball, watch, or pencil.

He enjoys fitting pans together.

He discovers that by doing something mischievous he can get adults to pay attention to him.

His interest in people is very great.

He points to attract the attention of another child or a grownup to something.

RESPONSES AT TWENTY-ONE MONTHS

He can go for walks on the street attended by an older person.

He walks backward.

He repeats things he has heard.

He tries to turn the doorknob.

He can name pictures in a book, such as "dog" and "baby."

RESPONSES AT TWO YEARS

He runs.

He can stand on one foot.

He asks for things at the table by name.

He combines words and is beginning to use sentences.

He uses pronouns.

If he wants to show something, he pulls at an adult or another child.

He plays ball.

He enjoys stories with pictures.

He can put blocks in a row to make a train.

He likes to play in the sand.

He is learning to co-operate with adults in following routine.

He can help to put on and remove his wraps.

He likes to build a tower and then knock it down.

He enjoys pulling toys after him, pushing a doll buggy, and pushing blocks along the floor.

Four-year-olds like to play on a slide, which they can go down frontwards, backwards, or face downwards.

He has nearly three hundred words in his vocabulary.

RESPONSES AT THIRTY MONTHS

He goes up and down stairs alone.

He can give his full name.

He helps his mother to put away things.

He can fit together nests of cubes.

He can keep time to music.

He is beginning to say "I."

His vocabulary contains about four hundred and fifty words.

He uses paints and brush.

RESPONSES AT THREE YEARS

He walks up and down stairs alone.

He can jump with both feet.

He uses a slide and climbs the Jungle-gym.

He enjoys simple picture puzzles.

He enjoys short walks and is interested in watching workmen.

He likes to wrap dolls, using pieces of cloth for clothes.

He thinks pulling a wagon is great fun.

He has a vocabulary of over a thousand words.

All the adult forms of mirth are fore-shadowed.

He likes to play with sounds, making up nonsense syllables.

He asks innumerable questions.

RESPONSES AT FOUR YEARS

He can manage his own clothes if they are simple.

He can button and unbutton.

He can lace his shoes.

He is interested in plants, birds, and all forms of natural life.

Many children at this age can hold, and even manipulate, scissors in the adult fashion.

Skipping on one foot, then the other, is achieved.

Imagination sometimes seems to run riot.

A few four-year-olds can hold fork and spoon in adult fashion.

He builds houses with blocks.

He likes to pull other children in his wagon.

He plays house.

He dresses and undresses dolls.

He shovels, sweeps, and rakes.

He goes down the slide frontwards, backwards, or face downwards.

He models dishes, baskets, beads, and so on from clay.

He uses eighteen hundred or more different words.

SIGNS OF SATISFACTORY DEVELOPMENT

How many parents know whether or not their baby is developing as he should? Among the signs that indicate satisfactory development, the most important is the continuing growth which goes on steadily—sometimes rapidly and at other times more slowly. Occasionally there are periods in which the child makes but little progress along a given line, but careful observation will show that he is growing or developing in some other way. First one thing and then another is emphasized during the process of growth.

As a child develops, his interests increase. He might be compared to the bee, gathering now from this flower, now from that; nothing that he absorbs is wasted. What the child does tomorrow he can do because of what he learns to-day. He does not always indicate immediately what he has gathered, nor is there much use in trying to put him through his paces. He is not developing in order to exhibit his progress, but in order to become a wholesome adult, able to do his share of work.

Happiness, the enjoyment of living, is another indication of satisfactory development. The healthy child is almost certain to be happy. The child whose development is not forced but is proceeding normally enjoys life, and laughter is one of the pleasant indications of this enjoyment.

How the Parent May Help the Child Develop

It is sometimes difficult to know just how much to expect of a child; parents should expect him to live up to the best he can do, and yet they should avoid expecting too much of him. Remember that he is not going to be exactly like anyone else in the world, so it is not fair to hold up some young cousin or playmate as a model to be copied.

No child can be expected to be perfect. As he grows, he learns; and learning includes mistakes as well as successes. At times he needs to learn for himself by making mistakes, and on other occasions he needs a guiding hand over rough places.

Sometimes it is possible to plan the environment so that a child will be helped in developing as he should. At other times when it is impossible to alter the environment, it is well to remember that children have a durability all their own.

It is helpful for parents to follow carefully their child's development and to compare it with the statement of what may normally be expected of children. Intelligent observation of children increases enjoyment of them. Through understanding his child the parent is able to guide development with sympathy and greater effectiveness. Give the baby a chance to be himself without expecting him to duplicate anyone else. Do not attempt to force development at a more rapid rate than is natural. Remember that each baby sets his own pace and that he needs an opportunity to discover for himself his own powers and to find out for himself about the world in which he lives.

SUMMARY

The normal rate of development is determined by a comparison of the records from birth to maturity of many different children. Studies of these records show similarity in the age at which children develop certain abilities. It must always be remembered, however, that both the rate and sequence in normal development may vary and that a precise statement is difficult to make.

The younger the child, the more rapid is the rate of development. This rate is greatest during the prenatal period and the first few months after birth; it then continues at a slower rate until maturity. Each of the organs or parts of the body grows at its own particular rate.

Even during the prenatal period the child is sensitive to various impressions and makes some responses to stimuli from the outside world. The perfecting of the development of the fetus determines the child's ability to meet the changes which birth brings and to function as an independent being.

As life goes on the child responds more fully to other people and to the world about him. He develops skills of all sorts. The finest thing a parent can give his child is the opportunity to develop both body and mind, to live and work with other people.

QUESTIONS

1. What does the newborn baby look like?
2. How does he differ in appearance from the child of a year?
3. How old is a baby before he recognizes his mother?
4. What can a two-year-old do with his hands?
5. Why does the brain grow most rapidly during the prenatal period?

6. How old are babies when they laugh out loud?
7. Why do little children enjoy pushing a doll carriage?
8. What do people mean when they speak of normal children?
9. How can parents help their children to develop normally?

READING REFERENCES

BOOKS

Aldrich, Charles A. and Mary M., *Babies Are Human Beings* (Macmillan). The interpretation of growth.

Anderson, Harold H., *Children in the Family* (Appleton-Century).

Arlitt, Ada H., *The Child from One to Twelve* (McGraw).

Bacmeister, Rhoda W., *Caring for the Runabout Child* (Dutton). Constructive guidance for the two-to-six-year-old.

Faegre, Marion L., and Anderson, John E., *Child Care and Training* (University of Minnesota, Institute of Child Welfare).

Isaacs, Susan S., *Nursery Years* (Vanguard).

Meek, Lois H., *Your Child's Development and Guidance Told in Pictures* (Lippincott).

Rand, Winifred, and others, *Growth and Development of the Young Child* (Saunders).

Reynolds, Martha M., *Children from Seed to Saplings* (McGraw).

Strang, Ruth, *Introduction to Child Study* (Macmillan).

Wagoner, Lovisa C., *The Development of Learning in Young Children* (McGraw).

PAMPHLETS

Murray, Marjorie F., and Eliot, Martha M., *The Child from One to Six, His Care and Training* (U. S. Department of Labor, Children's Bureau, Publication No. 30; Government Printing Office, Washington, D. C.).

U. S. Department of Labor, Children's Bureau, *Infant Care.*

Wellman, Beth L., *Learning to Talk* (Iowa Child Welfare Research Station).

BABY CARE

Louise Zabriskie

Every mother is anxious to learn all she can about taking care of her baby. Even the mother who feels she is well prepared for motherhood likes to know the most convenient and most practical ways of doing such everyday tasks as feeding, dressing, and bathing her baby. The author is Director of the Maternity Consultation Service, New York City, and lecturer at New York University. As a nurse she has had wide experience in all the practical aspects of baby care. She is also the author of *Nurses' Handbook of Obstetrics* and *Mother and Baby Care in Pictures*.

THE care of the baby, to be ideal, should begin in the prenatal state. The normal baby is nine months old when he is born. During the first ten months of a baby's life—that is, the nine months before and the one month after his birth—care is more important than at any other period. Prenatal care and the safeguarding of both the mother and the baby are of the utmost importance, and both mother and father should share in providing this protection.

Nature has given the father his share of responsibility for the baby. The new life begins to develop as soon as the two parent cells are united. Both the father and the mother share in contributing to the inherited characteristics of this new baby. Life begins with the union of the two cells, one from each parent. From these two cells the nuclei of the original cell is formed and from it millions of cells grow, developing into muscle, bones, glands, nerves, brain, heart, lungs, and skin. During the nine months of pregnancy the entire equipment of a newly born baby is developed.

It will be impossible to make up in the baby's later life for the lack of care during the prenatal period. Therefore, his future well-being depends largely on the care given—often indirectly—by the mother, father, physician and other capable advisers and assistants whom the parents may consult.

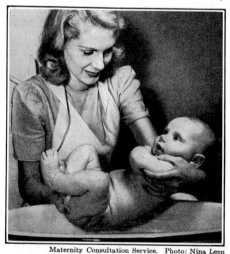

Maternity Consultation Service. Photo: Nina Leen

THE SAFE WAY TO BATHE THE BABY

Before putting baby in tub, the mother should place left arm and wrist under his head and grasp his left arm with thumb and fingers of left hand; with right hand she supports his buttocks and lifts him gently into tub. His back may then be rinsed without having to turn him over.

PRENATAL CARE

The first weeks of caring for the baby are chiefly the concern of the mother.

As soon as pregnancy is suspected, the prospective mother should place herself under the care of a competent obstetrician, not only for a complete physical checkup but for watchful attention throughout the entire period. The object of this safeguard to both mother and baby is to keep the mother in good health, to offer suggestions for overcoming discomforts, to detect and treat the first symptoms of complications, and to prevent further complications. Under normal conditions the skin, lungs, kidneys, and intestines throw off impurities from the body, and, as a result, the general health is good. If, however, these organs fail to act normally, poisons which should be eliminated remain in the body and cause various illnesses. While the baby is living and growing within the body he, too, is giving off waste materials through the mother's blood stream, to be excreted by her. This means that the mother's organs are taking charge of the waste materials for two instead of one.

Physical Examination. The prospective mother should have a complete physical examination early in pregnancy. Parents should acquaint themselves with what this examination should include. (Consult *Mother and Baby Care in Pictures,* or some other good reference.) In addition, an estimate of her general health and an inquiry into the history of her family, traits and tendencies should be made. A case history of previous diseases, pregnancies, and labors often reveals an inheritance of unusual physical tendencies. Frequent checkups during pregnancy are also essential. The obstetrician's supervision is often helpfully supplemented by visits from a competent nurse.

Dental Care. Adequate care of the teeth is especially necessary at this period. Good teeth are essential in masticating food, and good health is dependent upon adequate nutrition. If an acid condition is present in the mouth, it may be relieved by an alkaline mouthwash. When extensive dental work is necessary, the physician should be consulted. It must be emphasized that teeth in poor condition should be treated at once. Everything should be done to locate and eradicate any centers of infection. Such poison centers in the system may be the source of an infection which will spread to various parts of the body, and may also cause grave concern during the period immediately after the birth of the baby.

Diet. Perhaps the most important factor in the mother's care of herself is her diet. The proper amount of the right varieties of food is necessary not only to meet the requirements of the baby but also to aid in maintaining good health for the mother. Various foods with their different elements, such as minerals and vitamins, contribute to the building of the baby's body, serve to keep up the mother's daily strength, and build a reserve for labor and the trying period which follows. The mother's diet may greatly influence her ability to nurse her baby. The diet is all important to the baby, too, for on it depends his growth from week to week. The fundamentals of the daily diet consist of one quart of milk, vegetables (especially the green variety), fruits (fresh, canned, or dried), dark cereals, dark breads, and real butter. Fluids are also important because they aid in the assimilation of food and stimulate elimination.

Among the developments which take place when the baby grows from a single cell into a miniature human being is the formation of more than two hundred bones and two sets of teeth. The quality of the baby's teeth is established very early in pregnancy; and even the second teeth are present in the jaws and their durability is determined before birth. Strange as it may seem, the baby's physical needs are supplied before the mother's are met. If there is not enough food material for both, the mother's system becomes depleted in order to supply nourishment for the baby. During these vital nine months the baby is developing the entire intricate system of the human body, which, once developed, cannot be exchanged or remade. Even iodine, copper, and iron should be stored by the baby during this period in sufficient quantity to last until he is old enough to eat foods containing these elements.

Rest and Sleep. Individuals require different amounts of sleep and rest, depending on their nervous disposition, habits of life, age, and circumstances. Daily rest periods are beneficial, for rest prevents fatigue, the effects of which are harmful to the mother and baby. Sleep is especially important for the mother during pregnancy.

Sunshine and Fresh Air. Not only are sunshine and fresh air tonic in their effects, but since the cells require oxygen in order to utilize food, fresh air for the pregnant mother is a necessity. Cod-liver oil and the concentrates have been called "bottled sunshine" and, when taken during the prenatal period, are beneficial to the mother and provide extra protection for the baby.

Care of the Skin. During pregnancy the skin has added responsibilities as an organ of elimination. For this reason cleanliness is then of particular importance. Bathing stimulates the circulation and is restful and refreshing. Sponge or shower baths are advocated after the seventh month. Tub baths at this time are inadvisable because of the possibility of a fall and of the bath water entering the vaginal canal.

Recreation. Some form of recreation is necessary, and the mother should choose her own diversion. Perhaps some especially pleasurable or diverting trip or visit can be planned by the prospective parents. A happy outlook offers many benefits. Exercise, if it is a form of recreation, offers relaxation to the mind, stimulates the appetite, and strengthens the muscles. Fatigue should be avoided.

All these essentials during pregnancy have a direct bearing on the baby's development and should be made a definite part of his care during the nine months. It must be kept in mind that food, rest, fresh air, and proper elimination aid in keeping the mother well. When the mother is unhappy, worried, or disturbed, the body does not function as it should. This protection from worry for the sake of both the mother and the baby should be one of the father's major responsibilities.

Care of the mother and the baby during pregnancy prepares the mother to meet delivery and convalescence more adequately; and for the baby, a greater possibility for normal growth and development and ability to adjust himself to the changes in environment which take place at birth. This period of pregnancy should be one of happy anticipation for the parents and unhindered development for the baby.

DAILY CARE OF THE BABY

At birth the baby must begin to live as an independent individual. The physical changes which take place in the various systems of the baby's body at birth so that he may live in this new and different environment demand a great adjustment—probably the greatest he will ever have to make! He must now breathe, get his food by his own effort, and eliminate his waste. From the moment the baby is born he should be kept warm and comfortable. The schedule for his daily care should be planned. This should include regular feedings; sleep and rest periods; baths; fresh air and sunshine; attention to clothes; exercise and play; and an effort to provide a loving atmosphere.

FEEDING

The schedule for the baby's nursing time is advised by the doctor. Usually babies are fed at three or four hour intervals, with one feeding during the night for the first few weeks. The most important single factor in successful baby care is proper feeding. Regularity is also important, since a baby's stomach needs rest as much as the other parts of his body.

Most doctors agree that a baby needs an ounce or two of cooled, boiled water between feedings.

Milk. The best food for the baby is that designed by nature—breast milk. If the mother is unable to supply milk of proper quality and in sufficient amount for his needs, and if other breast milk cannot be secured, the next best food is cow's milk, properly modified to meet the requirements of the baby.

If artificial food is necessary, it should be prescribed by the physician, who will give directions for its preparation. Since modified cow's milk is commonly used, the mother should obtain information about the local milk supply. Certified pasteurized milk is the best, but it is not always available. Pasteurized milk, as a rule, can be used with safety. The physician may order dried or evaporated milk or some one of the patented foods. When such foods are prescribed, the doctor usually plans the formula in detail.

The care of bottles and nipples, which must be kept scrupulously clean, is another matter of great importance. There are a variety of bottles and nipples on the market. Choose bottles which are easily kept clean. Select nipples which can be thoroughly cleaned inside and out. If the baby has difficulty in nursing, it is advisable to find the type of nipple that is most satisfactory. Bottle caps should be used to protect the bottles after the formula has been prepared. The milk should then be placed in the icebox.

Cod-Liver Oil. When the baby is about two or three weeks old, cod-liver oil (or some other concentrated form of vitamin A and D) is added to his diet. The physician may order three drops

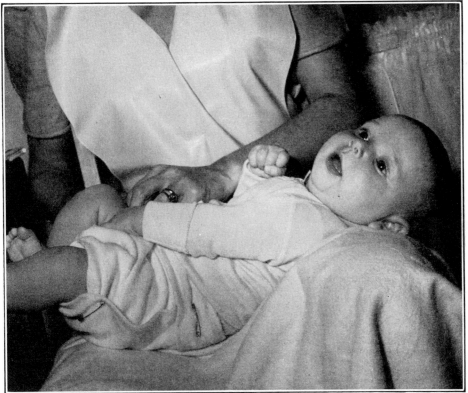

Taken at Maternity Consultation Service. Photo: Nina Leen

CHOOSE SUITABLE CLOTHING FOR THE YOUNG CHILD

Properly fitted diaper band, shirt, and diaper contribute to the baby's comfort and promote good posture.

daily, to be increased gradually. It may be given in one or two doses, with a medicine dropper, and it is placed on the tongue or the inside of the cheek. If the dosage is increased gradually, cod-liver oil is less apt to cause regurgitation of food. Because it is so necessary for the baby's health, pleasant associations will encourage him to enjoy this food. Concentrates are easier to take but are more expensive.

Orange Juice and Tomato Juice. At the age of one month the baby is usually given one teaspoonful of strained orange juice, to which an equal amount of boiled water may be added to prevent choking. Sweet oranges should be used and no sugar added. The amount of juice is increased by one teaspoonful each week until at the end of the third month the baby gets daily about eight or ten tea-spoonfuls. A baby that is given artificial food may begin his orange juice earlier. Tomato juice (canned may be preferred) may be substituted for, or alternated with, orange juice. Twice as much tomato juice as orange juice should be given. Orange and tomato juices are both rich in vitamin C, which prevents scurvy. The orange juice may be given in a bottle, but here is often a good opportunity to begin teaching the baby spoon feeding or drinking from a glass.

Other Foods. With the addition of a variety of foods the baby needs less milk. By nine months the baby should be having three meals a day. The doctor usually issues a food list with the different kinds of foods, stating when they should be added to the diet. At the age of two months the baby may be having cereals, prune juice (if he is constipated), and orange juice. Cereals may be fed to the baby with a teaspoon. At three months, cereals, vegetable waters, and banana pulp may be added. When the baby is four or five months old, vegetable purée, prune pulp (if needed for constipation), and butter for seasoning may be added. At six months the baby should be getting fruit pulp, stewed fruit, applesauce or baked apple, egg yolk, cereals, and vegetables. He should be drinking from a cup at this age. (See "Food and Nutrition," in this volume.)

Teeth. The baby's teeth may begin to erupt at about six months. When ten months old the baby may have from two to four teeth, although they may be slower in appearing. Some babies "cut" their teeth much slower than others. Cleaning the teeth regularly with a toothpick swab should be begun with the eruption of the first tooth. This eruption of the teeth may or may not be accompanied by gastro-intestinal disturbance and fretfulness. If any such disturbance occurs the doctor should be consulted.

Weaning. The time to begin weaning the baby is dependent on his physical condition, the season of the year (it is less advisable in very hot weather), and the amount of breast milk available. About the fourth month is the time to begin. Weaning should be done gradually at first by substituting one feeding a day. Bottles and cup feedings may be substituted for the breast milk. If the new foods are added gradually, the baby should pay little attention to the change. Care should be taken, however, to add only one new food at a time and this in small amounts.

SLEEP, FRESH AIR, AND SUNSHINE

A newborn infant sleeps most of the time; that is, from nineteen to twenty-one hours a day. This amount of time diminishes gradually as the baby grows older. Much is gained if the baby is put to bed at stated times and left undisturbed either to sleep or to rest quietly. He should be dry, comfortable, and clean.

Fresh air is as essential for the baby as for adults. It is, in fact, one of his greatest needs. The air indoors should be kept fresh but warm, and the baby must be protected from drafts. When he is taken out, he should be dressed according to the weather. Warm hands and feet and a tendency to sleep while outdoors are good indications that the baby is warm. Use clothing and covers that are light in weight but warm.

Sun baths are of great value to the

baby. In hot climates it is possible to give the baby sun baths throughout the year; but in colder climates, cod-liver oil or its substitutes must be given to take the place of sunshine. The baby may derive benefit from sunshine that comes through a "Do-plex" or "Cel-o-glass" screen. These screens may be made by covering an ordinary window screen frame with either of the above materials. Sunlight that comes through the ordinary window glass loses the health-giving ultraviolet rays.

The sun bath is usually begun about the third or fourth week, and in warm weather is given in- or out-of-doors. At first the baby's basket or carriage is so arranged that the sun shines directly on the baby's cheeks and hands but not in his eyes. He should be turned so that both cheeks will get the sunshine. Each day more of his body should be exposed, until finally the baby is completely undressed. At first the sun bath should last only a few minutes, two to five, but may be increased gradually to one hour. During the summer these sun baths must be given before 10:00 A.M. and after 4:00 P.M. The baby should be protected from the wind and must be kept warm and comfortable. Some mothers find it convenient to dress the baby in a sun suit (partly woolen) for these sun baths.

THE BATH

Frequent, regular bathing is a fundamental necessity in baby care. The first bath, given immediately after birth, is of oil. It removes the vernix, the protective substance covering the baby's body. After that the sponge bath is given until the cord has separated and the umbilicus has healed. From then on the tub bath is preferable. During the sponge bath it is important to bathe one part of the body at a time, such as the face, arm, or leg, drying it immediately so as not to expose and chill the baby. Giving the bath on the mother's lap is usually advisable. It is less fatiguing to her, since she does not have to stand. Furthermore, this intimacy makes an appeal to the average mother. Two other types of baths are sometimes used—the table bath and the spray bath. The *table bath* consists of having the equipment so arranged that both ends of the table are protected. The tub should be on one end and on the other the tray and clothing. The baby should lie between these on a well-protected surface. The disadvantages are that the mother must stand for these forty-five minutes and that the baby may have a fall if left alone on the table. The *spray bath* is seldom preferred because of the difficulty in regulating the temperature of the water and the chance of water getting in the baby's ears.

The temperature of the room, which must be free from drafts, should be from 72° to 80° F., and the bath water should be maintained at about 100° F. All equipment must be in readiness before the bath is begun. This forty-five minutes, when the mother and the baby become better acquainted with each other, is one of the delightful periods of the day. The bath is given preferably before the 9 or 10 A.M. feeding, for after this hour the baby has his longest nap of the day. Whatever the hour, it should be when

Taken at Maternity Consultation Service. Photo: by Nina Leen

THE BABY'S TOILET TRAY (*left*) AND BATHING EQUIPMENT (*right*)

This lap bath equipment allows mother to bathe and dress baby sitting down, conserving her energy. The baby's toilet tray is a necessity that should be prepared during the prenatal period:

Jar of boiled water: Day's supply for cleansing mother's nipples before and after nursing.
Jar of large cotton swabs: For cleansing mother's nipples.
Jar of small cotton swabs: For cleansing baby's nose, ears, genitals.
Jar for nipples and caps: Nipples and caps to be boiled after using and kept in dry jar.
Flat dish for soap: White, such as Johnson's baby soap.
Flat dish for oil: Day's supply of baby oil or abolene for cleansing nose, ears, genitals, buttocks.
Jar for cotton: Day's supply of cotton for applying oil.
Soap for pincushion: Easy to keep clean; points are lubricated and also kept safely covered.
Bottle of boiled water: Day's supply of "drinks for the baby."
Nursing bottle: For giving baby water. *Steri-seal cap:* To protect nipple.

the mother can give forty-five minutes of uninterrupted attention.

Preparations for the Bath. The mother should wash her hands before handling the equipment for the bath. The bath water, baby clothes, and equipment should be assembled before the baby is picked up. This sort of preparation makes the daily bath easier for both the mother and the baby. He should be bathed as quickly as possible so as not to cause chill or fatigue. His bath should be refreshing, and should never be given so slowly as to be irritating. He should be handled and turned as little as possible. The mother should be seated comfortably. On cold days the baby may be bathed before an open fireplace, radiator, or an open heated oven. It is well to sit so that the baby's feet will be nearest the heat, for if his feet are cold he may become uncomfortable and fretful. To protect him from drafts, a screen may be used or one improvised by draping a blanket or sheet over the back of two straight-backed chairs.

The mother should sit on a low chair without arms, while the bathtub is placed on another low chair or on a firm stool.

Equipment. The baby's toilet tray should be in a convenient place for use. This tray contains the bottle of cooled, boiled water to give the baby before his bath; the small swabs to use for cleansing the nose, ears, and genitals; the soap, cotton jar, oil dish, and soap pincushion; and a paper cornucopia in which to place the soiled cotton and used swabs. At the right place all the other articles needed. The complete outfit of clothing should include the band, shirt, diaper, pad, and square. Arrange these in the order in which they are put on, with the pettiskirt inside the dress as one garment, if a dress is to be worn. This prevents unnecessary handling of the baby.

The baby's bathtub should be about three-fourths full of water at 96° to 100° F. The safest method of testing the temperature of the water is with a thermometer. If this is not possible, water that feels comfortably warm to the elbow or the back of the wrist may be used. The washcloth may be made of an old piece of soft linen or baby washcloths may be purchased. A bath towel, bath blanket, and soft clean face towel should be within easy reach. It is a good plan to have a bath apron to use while bathing the baby. Inexpensive rubber aprons with a turkish toweling cover are good for this purpose if the rubber is not too light in weight to stay in place.

Disposal of Soiled Clothing. Spread a newspaper on the floor for the soiled clothes and a diaper pail with plain water or borax solution should be at hand for the wet diaper. When all the prepara-

tions are complete, wash the hands thoroughly before beginning the bath.

Details of the Bathing Process. In picking up the baby the mother must remember to support his head and neck most carefully. While the baby is having his bath is an opportune time to air his bed. After the mother is seated comfortably in the low chair, the baby may be given some cooled, boiled water. This is refreshing and makes him more contented during his bath. The bath should be given in the same order every day, not only because it may be given more quickly but also because the baby learns this system and before long responds by putting up a hand or foot to be bathed at the proper time. Place the bath blanket and bath towel under the baby and then, before undressing him, cleanse his nose and ears with small swabs of cotton that have been moistened in baby oil. A clean swab should be used for each side of the nose and for each ear. If the baby's head is held gently with the thumb and forefinger just above his temples he cannot wriggle. His mouth should be inspected but not cleansed. Any treatment necessary should be prescribed by the doctor.

In undressing the baby, he should be rolled on his side toward the mother. After the dress and pettiskirt have been removed and the neck of the shirt loosened, wrap him in the bath towel and blanket. With the face towel under his chin, wash his face with warm water, using no soap. If the ends of the washcloth are held in the palm of the hand so that the wet corners do not fall in his face, he will not be startled or annoyed.

Dry his face by patting with the soft face towel. The eyes are bathed as part of the face, as the mother would wash her own. Any discharge from the eyes should be reported to the doctor at once. Warm boric acid solution on cotton

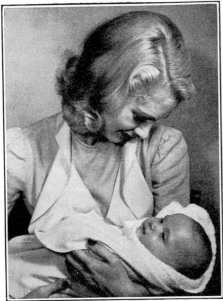

Maternity Consultation Service. Photo: Nina Leen

AFTER THE BATH

After the bath the baby is wrapped well in the bath towel (40 x 40 inches is a practical size) and receiving blanket and gently patted dry.

pledgets may be used to cleanse the discharge from the eyelids. Use these pledgets only once. Wipe the discharge from the nose outward. Wash the scalp and behind the ears with soap and water and rinse them by holding the baby's head over the tub. Carelessness in cleansing and rinsing the scalp may result in condition that is called crib cap. When the secretion from the sebaceous glands is mixed with dirt and soap, the

oil from these glands forms a yellowish-brown waxy-looking crust on the scalp. This will not form, however, if proper care is taken. When this condition is present, warm sweet oil or a paste made from baking soda and water should be applied and the crust removed gently and gradually. If the scalp is kept clean, the condition will not return. The baby's scalp and hair should be dried thoroughly. Rub the hair in swirls to encourage curling.

Chilling and exposure are prevented by not removing the shirt, band, and diaper until after the baby's face and head have been bathed. If, when the diaper is removed, the baby has had a bowel movement, the buttocks should be cleansed with oil. The soiled diaper should be placed on a newspaper for care later; if the diaper is merely wet, put it into the diaper pail filled with cold plain water or borax solution. To complete the undressing of the baby the shirt is removed (by turning the baby on his side toward the mother) and the band is slipped over the feet. The baby should then be wrapped in the bath towel and bath blanket to prevent chilling. The soiled clothing should be placed on the newspaper.

In order to protect the baby, only one part of the body should be exposed at a time. Apply the soap to the body with the hand, giving special attention to the creases in the neck, under the arms, at the elbows and wrists, between the fingers and toes, and in the groin. He is now ready to put into the tub. The left wrist supports the baby's neck and head and his left arm is grasped between the thumb and fingers; with the right hand under the baby's buttocks lower him gently and carefully into the water. Any sudden splashing or plunging may frighten him. If the baby's arm and shoulder are firmly held and supported, it is easy to steady his entire body and keep his head and ears out of the water. During the first few weeks the baby stays in the water only long enough to rinse him thoroughly. As he grows older he will enjoy being in the water five minutes or longer. Give special attention to rinsing the creases in the neck, under the arms, between the fingers and toes, and in the groin.

Lift the baby out of the tub in the same way that he was put into it. Quickly wrap him in the bath towel and blanket. Dry him thoroughly by patting, being careful not to overlook any creases or between his fingers and toes. Always remember that the skin of the newborn baby is so delicate that it is easily irritated, injured, and infected. After the baby's skin has been patted dry, remove the damp bath towel and wrap the baby with the bath blanket. A small amount of oil gently rubbed into the creases (any excess removed with the face towel) helps to keep the baby's skin in good condition. Talcum powder may be used if advised by the doctor.

In dressing the baby slip the knitted sleeveless band over the feet. In putting on the shirt grasp the baby's hand through the sleeve in order to protect the baby's fingers. Before adjusting the diaper, oil should be applied to the genitals. If the baby is a boy, retract the foreskin by gently rubbing it back with cotton, taking pains to pull it forward into its original position after the part underneath has been cleansed with oil. If the foreskin is tight the doctor should be consulted; he will decide whether or not the baby needs to be circumcized. If the baby is a girl, separate the labia and cleanse with oil. Report any discharge to the doctor at once.

Record of Weight. The baby should be weighed at a certain hour of the day, once or twice a week. Such conditions as feeding and clothing should be kept constant. The logical time to weigh the baby is after the bath. Considerable variations may occur and still be considered normal. A gain of four to six ounces a week, as a rule, results in doubling the birth weight by the end of six months. After six months the gain is somewhat slower, but by the end of the first year the baby should weigh about three times his birth weight. (See "Normal Rates of Development," in this volume.)

THE BABY'S CLOTHING

The baby's wardrobe should consist of bands, shirts, diapers, pettiskirts, dresses, nightgowns, flannelette squares, wool afghans, and light-weight wool blankets. The combined weight of one set should be about twelve to sixteen ounces. As the dresses and pettiskirts may be made long enough to cover the feet, many doctors think that stockings are at first unnecessary. For the first three months many mothers prefer to dress their babies in flannelette gowns open down the back. They can be washed and dried without ironing, and their use shortens the time of handling and dressing the baby.

For a month or two the baby scarcely needs special clothing for outdoor wear as he may be wrapped in a flannelette square and an afghan. This not only saves handling him but also is much more comfortable for him. The baby's

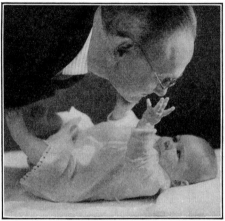

Photo: Lena Towsley

"The baby also derives a little exercise from being held for a short time each day. A good time is just before the baby's bedtime, when his father is home. In this way they can become better acquainted with each other."

clothes should be dainty, simple styles and should hang from the shoulders without any tight bands. The garments should be made of soft, light-weight material and should always be clean and dry. So that the baby may not become chilled or overheated, adjust his clothing to temperature, weather, and climate.

Bands. The first bands are really no more than bandages by which the cord dressing is kept in place. These bands may be made from a half yard of twenty-seven inch flannelette, cut into three pieces crosswise. The edges should be pinked, not hemmed. Several kinds of bands ready for use may also be bought.

As soon as the umbilicus is healed, these first bands are replaced by knitted bands with shoulder straps (sometimes called Vee bands, teething, or diaper bands). These are made of cotton-and-wool or silk-and-wool but never of all-wool, as an all-wool band might irritate the baby's skin. Such bands serve as a waist for pinning the diaper, and also aid in keeping the baby's abdomen warm. They are worn both winter and summer except on very hot days. When dressing the baby, this band should be slipped over the feet.

Shirts. The shirts should also be silk-and-wool or cotton-and-wool. The wool mixture is desirable because it absorbs the moisture from the baby's skin without causing him to feel cold and damp, as cotton does, thus preventing his body from being chilled. The shirts should be a simple coat style, with well-shaped neck and sleeves.

Care of Flannels. To keep the baby's shirts and bands in good condition wash them carefully. Use only white soap and lukewarm water. Squeezing, not rubbing, and drying slowly in the air but not in the sun keep them soft and help to prevent shrinking. A shirt drier, which can also be used for sweaters, not only maintains the shape of the garment but also aids in the drying.

Diapers. Make these twenty-four by twenty-four inches square, of cotton bird's-eye. A few patented diapers are on the market that are unusual, such as the Pantease, Curity, and Chix. The square diaper, pinned at the waist and just above the knees, makes no pressure on the genitals, and is therefore more comfortable. It is also easy to wash because it becomes soiled in but one spot instead of at the corners and hems. It also dries quickly.

Before putting this diaper on the baby, fold it straight through the center, forming a rectangle. If the baby is very small, fold down one-third, making an extra pad under the baby. For a boy baby it is well to have this extra flap in the front. Place the diaper lengthwise under the baby, draw the lower half up between his thighs, and pin it on each side at the waistline, through the band, having the back fold of the diaper overlapping the front. Adjust the diaper above the knees, not too high and not too tight, and pin. Use medium-sized steel safety pins, placing them crosswise through the sides of the diaper, so as to make them more secure. When the baby outgrows the folded diaper, this same method may be followed by sewing or putting two diapers together for extra thickness.

A wet diaper should be changed immediately, for it makes the baby uncomfortable. A dry diaper predisposes to healthful sleep and aids greatly in preventing skin irritation. The sooner the baby can be trained to use a commode the better, for it saves the mother a great deal of work. (See "Children and Their Habits" in the next volume.) Knitted protectors may be used instead of rubber pants because they are absorbent and less irritating. If rubber pants are used, they should be loose around the legs and never worn continuously.

Pettiskirts and Dresses. The pettiskirts (or gertrudes, as they are sometimes called) are very simple, opening down the back from neck to hem and fastened with ties or tiny flat buttons. All seams should be flat, the armholes and neck should be bound with taffeta or lawn seam-binding, and the drawstring at the neck should be tacked in the middle front to prevent it from being pulled out. When the baby is laid down, the clothes are separated at the back, so as not to become wet, soiled, or wrinkled. As soon as the baby is trained to use a commode, the back of the dress and pettiskirt may be closed.

The dresses may have kimono or bishop-style sleeves, with a drawstring at the wrist for any necessary adjustments. Both dresses and pettiskirts open down the back from neck to hem. Fasten them with tiny flat buttons or ties, with a drawstring at the neck (tacked in front as described above). Make the dresses of any fine material, such as nainsook or a combination of linen and lawn, trimmed with dainty thread lace. Make both pettiskirts and dresses short or just long enough to cover the baby's feet.

Flannelette Squares. Squares made of flannelette one yard wide are very practical. Use them at first in place of a coat and a bonnet, in order to avoid unnecessary handling of the baby. They may also be used as bath blankets. In fact, in these early weeks the flannelette squares often take the brunt of these services and save the fine little wool afghans from becoming soiled too quickly. Fold the square loosely about the baby and then pin it so that when he is picked up he is always protected from drafts and from being chilled. If the square is properly pinned, the baby may lie and kick and his feet will be covered and warm.

Wool Afghans and Blankets. These are necessary for warmth. They should be all wool and very light weight.

Nightgowns. Make or buy night-gowns of soft knitted materials or flannelette. Such gowns are not only light weight, loose, warm, and comfortable, but also absorbent, easy to wash, and they do not require ironing. Fasten them at the bottom with a drawstring or buttons so the baby will not get uncovered and so his feet will keep warmer.

Other Articles of Clothing. Quilted pads (about eleven by sixteen inches) or a substitute are necessary. These pads may be made of two thicknesses of absorbent toweling—sold as heavy toweling—stitched or quilted together. Under the pad use a piece of rubber sheeting, oilcloth, or some other waterproof material of the same size to protect the bedding and clothing.

Kimonos made of French flannel or flannelette and knitted sweaters are very practical for supplying extra warmth.

If the baby's feet are cold and he seems to need stockings, buy those with no seams and plenty large enough to allow for shrinkage.

For cold weather a bunting is a comfortable outside wrap. The hood protects the head but does not cover the ears tightly. Babies' ears need air circulation as precaution against infections.

Many other dainty and useful things for the baby's wardrobe may be bought, but only the essentials are mentioned here. (For the toddler's clothes, see "Clothing" in this volume.) Overdress-ing tends to cause skin irritability, digestive disorders, restlessness, and susceptibility to colds.

Exercise. During the first weeks the baby's only real exercise is crying. The baby also derives a little exercise from being held for a short time each day. A good time is just before the baby is put to bed at night when his father is home. In this way they can become better acquainted with each other. A baby should not be tossed about, played with, nor handled unnecessarily. He should lie quiet and undisturbed in his bed most of the time during the first three or four weeks. His position should be changed, however. Turn him from one side to the other and put him on his back or abdomen so that he will not lie too long in one position. The proper handling of the baby is of utmost importance. He must have adequate support for his head whenever he is lifted, since his muscular co-ordination is relatively insufficient.

The healthy baby will exercise and develop his muscles if he is not wrapped too tightly in his clothes. For this reason his movements should not be restricted by clothing. A mother may give a baby regular exercises, but this should be done only under the supervision of a physician.

Crying. A mother soon learns to distinguish the baby's condition and needs from the character of his cry. All babies cry as part of their needed exercise, and this is normal. The baby may cry because he is tired, uncomfortable, or wet. The mother can usually quiet him by changing his position, smoothing any wrinkles in his clothes or bedclothes, changing his diaper, adding more covers if he is cold, or removing some if he is too warm. Colic is denoted by a loud, insistent cry accompanied by a drawing up of the legs. Placing the baby face down on his mother's lap with a hot-water bottle next to his abdomen often gives relief. The hot-water bottle should be comfortably warm to the cheek and not too full. A fretful cry due to indigestion will be accompanied by green stools and passing of flatus; a fretful hungry cry with fingers in the mouth is easily recognized. If a baby has been spoiled, he indulges in still another form of crying. When the baby continues to cry over a long period of time, the doctor should be consulted.

TOILET HABITS

The regulation of the baby's bowel movements is influenced by feeding and habit. He should be trained as soon as he has established a regular time of elimination. Before beginning this training, the time when the baby usually has his bowel movement should be noted. At that time he should be held in a comfortable position with his back supported by his mother's arm, his buttocks touching the warmed commode. The baby should be put on the commode at the same hour or at the same point in his daily routine if the training is to be successful. The first time or two a carefully made soap stick, well lubricated and barely inserted in the rectum, may produce a slight stimulation. The mother should not expect the baby to learn too quickly; she should praise and encourage him when successful. The process is slow; more or less training will

be necessary. New foods and the eruption of teeth are apt to cause irregularity. Training the bladder takes longer, but is accomplished in a similar manner at more frequent intervals. Most babies prefer to be clean and dry. This standard of cleanliness is another of the good habits to cultivate.

CONDITIONS AFFECTING HEALTH

Since the common cold is highly contagious, babies should not be permitted to come in contact with infected persons. If the mother has a cold, especially while nursing or caring for the baby, she should wear an improvised mask or a clean handkerchief over her mouth and nose so that she does not breathe in the baby's face directly. The baby should never be kissed on the mouth. Neither should he come in contact with children who may have a communicable disease.

Babies, like adults, form habits by doing the same thing again and again. Thumb-sucking is an early habit which is easily formed and which should be corrected at once, since it may affect the development of the jaws and teeth. To teach the baby to put nothing in his mouth but food will take great watchfulness and much patience. He will be confused and learn slowly unless the mother is consistent in her treatment.

The baby is trained by everything that is done for him, to him, and around him —in fact, by everything that happens to him from the day of his birth. An atmosphere of justice, confidence, serenity, and courtesy should be provided for him. As he grows older, he should be dealt with according to his unfolding intelligence. (See "Emotional Problems of Children," in the next volume.)

Parents should be concerned not only with the baby's physical development so that he will have a body that will serve him well throughout a useful life, but also with the training of his character.

Every baby is a new individual, and while he may be trained and guided, he will also develop some ideas entirely his own. Parents should help him to develop all his potentialities and aid him in becoming considerate, self-reliant, and independent.

SUMMARY

The importance of prenatal care cannot be overemphasized. No amount of attention after birth can compensate for neglect during the prenatal period. The responsibility for the well-being of the unborn baby lies largely with the mother. Parents should consider it not only a responsibility but also a privilege to provide adequate care and so prepare during this period for the baby's full development.

Prenatal care includes a complete physical examination at an early stage by a competent physician, care and treatment of the teeth, attention to the diet, avoidance of fatigue, scrupulous cleanliness, and suitable recreation.

After birth the baby requires food and sleep at regular periods, bathing, fresh air and sunshine, proper clothing, exercise, and an atmosphere of love. Breast milk is the natural food for the baby; modified cow's milk and the other substitutes are second choice. Vitamins in the form of cod-liver oil (or concentrates), orange juice, and tomato juice are given at an early period. At about the age of two months other foods are added and weaning should begin at four to six months.

The baby requires from nineteen to twenty-one hours of sleep daily in the fresh air. The amount required diminishes gradually and should be divided into regular periods. Sun baths given properly should be a part of the baby's routine.

In bathing the baby all the bath equipment as well as the clean clothes and a means for disposal of soiled clothes should all be in readiness. Watch the temperature of the bath water and of the room. Weigh the baby at the same hour under uniform conditions of feeding and clothing, if possible.

Simplicity, practicality, and comfort should be the rule in selecting the baby's clothing. It should all be soft, light in weight, and adjusted to the temperature and climate. Wet diapers should be changed immediately, and the baby trained to use the commode as early as possible.

Except for normal crying, quiet is more important than exercise during the first few weeks. Change of position is necessary. Proper handling with the head supported is imperative. Tossing, playing, and other unnecessary handling should be avoided. Care should be taken to avoid contacts with persons infected with colds and communicable diseases. Thumb-sucking is an undesirable habit. Remember: "A baby is both a job and a joy."

QUESTIONS

1. What are the essentials of prenatal care?
2. Why is care during the prenatal period so important?
3. Of what value is dental care during pregnancy?
4. Give several reasons why the diet during pregnancy needs to be considered.
5. What foods are of special value? Why?
6. When should the baby's care begin?
7. What constitutes an adequate layette and the necessary equipment for the care of the baby?
8. Give a routine of care which might be carried out for the baby.
9. Why is breast milk the best food for the baby? What substitutes may be used if necessary?
10. Why should the baby's clothing and equipment be as simple as possible?
11. What habits may the baby develop?

READING REFERENCES

BOOKS

Aldrich, Charles A., and Mary M., *Babies Are Human Beings* (Macmillan). An interpretation of growth.

Carroll, Eleanor G., *Is There a Baby in the House?* (Doubleday).

Dafoe, Allan R., *Guidebook for Mothers* (Messner).

Eastman, Nicholson, *Expectant Motherhood* (Little).

Gilbert, Margaret S., *Biography of the Unborn* (Wood).

Goodenough, Florence L., *Developmental Psychology* (Appleton-Century). Behavior of the unborn child.

Hurlock, Elizabeth B., *Modern Ways with Babies* (Lippincott).

Kenyon, Josephine H., *Healthy Babies Are Happy Babies* (Little).

Lowenburg, Harry, *Care of Infants and Children* (McGraw).

Tenney, Horace K., *Let's Talk about Your Baby.* (University of Minnesota). Book for parents on child care and training.

Woods, Linda M., *Your New Baby; How to Prepare for It and Care for It* (McBridge).

Zabriskie, Louise, *Mother and Baby Care in Pictures* (Lippincott).

PAMPHLETS

American Medical Association, *A Child Is to Be Born* (Chicago, Ill.).

De Normandie, Robert L., *The Expectant Mother and Her Baby* (Funk).

Parents' Institute, Inc., *Baby Care Manual* (52 Vanderbilt Ave., N. Y.).

U. S. Department of Labor, Children's Bureau, *Appraisal of the Newborn Infant; Infant Care;* and *Prenatal Care.*

PLANNED CONVALESCENCE FOR MOTHER AND BABY

Louise Zabriskie

Every mother should know how to take care of herself after her baby is born as well as during pregnancy. The author is particularly well fitted to give such advice because of her years of experience in caring for new mothers and new babies. She is Director of the Maternity Consultation Service of New York, and lecturer at New York University. She is also the author of *The Nurses' Handbook of Obstetrics* and *Mother and Baby Care in Pictures*.

IN ORDER to make the necessary preparations for convalescence following labor and the birth of the baby, it is important to understand some of the changes and readjustments that take place in the systems of the mother and the baby. Labor is the crisis of the maternity period. Before the onset of labor every organ and every system in the body have contributed to the changes which have occurred. These include changes in the secretions from the internal glands or endocrines, some of which have been suppressed, some increased; also changes in those muscles which must stretch and enlarge; and changes in the breasts before lactation is established. Preparation for aftercare

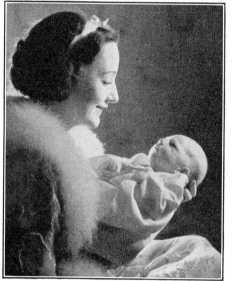

Photo: Doris Day-Loder

Every mother should know how to take care of herself before and after her baby is born.

must begin in the prenatal period, when the mother is planning for labor and delivery. The manner in which she reacts to this crisis and the kind of care she has at this time greatly determines the type of convalescence she will have and the progress which might be expected for the baby.

The preparation for delivery is comparable to the preparation for any major operation. This means building up the general system to offer the best resistance at the time of need. In addition, the obstetrical patient is not only preparing for delivery and the expected normal convalescence, but she is also preparing herself for the time when she will be ready to nurse her baby.

Care Following Delivery

The three major considerations in the period immediately following delivery are: (1) protection from infection, (2) maintenance of the daily strength by diet and rest, and (3) emotional adjustment.

The care following the birth of the baby should include also the following:

Aseptic care of the genitals and careful observation of the state of the uterus and the type of vaginal discharge or lochia.

Care of the breasts and means of aiding lactation.

Consideration of adequate diet and fluids.

Rest in bed ten to fourteen days followed by guarded convalescence.

Plenty of rest and sleep.

Attention to intestinal and urinary elimination.

Daily routine for both the mother and the baby.

Provision for diversion, and protection from anxiety or emotional stress.

Significance of the return visit to the doctor in about six weeks after the birth of the baby.

PROTECTION FROM INFECTION

Unless there is some focus of infection in the body, the meticulous care of the mother by the doctor, nurse, or whoever is giving the care, offers the best means of protection. The uterus at this time has a denuded surface, which may be compared to a surgical wound. It is, therefore, extremely susceptible to infection. Scrupulous cleanliness in the mother's daily care must be maintained, and she must also be protected from contacts with people who have colds, local infections, or communicable diseases.

Aseptic Care of the Genitals. Following delivery, asepsis is one of the important ways for preventing infection of the genitals. Hospitals have various techniques for this care, but the object is always the same: to protect the mother from infection from without, since the inner surface of the uterus is still regarded as an open wound. This treatment also makes the mother more comfortable.

The procedure usually consists of cleansing the external genitals with sterile soap and water or some antiseptic solution and drying with sterile cotton. This care is usually given after each urination and defecation, or about every four hours. The vaginal discharge, or lochia, is quite profuse at first and dark red in color much like the menstrual discharge. It becomes less day by day. On getting out of bed this discharge may increase, but normally will not be profuse. By the end of the fourth to fifth week the discharge has usually completely disappeared. Lack of proper rest and overexercise will tend to increase the amount of discharge.

Care of the Breasts. The breasts as well as the nipples need special daily care before and after nursing. Hospitals also have various techniques for this procedure. During the first few days there is only a grayish, watery secretion (called colustrum) from the breasts. About the third or fourth day the secretion of milk begins, and the breasts become quite full, sometimes engorged. It is important that the nipples be kept covered and the breasts supported. The nipples should be watched very carefully for any irritation or fissures (cracks) because these signs are often the forerunners of breast infections. The first consciousness of irritation or discomfort in the breasts should be reported to the doctor.

Breast milk is stimulated by regular nursing and complete emptying of the breasts. Worry and emotional disturbances influence the amount and character of breast milk and react on the baby. After the milk is finally established, the amount secreted is usually regulated by the baby's needs. Both the mother and the baby should be comfortable during nursing. Even at this early time the baby should not be encouraged to dawdle over his feeding.

MAINTENANCE OF THE DAILY STRENGTH BY DIET AND REST

Diet. The mother's daily strength must be maintained by proper diet and sufficient rest. These are necessary not only for a more rapid convalescence, but also to build up resistance against infection. Diet is of special importance because of the numerous changes going on in the body at this time. This is the period when the uterus begins to return gradually to its almost normal state, size, and position. The foods which stimulate muscle tone help the uterus to discharge the degenerating mucous membrane and aid in the building up of the new tissue. (See article on "Food" in this volume.) Muscle tone is also necessary to contract the uterine muscles in an effort to reduce the size of the uterus. During these days the uterus must change its position and in time return to the pelvic cavity. This, too, is aided by the strengthening of the ligaments and muscles which support the uterus. In fact, all the organs of the generative system as well as the abdominal muscles are involved and are, therefore, aided by proper diet and rest.

While the mother is in bed, the diet should be light and easily digestible. After there has been a satisfactory elimination, the mother may have a wider selection of foods.

Fluids are especially needed to replace those lost during labor and delivery. They also aid and stimulate elimination. If the mother is nursing her baby, his normal development will depend on the quality and quantity of the foods and fluids she takes. A well-balanced diet is one of the best means of maintaining adequate breast milk.

Elimination. Many doctors order a cathartic about twenty-four hours after the birth of the baby. After this, daily elimination aids in the patient's general progress. The mother is also urged to void a few hours after delivery; this helps to re-establish the regularity of urinary elimination. Food and fluids aid in these bodily functions.

Rest. As for rest—this in-bed period of ten to fourteen days following the birth of the baby prevents any strain on the ligaments and muscles which support the uterus. The ordeal of labor and delivery is so strenuous and exhausting that rest is essential to restore the mother physically.

During the first three or four days she may be allowed to turn from side to side or to lie on her abdomen for a few minutes at a time. After this time she may be allowed to be in a semisitting position; and by the ninth or tenth day she may be permitted out of bed for a few minutes. Because of the change in position the mother may feel weak and faint on this first adventure out of bed. Sitting up in bed is a preparation for getting out of bed. It is important that the mother go back to bed before she is tired. The regaining of strength comes gradually. The stimulation created by the advent of the new baby should not be mistaken for physical energy.

Sleep. Sleep, too, must be emphasized during these days in bed, because the night's rest will be interrupted from now on. Even after the baby's night feeding has been discontinued, the mother has his responsibility constantly on her mind. The mother should be encouraged to nap during the day and establish a habit which will be so necessary to her health during the weeks to come. Rest and sleep is always an individual consideration. Some mothers need more sleep than others, and it should be regulated according to the individual nervous disposition and habits of life. It is wise also to limit the number of visitors in these early days of her convalescence, because too much company is often exhausting.

Daily Routine. During these first few weeks is the opportune time to begin a regular routine. Not only will this be advantageous to the baby's general health and development, but it will also help the mother to adjust herself to the added responsibility of the baby, so as to fit his care into her usual household routine. If the mother is in a hospital, she should take advantage of the opportunity to rest while the nurse assumes the care of the baby. When the mother has to take over this responsibility, she should be able to discriminate between the more and the less important tasks in order to conserve her energy and strength. One can imagine that it is also difficult for

the baby to make the adjustment from hospital to home routine. While the time and regularity for feeding and bathing may be the same, the baby must become accustomed to different surroundings, clothing, a strange bed, and inexperienced handling. All these readjustments may take one or two weeks. Everything should be done during this time to aid his adjustment and the mother should be protected from emotional disturbances and worry. These first few days at home with the added responsibility are exhausting and may influence the amount of breast milk. As soon as the mother becomes accustomed to the routine and is getting sufficient rest, the amount of breast milk will be increased.

EMOTIONAL REACTIONS

The mother also must make an emotional adjustment which is not comparable with any other experience in life. It is impossible to evaluate the emotional response involved in bringing a brand-new human being into the world.

The baby may be anticipated by both parents with great enthusiasm and happiness, or his arrival may be looked forward to with agony or indifference. The attitude toward this newcomer during pregnancy and the attitude after his arrival may be the cause of considerable emotional stress. All kinds of emotional disturbances affect the general physical condition. Distress and worry particularly contribute unfavorably to the mother's convalescence, not only interfering with the normal rehabilitation of her body but also with the progress of lactation. The father and other members of the family should endeavor to make this a time when the mother is as comfortable and as free from anxiety as possible.

Diversion. When the mother begins to feel stronger, she will need some diversion. It may be very relaxing for her to be away from the baby for an hour or two, leaving him with some dependable person. The father may be a great help to the mother by relieving her of some household responsibilities and helping to create a happy congenial atmosphere.

Return Visit to the Doctor. About six weeks after the birth of the baby, the mother should make a return visit to the doctor or clinic. At this time the doctor is able to judge whether or not the internal organs are returning to their almost normal size and position. This is also an opportunity for the mother to discuss any problems with the doctor.

Certificate of Birth. Within the first few weeks the parents should receive the baby's birth certificate. The legislation in all states now requires the registration of all births. This is an important document for the baby to have in later years.

A mother who is well, a father who is really interested and shares the responsibility, a home that is well adjusted and has a happy atmosphere—all these influences offer the baby the best fundamentals for a good start in life.

SUMMARY

1. Prenatal care is important in preparing the mother for the strenuous time of labor and delivery. Frequently aftercare depends on how well the mother has taken care of herself and the kind of supervision she has had during pregnancy.

2. Care following delivery means protecting the mother from infection, maintaining her strength by diet and rest, and establishing a healthful routine.

3. Of major importance at this time is protecting the mother from emotional upsets.

QUESTIONS

1. How does the kind of care and supervision during pregnancy influence convalescence?

2. In what way does diet prepare the mother for labor, convalescence, and lactation?

3. What value is derived from the rest-in-bed period following delivery?

4. How can the mother be protected from emotional distress and worry?

5. Of what value is breast feeding?

READING REFERENCES

Dafoe, Allan R., *Guidebook for Mothers* (Messner).

Eastman, Nicholson J., *Expectant Motherhood* (Little).

Irving, Frederick C., *Expectant Mother's Handbook* (Houghton).

Kenyon, Josephine H., *Healthy Babies Are Happy Babies* (Little).

Maternity Consultation Service, *Maternity Handbook* (Putnam). This may also be obtained direct from the Maternity Consultation Service, 1359 York Avenue, New York, N. Y.

Washburn, Helen, *So You're Going to Have a Baby* (Harcourt).

Zabriskie, Louise, *Mother and Baby Care in Pictures* (Lippincott).

WORK AND PLAY FOR THE PRESCHOOL CHILD

Helen G. Sternau

A happy childhood, with just enough responsibility to give life meaning, is the birthright of every child and the very foundation of a purposeful and contented maturity. It is, therefore, every parent's duty and privilege to direct the little child's play into wholesome and imaginative channels, and his small tasks so as to give him the greatest enjoyment and benefit from them. The author, who is Associate Editor of *Child Study Magazine,* has written numerous articles on this subject for her own and other periodicals. She has been a teacher in nursery schools, has had experience with special guidance problems, and is the mother of two children.

How anxious the small child is to learn! He has the "insatiable curiosity" of the Elephant Child in the story and the ceaseless energy of a young monkey. He wants a part in everything that goes on, and he imitates everything he sees; especially he wants to please the people he loves.

Of course he gets underfoot and in the way, and his experiments often end in minor mishaps; but his drives to know and do and try for himself are priceless assets for his education. Too often they are wasted or deliberately stamped out by busy adults who don't know what he is after. It is hard to learn anything if someone is always saying, "Don't touch! Don't bother me! Don't be silly! Don't get dirty! Don't get wet!" or, most ignominious of all, "You're

Photo: Black Star-Haller

Water play of any kind, but especially blowing soap bubbles, is a favorite pastime of little children.

too little!" And there is so much for a small child to learn about the everyday world of things and people, about managing his body and his feelings, about his own native language.

When he is learning, he is busy and happy, most of the time. Much of the "naughtiness" of little children springs from sheer restless boredom. How then can we help our children toward this happy kind of education?

The little child learns largely through play. Play builds body and mind and develops skills of many kinds. It is the child's way of digesting ideas and working through problems. But he must have things to play with. Good play materials need not be expensive. Most of us throw away daily much that our children could use in creative play, or

112a

that we might use in making simple toys for them. Children know the charms of our cast-offs at once, but too often their treasure hoards are thrown away in the cause of neatness. A painted orange crate will frequently solve the storage problem.

PLAY MATERIALS FROM SCRAP

Cartons can be turned into dollhouses, stores, or dry-land boats. Trucks, cars,

Photo: F.P.G.-Baker

Playmates are as important as playthings in a child's education. The good nursery school provides the proper toys and the most suitable companions; but be sure the school is run by trained persons.

boats, and planes, wagons, and doll furniture can be made from boxes and spools, or with ends of wood, or with cardboard and glue or adhesive tape. (See "Handwork Experiences," Volume Thirteen.) Scraps of cloth make rag dolls, beanbags, or clothes, draperies, and covers for the doll family, while ends of lace, ribbon, and wool supply the priceless details of fashion. Bits of rope, wire, and tubing, odd screws and bolts and broken fixtures become "machinery," dear to the small boy. Empty cans serve as nested blocks or flowerpots, or make boilers and smokestacks for trains and boats. Towel rollers, when painted, are useful as trumpets. Add a folded newspaper hat and a small boy and you have a soldier.

Colored papers are fun to cut and paste. Magazine pictures can be saved for scrapbooks or, when pasted on cardboard, may be cut into simple puzzles. Fashion advertisements, colored and backed with stiff paper, make fine paper dolls; and collections of auto, ship, or animal cutouts can be made in the same way. Shells and seeds and pebbles become doll dishes and food, or may be used to make gay designs. Linoleum scraps are useful for block printing; wood ends and scraps of plasterboard, for carpentry; old pans and sieves make fine sand toys.

A shabby handbag, filled with this or that, turns the child into traveler, carpenter, plumber, or doctor at will. Old clothes are good for dressing up. Play materials are everywhere, once one learns to see them.

HOUSEHOLD EQUIPMENT AS TOYS

Nor need the child be limited to such discarded oddments. Everyday household equipment has great possibilities if we are reasonably generous about lending our possessions to our children. Caves, tents, and playhouses, trains, boats, and airplanes grow from ingenious arrangements of furniture, blankets, and pillows. Merchandise for a store and food for a tea party are always on hand. A basin of water with a soap shaker, a cooky cutter with a pan of dough or wet sand, buttons to string or the spool box to arrange will amuse a child for many happy hours. Nests of pots and lids make fine put-together toys for the tiniest; so do poker chips and a box with a slit in its cover through which to poke them. Cans or bars of soap will serve as building blocks. The imaginative child will have many ideas of his own. The ironing board becomes his cow, the alarm clock his engine headlight, an old lantern his outboard motor.

PLAYING OUTDOORS

Water and mud and sand are the cheapest toys in the world and the most universally satisfying. They are best, perhaps, in their natural setting of beach or pond or running brook, but endlessly entertaining in any form. The hose, a sprinkling can, or a tub of water in the yard are fine playthings in warm weather. The city child makes a beeline for drinking fountains, dripping hydrants, and puddles of rain water, if only he is allowed to get dirty. After all, sunsuits and overalls are easily laundered, and getting wet in warm weather never hurt anyone.

PLAYING INDOORS

Water play indoors is fun, too: washing clothes, sailing boats, filling and pouring, "painting" with plain water and a big brush, washing shelves, blowing soap bubbles, or scrubbing vegetables for mother. This kind of play had best be limited to bathroom or kitchen, and it does require an oilcloth apron to protect the clothing; but any child will accept such reasonable restrictions. What a boon this quieting kind of play can be on a long rainy day in the house!

BOUGHT PLAYTHINGS

If there is money to buy play equipment, the list can be enriched; but elaborate and expensive toys add little to the child's happiness. Buy him materials for making and doing: *blocks above all,* clay, poster paint with large brushes and paper, jumbo crayons, scissors and paste, simple carpentry tools. He enjoys store toys, too: boats, trains, trucks and cars, housekeeping equipment, dolls and animals. Simple, sturdy toys are best, and not the easily broken mechanical gadgets. Washable dolls with clothes that come off are far more fun than the fancy show type.

Equipment for outdoor play is worth buying if one can afford it: tricycles and wagons, large hollow blocks, climbing apparatus, a swing, packing cases and boards, a sandbox. Much of this can be made inexpensively by a handy father. Getting together with the neighbors on play-yard equipment is often possible and an excellent way to save space and money and time for supervision.

SUPERVISING PLAYTIME

Just how much supervision *is* needed? Certainly some adult should know what is going on at all times; and for some sorts of play with tools or on climbing apparatus or beside deep water, an adult should be close at hand, but the child should plan his own play and carry out his own ideas. Even the sheerest messing with paint or clay or mud serves a real purpose for him. Of course, one should give help when it is needed, prevent accidents and destructiveness, and be ready with suggestions when interest wanes; but give the child freedom to experiment and learn.

PLAYING WITH OTHER CHILDREN

Playmates are as important as playthings for the child's education. Nor should he play exclusively with his own brothers and sisters. Where there are differences in age and strength, the pattern of slave and master grows up too readily. Play groups and nurseries are fine if they are run by trained people; but beware the purely commercial venture. It will prove worse than nothing.

Visiting children help to provide suitable companionship, but such visiting should be an informal affair, preferably with one mother caring for the two youngsters and the other freed for an afternoon's "vacation."

Company manners are meaningless to the small child. The same code of sharing and fair play which prevails among brothers and sisters is quite enough. Of course, the parent must expect some quarreling when children play together. It is well for an adult to know how each child is faring, and sometimes interference will be needed; but it is wiser to suggest compromises and explain divergent views than to act as judge. Helping the child to learn how to play happily with another is the real point of such associations.

COMPANIONSHIP WITH GROWN-UPS

The child needs some chance to play with the grown-ups in his family, too. It helps him to feel close to them and leads him on to new experiences. But a word of warning here: Too much play with adults can be overstimulating, and it may make the child too dependent. Don't overdo it.

There is a happy kind of dramatic play with little children which grown-ups can carry on while their hands are busy with routine tasks. The child takes the lead and sets the pace. The adult adds just enough to keep the game going. Perhaps they play store or house or doctor or traveling, or that the carpenter has come to fix the house. Such simple games develop imagination and language skill. Above all, they give a warm sense of togetherness.

Children love stories and songs and rhythmic play. Stories and picture books about everyday things and people are best in the preschool years, and songs with easy tunes, which the child can learn to sing. (See "A Library of 300 Titles" in Volume Nine, and "Music" in Volume Thirteen.) He enjoys rhythms, too, free body movements to simple music, but not set dance steps and recitations to show off for company.

Nature study and science can yield happy shared experiences, too. Making things grow, caring for pets, noticing form and design, color and texture, watching the seasons and the ways of wild things, such experiences have meaning for the child. (See special articles in Volume Ten.) He needs simple answers to his questions but not long, wordy explanations. He will ask for more when he is ready. Questions about his body and its functions, about sex differences and babies, should have the same simple, honest answers. Even if he doesn't understand—and often he won't—it is important that he should feel free to ask again, to talk to his own parents about any of the things that puzzle him. (See "Sex in the Young Child's Life" in this Volume.)

Time To Stand and Stare

Most of all he needs time to watch and experiment and wonder. "The world is so full of a number of things!" Too often adults are slaves to time, and hurry a child past his learning experiences. Routine and order are important in the life of a small child, but not hurry and rigidity. Routines should be planned with leeway for fruitful loitering. One's child is not wasting time when he stops to watch the birds on the lawn or the steam roller in the street, or when he plays with the water tap, or gazes fascinated at the ripples on the pond. This, too, is part of his education.

Trips and Excursions

Exploring the larger world comes next, and here is a fine way for fathers to get acquainted with their toddlers. How much there is to see near at hand! There is never any need for fatiguing or overexciting trips for the preschool child. A visit to a train yard or dock, or to watch the boats on the river makes a fine outing. Try a morning at the zoo or the playground, or one just feeding the pi-

geons in the park; a ferry-boat ride; a trip on the electric car or subway, when the child can stand on the platform to watch the tracks and signals.

Those who live in the country might follow a brook or a woodsy trail, explore a cave, sailboats on a pond, or fish for minnows, visit a nearby farm or dairy, drive to market, or collect shells on the beach.

An occasional all-day picnic or beach party for the whole family is fun, but

Black Star-Titcomb

Allowing this toddler to dig while the garden is being spaded gives her a feeling of importance, especially when father praises her and tells her what a big help she is.

careful plans must be made if the young child is not to suffer. Some youngsters can stand more than others. One will rest on a rug out-of-doors or fall asleep in the car. Another grows more and more tired and cross as the day goes on, sleeps little that night, and shows the ill effects for days. One must watch the child and plan accordingly.

Movies, museums, and amusement parks, the circus, and similar exciting ventures are really not intended for the preschool child. Of course, if older brothers and sisters are going, one may be tempted to break the rule at times. It is hard to be the youngest and to be left out again and again. Often, exceptions do less harm than hurt feelings; but often a substitute treat with mother or father may be enough. It depends on the child's reaction. There can be no rigid rules for living with children.

HELPING IS FUN

Working together is one of the best forms of companionship for parents and children. Fathers are often especially good at this sort of thing, and their children always enjoy the chance to work with them. Simple carpentry, modeling and painting, making or mending toys and household equipment, repainting furniture and fences, gardening, jelly or candymaking, house-furnishing and dressmaking for the doll family—these are only a few of the creative tasks which parent and child can share.

Let the child do his own job. If you are helping with *his* plans, do not insist on adult standards of perfection and spoil his fun. Of course, if it is *your* project and he is "helping" you, then your standards prevail. But it is always possible to find some part of the task that a child can do well enough, if it is only stirring paint or measuring sugar. He is happy

if he has a finger in the pie—literally or figuratively—and, "See what *we* made!" is a phrase that fills his soul with pride.

The toddler always wants to help with whatever you are doing. Of course, he is a nuisance at first, but his spirit of helpfulness is worth encouraging. If you keep telling him he is too little, he will soon stop wanting to help. Even a tiny tot can dust the rungs of chairs, shell peas, or scrub potatoes, drop seeds in a furrow, or throw corn to the hens, gather weeds and fallen leaves in the garden, wash silver, empty trash baskets, paint a board, sandpaper an edge, or pound a nail here and there. It is quicker to do it yourself, of course, but that is not the point. It is worthwhile *finding things he can do* at first and adding more skilled tasks as he is ready.

Let him try the harder things, too, but give him plenty of time and be prepared for some mishaps. Three- and four-year-olds can be amazingly careful with "spillables" and "breakables" and they love to try. Mishaps constructively handled can become learning experiences, too. Treat them calmly. Let the child clean up the mess himself. *And don't scold!* Then let him try again.

NEVER OVERBURDEN WITH RESPONSIBILITY

Do not expect too much work or too much responsibility. The young child's attention is brief and his interest soon lags. *As much as he wants to do,* is a good rule at first. By the time he is five or six, he will see a task through in most cases, but only if you are working, too. Carrying on all alone is a more mature accomplishment. This goes for cleaning

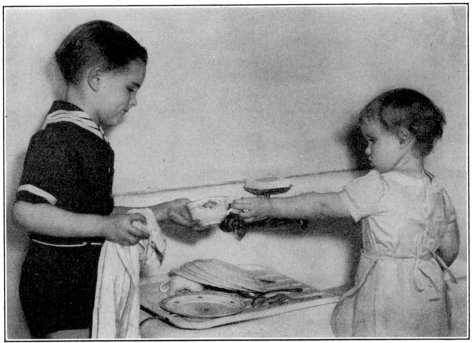

Photo: F.P.G.-Burnham

Three-year-olds can be amazingly careful with breakables. Let them wash the dishes, especially if there is an older brother or sister standing by to enjoy the fun as well as the responsibility.

up the playroom, too—unless there are big brothers and sisters to help. Working with a child is the best way to teach him to work. Do not discourage him by too much criticism. Praising him for a job well done is a better way of improving his standards.

LEARNING INDEPENDENCE

Let your child help himself. Give him time and encouragement. Of course, it is quicker to wash and dress him yourself, but he wants to try it alone. It is important for him to learn and feel capable of accomplishment. Low shelves and hooks should be provided for his possessions, a sturdy step for the bathroom basin and toilet, clothes that are simple and easily managed. All these encourage independence.

Again! Do not expect too much! After a child once knows how to wash and dress himself, his interest wanes. Doing these things all alone may be too hard.

Sometimes a child just wants to be babied, especially if he is tired or life has been hard that day. Help him along at such times, share the job, make it a game—and expect to do plenty of reminding for years to come. Pushing won't make a child grow up. It is as bad as holding him back. Independence can't be forced; it must be fostered.

SUMMARY

The little child learns largely through play but he needs things to play with and suitable companions. Elaborate toys and games are unnecessary but a chance to make and do, to experiment and explore, is every child's birthright. There is good play material in every home if one knows what to look for and how to use it.

Adults can enrich the child's experience with stories and music, nature study and outings. They can add to his skills by working and playing with him. Little children love to help and to try for themselves. It is important to encourage their efforts at helpfulness and independence, but one must not expect too much or force the child too fast.

QUESTIONS

1. What are some of the scrap materials preschool children enjoy having for their own fun?

2. What kind of equipment can a father build for his children's outdoor play? Indoor?

3. Name some benefits of local excursions for the preschool child.

4. What are the harmful effects of all-day excursions for the highstrung child?

5. In what ways do you permit your child to help about the house? In the yard? On shopping trips?

6. What responsibility should the little child take for keeping his room in order? For remembering to bring outdoor toys inside?

7. How can you encourage his independence?

READING REFERENCES

BOOKS

Baruch, Dorothy W., *Parents and Children Go to School* (Scott, Foresman).

Boettiger, Elizabeth F., *Children's Play, Indoors and Out* (Dutton).

Frank, Josette, *What Books for Children?* (Doubleday).

Hart, Beatrix T., *Play and Toys in Nursery Years* (Viking).

Isaacs, Susan S., *The Nursery Years* (Vanguard).

Wolf, Anna W., M., *The Parents' Manual* (Simon & Schuster).

PAMPHLETS

Lambert, Clara, *Play, A Yardstick of Growth* (Play Schools Committee, Child Study Association).

Staff, Child Study Association, *Will Your Child Be Ready for School?* These two pamphlets and others on related subjects may be obtained from Child Study Association of America, 221 West 57th Street, New York, N. Y.

SEX IN THE YOUNG CHILD'S LIFE

Newell W. Edson

Perhaps no other problem of child training causes such acute concern to parents as how to answer children's questions about sex. The childhood experiences of the parents themselves seldom furnish a usable precedent, since the generally accepted attitude toward such matters has changed rather radically in the past few years. The author tells exactly how to handle the questions and situations that are certain to arise, and he gives sane advice about the necessity for a wholesome point of view. He is well known as a writer and lecturer on social-hygiene problems. Formerly with the American Social Hygiene Association of New York, he is now executive secretary of the Social Hygiene Association of Erie, Pennsylvania.

For most young children sex plays a comparatively minor role. Experience indicates the wisdom of keeping it so. This does not mean that it should be either ignored or emphasized, or that it should be feared or evaded or made a cause for emotional disturbance.

Usually sex is a normal factor in the young child's life; and to continue normal, it needs to be handled like any other factor—simply, calmly, and appropriately.

Since it is interwoven into the fabric of the child's nature, parents should not attempt to separate it from the situation of which it is a part, but should deal with the total situation. This means that when a child's curiosity is aroused about his body, for instance, he should not be put off until some particular moment "when such things are talked about," but the immediate situation should be treated then and there as a part of the total experience of body exploration.

In the average household, it is not a question of whether or not sex is a fit topic about which children should be informed. They get information regardless of what the parents may wish in the matter. It happens that humans are of two sexes, both of which share in the gendering and rearing of the child. Thus there are constantly manifested in the daily life of the child the sex differences and

Photo: H. Armstrong Roberts

ANSWERING QUESTIONS

When the child asks questions about sex, he should be given calm, matter-of-fact answers.

the sex conduct of his parents and, if there are other children in the family, their various stages of sexual differences and conduct. Father is different from mother not only in size and shape but in dress and manners and occupations, as any child quickly learns. Big brother resembles father in all these things, while sister resembles mother. Other children and adults fall into one or the other of these classes. Bits of open conversation, suppressed comments for "little pitchers," unintended remarks about coming babies, sister's growing interest in boys, brother's satisfaction with his "blind" date, mother's shriek of "Don't come in here, I'm only half dressed," sister's confusion at finding father in the tub, father's markedly different affection and admiration for mother, mother's unconscious jealousy over a new maid, an aunt's expostulations at the modern freedom of talk between boys and girls—all these fragments of everyday life are informing the child about sex. So also are the vulgar or silly remarks of servant, farm hand, or grocer boy. Everyone avoids telling the child why kitty is so big or why a neighbor went to the hospital and came back with a baby. The child's family may not be willing to tell him where babies come from, but older companions or chance remarks or vulgar stories soon inform him.

These common experiences may not seem to the average parent to be significant sex education, but nevertheless they lay the foundation of fact and attitude that colors the child's later responses and attitudes as well as his acceptance of facts. If this foundation of sexual knowl-edge is to be secure and effective, it needs to be built carefully, not left to chance discovery or ashamed revelation.

An easy-going father may say, "Why not let him pick it up? He'll learn soon enough." The answer to this is that "picked-up" education is the poorest the child can have. It is given not by people who love him and want him to have the best information and ideals on sex, but by those who like to share their vulgarities or superstitions. The child is without the ability to discriminate between the sound and the unsound. The tragedies poured out to physicians and psychiatrists are many of them founded upon "picked-up" education about sex. Our jails and hospitals hold many persons who have been the victims of the same haphazard sex education. Not only is the child entitled to the best that parents can give him, but their neglect is often serious for him. Perhaps in no phase of the child's life is a right start so important.

CHILD'S ATTITUDE TOWARD SEX

Lack of Meaning in Sex Manifestations. There are a few things for parents to remember in directing the sex factor in the life of the young child. Sex manifestations have little meaning for a child until they are given such meaning by others, usually adults, to whom these manifestations have much meaning. To the child, sexual organs have no more significance than other body parts. The sudden appearance of either of his parents nude becomes important only when they make it so by hurriedly covering up and showing their

agitation in flushed cheeks, startled ex-
clamations, or angry command. The
vulgar vocabulary he picks up in the yard
or street is only the conversation of his
friends, until parents or relatives show
disgust or shame or righteous indigna-
tion over it and try to stop it. The child
begins life with no sex consciousness;
that is set for him by his home associates.
Hence his parents have in their hands
much of the shaping of his attitudes. If
they, no matter how they feel themselves,
can give him the impression that sex is
a natural and fine part of him, to be
directed wholesomely like any other factor, they will give him a foundation that
will likely last throughout most of his
life.

There is apparently no sex drive behind the young child's conduct, however much he may shock and startle his
family. The undressing of a little girl
by a little boy can hardly be laid to sex
desire, but rather to a feeling of adventure or of curiosity to see if she is made
like himself. Blunt questions about
coitus between dogs, frank revelations
about family intimacies to strangers, and
a sudden appearance without clothes before guests are usually evidences of un-
familiarity with adult codes. Probably
the greatest mistake that parents can
make in such instances is to attribute to
children the mature feelings of adults.
Adult motives come only from adult experience. The child's experiences are
limited and his sexual mechanism is immature. Most of his early adventures,
therefore, are due to curiosity or play-
hunger or desire for companionship
rather than to anything that could be

called sex in the adult meaning of the
term.

*Natural Curiosity about Sex Easily
Satisfied.* The child's curiosity about sex
is wholly natural and is ordinarily easily
satisfied. In the beginning, sex is an un-
differentiated part of the life around him,
and he inquires about it as he would
about any other thing that interests him.
To him the physical sex differences and
the coming of a baby are not sex but
merely things about which he wants to
know. Their sexual significance comes
out only after it has been made evident
from the explanations and emotional responses of those around him. Hence
many queries about sex are included
among the hundreds of questions which
a normal child asks. Curiosity is too valuable an asset to be denied, for it is the
motivation of much of his learning. If
information is made understandable, the
young child's curiosity is easily satisfied.
If his curiosity is not satisfied, it might
perhaps die out if sex were not so much
—and so early—a part of the environment outside the home. Other children
are curious about sex also, and they are
usually eager to share their meager and
often fantastic information. Therefore,
sex curiosity is far better satisfied at
home, where parents can be sure of the
information and attitudes given the child.

If the objective of education is to help
the child meet his life situations, helpful
information should be given before a
situation develops rather than after. For
example, normal attitudes toward body
differences had better be set by parents
before a conservative grandmother or
prudish aunt or vulgar servant initiates

the child to shame or squeamishness. The coming of a baby can best be explained by mother and father before others surround the event with mystery or fear or hilarity. The father's part in reproduction had better be told by the parents than by companions or "wise guys" during the first week or month of school. Too many parents, through dread of the task or through failure to realize the influence of others, do not anticipate likely or obvious situations. They have to overcome wrong emotional attitudes on the part of the child. The relearning of facts is not difficult; the relearning of attitudes may be very difficult indeed for the child. Wise anticipation is better than slow relearning.

No Emotional Disturbances about Sex. The parent needs to realize that emotional disturbances are usually in the parent and not in the child, except where the child copies parent emotions. If the parent can conceal or check his own emotion, he can limit the emotional response in the child. This is not always easy, especially if the parent is emotionally sensitive, as he may be in regard to sex.

Many parents, however, have found that they can largely overcome their emotion by concentrating on the child's needs and point of view. In substance, therefore, this sort of reasoning may develop in the parent: "Ralph wants to know about babies. Of course he does. They are alive, near his own size, not grown-up, and hence understandable. For him they have no connection with sex. He certainly doesn't want to know all that I know about them, for he couldn't absorb it all and probably wouldn't listen to most of it. Then just what does he want to know? Why, just what he asked, where babies come from. That's easy. They come from their mother's bodies. Nothing difficult in that, either for him or for me. And of course the next question—which may not come till tomorrow or next week—will be, 'How do they get there?' That's not difficult to answer either. They grow from tiny eggs in the mother's body." This method seems a more rational one than for the parent to fight down his own dread or shame and become so absorbed in the fight that he entirely loses from sight the simplicity of the child's question and the ease of answering it. After all, the essential in such situations is not how the parent feels but what is the best education for the child. It certainly cannot be effective education if the parent is so involved in his own emotion that he cannot sense the child's need or the best way to meet it.

The child grows up without waiting for the parent to feel just right before acting. This statement seems necessary for those parents who are constantly postponing answers or sidestepping situations until a better time and for the few parents who have been swayed by the argument, "If you can't become emotionally adjusted, you'd best not undertake the task." The child has to meet his situation whether the parent helps him or not. A curiosity made dormant for the time being by evasion or rebuff may easily be revived by the chance remark of a playmate, and the curiosity may be satisfied by the same source. And as for emotional adjustment, in how many situations that one has to meet with the child does one become emotionally adjusted? There is very likely to be at least a residue of emotion when one rescues his child from playmates who are making him eat dirt or pulls him away from the hot stove or mops up the spilled ink. Yet these situations have to be met, and promptly, whether one is emotionally adjusted or not. Life does not wait until one has trained oneself to be calm under all circumstances, including those concerned with sex. Meanwhile, the child is growing up and is getting experience and information elsewhere, both of which may be unwholesome. For the unwholesome person does not hesitate to tell the child all he knows, with all the intrigue of humor and vulgarity and mystery and fear he can pack into the experience. While parents hesitate, the back yard and the street are right on the job!

The Child Discovers Himself

The young child is a discoverer. His first area for discovery is himself. He tests the movements of arms, legs, trunk, and head, and gradually learns some of the things he can do with them. He tastes and smells and feels everything that comes within reach. His body becomes an exploring ground. Some parts of it respond more pleasurably than others, among them the external sexual organs, which are more sensitive than most body parts. It is natural and apparently not harmful for him to feel these, at first casually, then more purposively, and sometimes, if he is not checked, to repeat the experiment until it

becomes a habit. Alarmed parents, especially fathers, who have been brought up with the feeling that handling is harmful or unnatural or degrading, need to watch their own emotions quite carefully during such times and to remember that no dire results will take place. This child experimentation is no excuse for emotional outbursts, punishment, or hand-gags. Attractive substitutes—mother's finger, a rattle, a gay-colored ball, some soft-feeling object—will commonly divert the attention of the child without much difficulty. The parent should remember that there is no sex drive to make the child persist in the handling habit the moment parental attention is relaxed. Cleanliness, especially for the boy, where the foreskin needs to be pulled back occasionally and the uncovered part washed gently, and sufficiently loose clothing are aids in preventing the formation of the habit.

Child's Questions Regarding His Body. As a natural result of body exploration, questions arise concerning the body and what it is for and how it works. Not all the questions are asked at once; they are scattered over a considerable period, although at times bunched in a somewhat parent-alarming way. Among these questions there are some about sexual organs, of course, for the young child does not differentiate between sex and other functions. "What is this for?" "Why am I different from Harold?" "Why can't I go to the toilet with Jean?" "Is Daddy like me?" These are simple questions calling for simple answers. In none of them does the child need or want to know a tithe of what the parent knows, nor is the child interested in parent confusion over the question. "Those are testicles. You have two of them. When you are grown-up they will contain sperms that help to make a baby." "Because you are a girl and Harold is a boy. Girls are different from boys." "Going to the toilet is a private matter, and as soon as they know how, people usually go alone." "No, dear, Daddy is like Harold. Mother is like you."

The parent who is likely to become confused by such questions can, during the answer, turn to some simple activity, such as washing the dishes, straightening out the towels on the bathroom racks, or stooping to pick up something from the floor. The activity is an emotional release which helps prevent confusion. Then the parent can realize that she or he did not need to be disturbed; the child was not. After all, the situation was not really difficult. If the parent is able to answer the question in a matter-of-fact way without show of emotional disturbance, so much the better. The parent who is determined that the child shall have a fair and right answer will soon learn that these questions are only momentarily confusing and that any one of them can be answered in a satisfactory way.

"But," you say, "that's all right for the first question, but what about the second and the third and the fourth?" This question implies that children are like adults. Grownups ask strings of questions; children commonly do not, for it takes knowledge and experience to ask questions and the child's range of both is limited. Moreover, the child's interest soon passes to something else. Parent experience with these situations shows that children are often satisfied with an answer to one question, and rarely does the parent have to undergo a questioning ordeal. If a second or a third question does arise, it can be answered in the same simple way as the first. If children are persistent in their questions, the parent can use discretion about how much to answer at one time and when to turn the child's attention to some other matter that interests him.

EXPLAINING LIFE ORIGINS

Next to the child's interest in himself is the fascination which other children, especially babies, have for him. At almost any time the young child will turn from his toys and often from his food to watch children of his own age or younger. They are understandable; adults, including parents, are often beyond understanding. Parents want the child to do all sorts of things he does not want to do, and instead of explaining why, they enforce their authority. Questions about other children are natural, including questions as to where they came from originally. From the child's point of view these are not sex questions. Like the queries about his body, they are merely an expression of interest in the life around him. Thus he needs an answer of the same sort, that is, a reply as natural as that to any other question about daily situations. As with the demands for information about his body, he does not want to know all that the parent knows. Parents who have tried to answer questions about life origins by starting with reproduction in the amoeba and continuing up the scale to human babies usually find that young children absorb little and are often confused. Learning is a slow process, and in the early years takes time.

How Much Should the Child Be Told? The inquiries about life origins take many forms: "Where do babies come from?" "Where did you get me, Mother?" "Why did Mrs. Gerald go to the hospital for her baby?" "Why does Mrs. Bates walk so funny?" "Can't we have a baby, too?" "Do you have to sit on the egg?" "How did she know she was going to have a baby?" "Can't I have a baby?" "What is Auntie making those clothes for?" And many others. The child's query may take an unexpected form, but the essence of the answer is the same: simple statements which answer the child directly, given in as matter-of-fact a way as anything else the child is told. "Babies come from their mother's bodies. They grow from a tiny egg there. The egg stays in the body until the baby is big enough to live by itself." "A mother goes to the hospital so that she can be cared for when she has a baby." "The baby is heavy in Mrs. Bates's body; that's what makes her walk funny." "Yes, we can have a baby when we are ready for it and can look out for it well." "No, a mother doesn't sit on the egg, because it is carried inside her body." "There are several ways to tell when one is to have a baby; one of them is that the mother's body begins to grow large." "You can have a baby when you get old enough to look out for it well." "Auntie's making clothes for a new baby."

Just as there are many variations to the questions, there are many possible answers. The main point is *to answer the question the child asks.* Giving many facts at one time appears useless, for even the simplest facts have to be told to some children over and over again, as many parents can testify. Probably, after all, facts are not so important to the child as proper attitudes.

Eventually the child will need the whole story of reproduction, the mother's part in it, the growth of the embryo and fetus, birth, care of the baby, and the father's part. (For the complete story read *Growing Up,* by Karl de Schweinitz. For the manner of giving the story, read *Step by Step in Sex Education,* by Edith Hale Swift.) The last point—that is, placing the sperms inside the mother's body to join the egg there—is for many parents the most difficult to develop because it seems to them to reveal intimate relations not commonly talked about. But to the young child intimate relations mean nothing. Moreover, sexual intercourse is a universal process by which all fathers and mothers—human, dog, horse, rabbit, and all the other animals the child knows—have their babies. Babies are more important to the child than any process by which they are made. If one keeps in mind the interest of the child in life and its origins, the fear of intimate revelations disappears. The parent who, in addition, is well versed in nature study can not only bring out the universality of the reproductive process but can give to the child some of the wonder of life, so that its beginnings will always seem a marvel—as they are.

When Should the Child Be Told? The importance of the life-origins story is not in the facts given but in the emotional responses set up in the child. Unless facts are tied into some definite interest, they may soon be forgotten and

Photo: Elizabeth R. Hibbs-Loder

"Telling the story of how life begins is aided by the rearing of animal pets."

will have to be relearned. Incorrect facts may be corrected. But emotional responses tend to remain, especially if they impress the child, as the deep confusion of the parent or the vulgarity of the street is likely to do. Therefore, it is important for the parent to set the trend of the child's emotional responses before uninformed companions or vulgar-minded adults—servants, tradesmen, passers-by—

get to the child with their facts and attitudes. This means that the whole of the life-origins story should be given to the child before he goes to school. Just when and how to give it depends upon circumstances. The first questions usually begin at three to three and one-half years. By the age of six, the child should have the elements of the story.

If he is in a neighborhood where he is likely to associate with older, more sophisticated companions or grownups, then their remarks and acts need to be forestalled by previous information from the parent. Fortunately, home interpretations and attitudes are more acceptable to the child than are those of people outside. The child has confidence in his parents and in their knowledge. Hence, the chief value of the life-origins story as given by the parent is that it tends to immunize the child against the unwholesome.

Using Pets To Help Tell the Story. Telling the story of how life begins is aided by the rearing of animal pets (in pairs) and by the coming of their young. The discovery of a litter of pups or rabbits or kittens is an event of great importance to the child, and a flood of questions about their coming will arise. Such questions and the comparison with human reproduction are not difficult to handle when the child is eagerly interested in the animals before him, for to him the process of their coming is not so vital as the fact that they are actually here. Alert children may discover the pair mating and will ask the significance of this act; they will see the mother increase in size and will treat her tenderly, and they may even be present at the birth of the litter. "Why did Daddy put my squirrel into the cage with yours?" "Is the rooster fighting with the hen?" "Did Maltie have a husband?" "The old mother rabbit doesn't hop around as fast as she used to. Is she going to have her baby bunnies soon? I hope so!" "Daddy, can you guess how many darling puppies she is going to have? And can I name them all? And how soon will they be here?" "Molly gave a little yowl and then a tiny kitty popped right out. How did she do it?" Children whose parents have explained such mysteries of life for them in simple, dignified, and interested fashion are little influenced by the hearsay gossip and incorrect facts that circulate among their comrades, and they will oftentimes dispute the inaccuracies, supporting their statements with the authority of their parents. In order to be authoritative, however, some parents will have to increase their own information about the life histories of the animal pets which interest their children so much.

Technique in Answering Questions. From four years on, the world of the child increases rather rapidly and he becomes greatly interested in what it is and what it is all about. Many questions naturally arise from this interest, including those about sex. Katherine W. Hattendorf's study (see Reading References at the end of this article) of 1,763 sex questions asked by children shows that one of the peaks of child questioning comes at the age of four to five years. She has classified these child questions into eight groups: those concerned with (1) the origin of babies, (2) the coming of another baby, (3) intra-uterine growth, (4) process of birth, (5) organs and functions of the body, (6) physical sex differences, (7) relation of the father to reproduction, and (8) marriage. Questions about groups (1), (5), and (6) were asked more frequently by children of two to five years than by children of six to nine years. Naturally the questions about the more complicated functions and development increase as the child acquires more of a background of fact and experience.

As a matter of protection from shock and as a timesaver, most parents will acquire a technique for handling these questions. The following suggestions from those who have tried them out are offered as of value:

1. Treat all questions with respect. Few children ask questions for the fun of it. Most questions represent a situation of importance to the child, for the meeting of which he needs certain information. Child needs are not to be judged by adult standards. It may be quite as essential for the child's happiness to know how eggs get inside a mother's body as for father to know how many home runs his favorite ballplayer has made this season or for mother to know the latest style in hats. Even if the information received is not apparently of great moment to the child, the sense that he has an unfailing source of information to which he can turn at all times is a part of the security he needs for his happiness.

2. Try to see the child's need and satisfy that. This point has already been referred to above. One's own emotion

does not easily get the upper hand if one is deeply interested in figuring out and meeting the child's need.

3. Simple, matter-of-fact answers in your own words are preferable to book replies. The child is accustomed to your words and manner and accepts them as a matter of course. The statement from the book may not answer the question. Your words will.

4. If you are not able to answer the question, say so. "I don't know, dear, but I'll try to find out and answer you tomorrow." Then be sure you do answer him tomorrow, for an appointment with a child is as important to him as an engagement with an adult is to the latter. If you are so upset emotionally that you cannot trust yourself, postpone the matter until you have had a chance to think it through and become calmer; then answer him as promptly as you can. "Father is ready now to tell you how babies get out of their mother's bodies. They come down a special passageway made for that purpose and are slowly and gently squeezed out of the mother's body."

5. Never evade a child's question. Evasion does not help him, and it may send him elsewhere for information.

6. Don't be so matter-of-fact that you are not interesting to the child. Probably you are not coldly scientific with him about other things; why should you be so about sex? "Of course it hurts when babies are born. But not too much. And mothers are so happy to have the babies that they soon forget the hurt."

7. If you find that your child is a chatterbox and asks questions as a social accomplishment rather than as a means of securing information, turn him to some lively activity that will absorb him.

8. Don't rely too much on one technique. Study Hattendorf's pamphlet, already referred to, and turn to *New Patterns in Sex Teaching,* by Frances B. Strain, for some of the replies that she has worked out, remembering that she would modify her answers to meet differing situations. Then develop your own way.

The Child Who Asks No Questions. "But," some parent may say, "my child doesn't ask questions. What shall I do?" Try to find out why. It may be that unconsciously you have already given him the information wanted, or perhaps someone else has. Parents tell things without realizing that they have done so. Recently a father, in telling his six-year-old boy about fertilization in fishes, spoke of the female habit of clearing out a place for her eggs on the sandy bottom of a swift-running brook. He was reminded by the boy that he had pointed out such a place in the brook the summer before, an item which the father had completely forgotten. Aunt Sally's "She had an awful time with her second—hospital, special nurses, and all that. Oh, I forgot Jean," may be quite informative for Jean. Children at play may be equally informative. If parents are sympathetic and do not scold, it may not be too difficult to learn what the conversations of the playground include and to clear up confusions caused by them.

But whatever the reason for the lack of questions, if by the age of six the child has asked few or none about the origin of babies, the organs and functions of the body, and physical sex differences (the three groups mentioned by Hattendorf as common to children of four and five), probably the safest procedure is for the parent to tell the child what he needs to know. Staged conversations between father and mother about the expected arrival of a neighbor's baby or the "fixing" of a pup or Cousin Genevieve's inadequacy to nurse her child may stimulate the non-questioner to start a barrage. Sometimes the casual remark will start him: "Long before you came, . . ." "Well, she is Daddy's child too." "Of course boys are different from girls." Some children seem to be content to wait for information. It can be given just as though the child asked actual questions. Everyday events provide frequent occasions.

OBSERVING BODY DIFFERENCES

One value of having animal pets and their families is that information is given the child through his eyes as well as through his ears. There is a similar value in having children of both sexes romp nude about the bedroom, in having them present at the baby's bath, and in having them share the dressing-room with their parents. The child sees for himself that fathers and mothers, as well as brothers and sisters, are different. Nudity means nothing to the young child, unless it be freedom from the restraint of clothes. Parent nudity means little more, except that parents are grown-up. In addition, a sense of unity and sharing develops when children have ready access with their parents to any part of the house and do not have

to face the exclusiveness of unexpectedly shut bedroom doors and locked bathrooms.

Provision to observe body differences should be made for the only child of the family. This can be accomplished by taking him to see the neighbor's baby bathed or by having friends for an overnight visit, with the usual nude romping. Or if that is too difficult to arrange, pictures and statuary are available for parents who sense the values of learning through the eyes.

Unsatisfied curiosity about body differences sometimes leads to the examining of other children, in the same family or in another, or to showing themselves to each other. Such conduct is inexcusable in the adult code, and adults are likely to rate similar conduct in children by the adult code, which is quite unfair, since children do not know adult standards. Parents who were brought up to be afraid of what people will say find it hard not to be badly shocked at this childish action, although other situations would not be upsetting. Such parents should realize that this is not sex conduct so much as curiosity conduct. Experience shows that where children have had opportunity to observe body differences, this manifestation of curiosity is not common. However, there is little evidence that it is harmful to children, except where they have been made very sex conscious by scolding or by shame or have been punished by neighborhood ostracism. In such a situation parents need to protect children from their own emotional outbursts and also from those of the neighbors.

INFORMATION FROM OUTSIDE THE HOME

At this point some fond parents believe that their job is done. Actually it has only begun. For the child will have many informants, and some of their information and vocabulary and attitudes will be confusing. If the parents are sympathetic and companionable, the child will come to them for explanations. "Father, why did Bill do that?" "What made Marguerite laugh when she said that word?" "Mother, what made the boys laugh at the picture?" "What does this word mean? I heard it today." Or, with a good imitation of the knowing leer of his companion, the child may try out on his parents some of the pungent one-syllable words from the gutter, words that have been handed down from older child to younger from time immemorial. Few parents can help being shocked, especially fathers, most of whom have had an unwanted overdose of just such words and are not eager to have their children go through the same experience. It therefore requires heroism not to show resentment at this vulgarity and not to burst out into, "Don't you ever let me hear you say that again!" or to wail, "Why must *my* child have to learn such dreadful things?"

Among the many ways to meet this emotional difficulty are: (1) to ignore the situation until one has had time to cool off, but to come back to it later; (2) to say with what poise one can muster, "But you know, dear, that isn't the word Father and Mother and the family use. We have taught you this word," or, "That isn't a very good picture, is it?

Let's find a good one," and suit the action to the word; and (3), in any case, to give to the child the information he needs, along with a wholesome and matter-of-fact attitude to offset the new attitude he has acquired. Whatever the method, the parent should focus on the child's need rather than on his own emotional disturbance. For again, to the child this is not a sex situation; it is merely a part of the interesting experiences he is having with the world around him, and he wants to share this experience with the people he loves most —his parents. If the parents frankly but gently straighten out his confusion, explain the word simply and why the companion used it, and give the preferred word, the child is likely to follow the parents' preference. It may take several experiences before this matter of street interpretations is cleared up, and the parent may get some bad shocks in the process. The child may later occasionally revert to street talk. But few lessons that the child has to learn are more important than these early experiences with the outside world and the sound judgment acquired in interpreting them. For this beginning judgment is the foundation of most of his later judgments about sex and sex conduct.

Some parents say, "My child never has such experiences, I know where she is every minute. She never associates with such vulgar people." Those parents should know that the girl of today is far less protected from frank and often vulgar talk than she would have been a generation ago, when there was less general conversation about sex. They should realize that in the best of schools, public or private, there is more or less interchange of ideas about sex, some of it very unwholesome, and they should therefore prepare their children against it. An immunized child is safer than one who runs the risk of exposure, no matter how protected he may be for the time being.

INTERPRETING FAMILY RELATIONSHIPS

However much the young child knows about sex and sex conduct and whatever the quality of that information, he is going to be a family member all his life, not only in the family in which he grows up but later in the family he establishes for himself. These families are important factors in shaping his character and conduct. It is necessary, therefore, not only that his first family should interpret life to him adequately and soundly, but that he should understand thoroughly the relationships of its members, their method of getting along together, and their essential spirit, in order that he may carry these over into his leadership of the second family. Too frequently such understanding is left to chance absorption or to hasty contacts with people who are so occupied with their adult affairs that they have no time to interpret them to children. To be effective, this understanding of family relationships should be definite and purposive. It is true that many of its factors are too complicated for the young child to grasp, but before he enters school he can get the beginnings of most of them, and by the time he is nine or ten he can be well on the way to such understanding.

Father-mother relationships are the background of the family spirit and achievements as well as the basis of the child's security and happiness. Their love for each other, their teamwork, their adjustments of differences, their ways of meeting difficult situations, and their joint responsibility for the success of the family group are vital to the child's welfare. If the child is really to comprehend them, they must be interpreted concretely and simply. He needs to know why father and mother love each other, as well as to feel that love. "Your father is a fine man and I'm proud of him." "I've always loved your mother for her patience. And she has needed it to get along with me." "Barbara, our affection has helped us over some pretty rough places, hasn't it?" "Jim, how can I help loving you when you are so thoughtful of the children and me?" Such love is not only seen and felt by the child but is made more real by expression in words.

So with teamwork. "Margaret, I knew I could make good, for you have always pulled together with me." "Paul, if you and the children will help, I'm sure I can save enough to buy that refrigerator." The same method should be used with the other phases of parent relationships. It is not enough, apparently, that mates shall live together successfully in the home. Example is not enough, as many family tragedies prove. The success of mates in living together needs definite interpretation to the child. This interpretation cannot be given in a short time; it must be spread over many years. It may be given casually or impressively, according to the occasion.

The same kind of interpretation is needed for relationships between parent and child and between brothers and sisters. Adjustments are made possible by understanding, and parents are both the chief adjusters and the chief interpreters. "Polly, you will understand brother Tom after you have worked with him the way I have." "But why get angry when you know you both are driving at the same thing? You'll get the job done quicker if you forget the anger and get busy together." "Sam doesn't say much, but have you realized that he is always helping his mother? That's how she has time to make dresses for you."

Bits of family history, father's struggles to make good, grandmother's management of a headstrong husband, the building up of certain family traditions, the joy over the first homestead and the hard work that went into keeping it during the lean years, mother's achievements with pen or pencil or with the committee that fought for community decency or adequate recreation—all these points, given simply, lay family foundations for the child. Successful families do not grow; they are an achievement based on knowledge and skill and spirit. Your child as mate and homemaker will need your best interpretations and long experience if he is to acquire this knowledge and skill and spirit. The time to begin is when his interest in the home is strongest, that is, in the early years.

In many homes this sort of family interpretation is going on all the time, often unconsciously. In others, parents will have to train themselves to interpret family life to the child. But if he is to be a successful homemaker, he will need definite interpretations of what a happy and well-adjusted home can be. Homemaking is too difficult to take for granted. Altogether too many homes have failed because of this parental error. On the other hand, the child so fortified does not commonly fall into foolish sex conduct during adolescence or later.

By the age of six, the child should have acquired: (1) some knowledge of body parts—including the sexual organs —and their functions, with correct vocabulary; (2) a simple knowledge of physical sex differences and a general understanding of other differences between the sexes; (3) the elements of human reproduction, with both the mother's and the father's part in it; (4) habits of cleanliness (with no unnecessary handling of the sexual organs); (5) an appreciation of his family and of his place in it; and (6) an attitude of frankness rather than of secrecy about sex, with some reticence about it outside the family. The child needs these acquirements as a basis for his own understanding of sex and for meeting situations that will arise in his contacts with other children and with adults.

THE SCHOOL AGE

As the child's social contacts increase during the early school years, he will meet children from homes that have other standards and attitudes about sex and sex conduct. Their responses of snickering or blushing or mystery or shamed silence or matter-of-factness, their vocabulary and knowledge, their acts, such as sharing sex secrets or telling salacious stories or making hand signs or drawing crude pictures or occasionally inspecting each other, will supplement or challenge what he has learned at home. If his parents have been sympathetic and helpful, he is likely to bring home these experiences, often unconsciously, for further understanding and interpretation. Parents who have laid solid foundations of correct facts and vocabulary and attitudes will usually find these important problems not too difficult. Those parents who have let the sex education of the child drift through the preschool years are likely to face not only a somewhat sophisticated child but one who prefers the crude and jocose attitudes of his companions or one who is wholly silent about sex. The conscientious parent, under such circumstances, will need much patience and persistence in re-educating his child. It can be done; it has been done. But the sounder method and the fairer one to the child is to start in the preschool years and meet every situation as it comes.

Where parents have wholly neglected or sidestepped the matter of early sex education, some school systems have taken up the task in self-defense. Behavior difficulties and embarrassing situations arise in the early grades because children have had little or wrong information. Here and there teachers have done very effective work in this field. But most schools are reluctant to take over this task which is so obviously that of the parent, and the parents who will not do the job themselves seem equally reluctant to have the schools do it. Meanwhile, these neglected children grow up under the sex guidance of the back yard and garage and gutter.

The elementary schools have a very real opportunity for supplementing the efforts of the home. Through nature study the school can reinforce the facts about animal reproduction and families and can continue the comparisons with human situations. The breeding and raising of pets add to the value of this work. Such projects are far beyond the experimental stage, so that schools and parents desiring to carry on similar work can find an abundance of successful examples.

Where boys and girls have satisfactory experiences with wholesome conduct, they come to prefer it to the unwholesome. The elementary school, even better than the average home, has many opportunities for boys and girls to work and play and think and plan together, and thus to understand each other. When, in addition, the school definitely fosters fine traditions of boy-girl attitudes and conduct and maintains high standards of self-control, fair play, and comradeship, some of the early deficiencies of the home are made up for. Whatever the school does, it should always provide personal counsel for the boy or girl with problems, whether through principal, dean, school nurse, or teacher. Such counselors can not only direct children but can also co-operate with their homes in guiding the sex conduct of the pupils.

SUMMARY

The young child is being educated about sex, whatever may be his parents' wishes in the matter. It is sounder to direct this education wholesomely than to leave it to chance. Parents have in their hands much of the shaping of the child's attitudes about sex, as well as the wholesome direction of his curiosity. Despite their own disturbances, parents are not justified in letting emotions block their best efforts at educating the child or in postponing his education until it is too late. In general, it is better to anticipate situations before they arise than to try to educate the child out of unwholesome reactions. It is natural for the child to discover his own body and to ask questions about it, where he came from and why others are different from himself. These questions should be answered simply, promptly, and specifically. Most parents can, without too much difficulty, acquire a technique for doing so. Sex education from outside the home, however, is inevitable and will need both anticipation and interpretation. It is important, also, that the growing child know much about family relationships and about ways of adjusting himself to such relationships.

QUESTIONS

1. In what ways does the child in the average home become aware of sex?

2. Why is it unwise to neglect or postpone the sex education of the young child?

3. Why is shaping the child's attitudes more important than correct or incorrect facts?

4. At what point should the parent curb the child's curiosity? Why?

5. How should a parent handle the problem of the child's sharing information with neighbor children?

6. What can be done when children from outside the family bring up sex questions?

7. Under what circumstances would it be preferable to give the story of reproduction at one time rather than piecemeal?

8. Why are the interpretations of family experiences important to the sex education of the young child?

9. What can be done when parents cannot or will not give them sex education?

10. In what ways can the school supplement the efforts of the home?

11. Why is guidance of sex conduct more important than giving of sex information?

12. In what respects is sex education more important than other education? Less important?

READING REFERENCES

FOR THE PARENT

Cady, Bertha L., and Vernon M., *The Way Life Begins* (American Social Hygiene Association).

Groves, Ernest R. and Gladys, *Sex in Childhood* (Macaulay).

Gruenberg, Benjamin C., *Parents and Sex Education* (American Social Hygiene Association).

Strain, Frances B., *New Patterns in Sex Teaching* (Appleton-Century); *Sex Education in the Home* (Grolier).

Swift, Edith H., *Step by Step in Sex Education* (Macmillan).

When Children Ask about Babies (Child Study Association).

The Wonderful Story of Life (U. S. Public Health Service. A father's talks with his little son; a mother's talks with her daughter).

FOR THE CHILD

Baruch, Dorothy W., and Reiss, Oscar, *My Body and How It Works* (Harper).

De Schweinitz, Karl, *Growing Up* (Macmillan).

Ets, Marie H., *Story of a Baby* (Viking).

Levine, Milton I., and Seligmann, Jean H., *The Wonder of Life* (Simon & Schuster).

Strain, Frances, *Being Born* (Appleton-Century).

POSTURE

Charles H. McCloy

Scientific study of the subject has shown that some of our notions regarding correct posture have been fundamentally wrong. Since proper posture is necessary to the most efficient functioning of the entire body, parents need to know how to train their children to form the right habits of posture. The author is Research Professor of Physical Education and Anthropometry, State University of Iowa, and has made many studies of the growth and development of children.

"DO STRAIGHTEN up!" How often a child hears these words from parents or teachers, and how seldom does he have a proper conception of what it means! Perhaps parents do not really know what it means either. Is the child, then, to blame if he stands or sits in the way that seems comfortable to him?

Unfortunately, present-day posture is derived from soldiery. "Straight as a soldier" has for years been considered as the ideal to be attained. This concept has come largely from the military practices of the Swedish army of the nineteenth century. In that country gymnastics were developed and controlled by a normal school, whose teachers were all army officers. These teachers supported the theory that everyone should stand as straight and as rigid as a soldier at attention or in salute. They wrote this theory into textbooks on posture; these were read by instructors of physical education, who, in turn, wrote books and articles which led teachers and parents in America to endorse the military ideal.

The only contradictory popular notion concerning posture was that fostered by the more artistic group—mostly teachers of the dance—in physical education.

Photo: H. Armstrong Roberts

AN EXAMPLE OF GOOD POSTURE

This group taught grace, freedom, balance, poise, and relaxation, but they were in the minority, and until very recently the military ideal was the standard for correct posture. The mother, then, when she says, "Do stand up straight!" means that she wants her child to "stand like a soldier." This same parent would

129

not think it at all sensible to exhort the child to use correct grammar without first teaching him what correct grammar is and pointing out to him his mistakes. She knows that he would be unable to speak correctly if no standards of correctness were known to him. The simple direction to "straighten up" is just as futile when the child does not know what is incorrect about the thing he is doing.

Many of the current generalizations upon posture have come from theories based upon the facts of anatomy rather than from the effects of posture upon children themselves. One of the most curious aspects of posture teaching is that almost all the emphasis has been put upon standing posture—the bearing of the soldier. Any parent knows that the child is not required to stand at attention except during a few moments of the day. His posture in walking or running or sitting presents much more important problems than his standing posture.

DEFINING POSTURE

Good posture can best be defined, not in terms of a set of lines or positions, but in terms of balance, poise, and function. Good posture has been defined by one authority as "The relationship of each part or segment of the body to each other part and of the whole body to its task or work." As we study this matter of relationship of each part to the other parts it becomes clear that the most important thing is that all the parts should be properly balanced. The trunk is balanced on the legs, and the neck and head upon the trunk.

Let us consider an analogy. If one wished to support a weight of one hundred pounds six feet above the ground, it could be done very easily by placing a half-inch water pipe under the exact middle of the weight, in a position perpendicular to the ground. If, however, the pipe were curved even slightly, the weight would quickly bend it and the load would fall to the ground.

Now let us consider a somewhat larger and stronger pipe. Suppose we think in terms of a pipe one and one-half inches in diameter. Such a pipe might be slightly bent and still be strong enough to support the weight. If the pipe were bent very much, how-

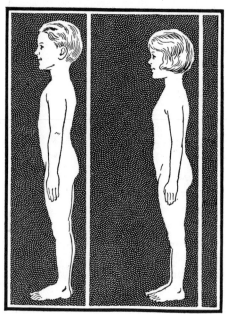

GOOD STANDING POSTURE

ever, the leverage of the weight on the bent pipe would become so great that the pipe would eventually give way.

The support of the body presents a similar problem. The straighter the line of the different segments of the body, the more easily the total body weight is balanced and supported. The less the strain upon the muscles and ligaments, the more the individual can relax and be at ease. The greater the deviation from this straight line, the greater the strain and the sooner does gravity overcome the support afforded by the muscles.

The problem of posture, however, is not quite as simple as that of the weight and the pipe. One of the disadvantages of having everything in an absolutely straight line is that every jar or jolt is transmitted almost undiminished to the upper parts of the body, including the head and the brain. This danger is avoided, however, by the curves in the spine. Starting from the hips, the lower back is curved forward, the upper back is curved backward, and the neck is curved forward. This triple curve functions much as do the springs and shock

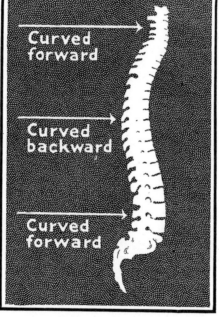

This side view of the vertebral column shows the triple curve which functions much as do the springs and shock absorbers in an automobile.

absorbers in an automobile. Jars to the body produced by walking, jumping, or suddenly stepping from the curb to a lower level of the street slightly compress this spring of the spine and prevent the jar from reaching the more sensitive and more easily injured portions of the trunk and head. These jars are also absorbed by striking first on the heels in walking and by a slight bending of the knee, ankle, and hip.

Those who have thought constructively on the problem have come to the conclusion that the over-straight and rigid posture of the soldier is not the ideal one. One should seek, instead, a relaxed but balanced and poised posture which will straighten the curves of the spine and head to give freedom and ease of movement, but which—because of its poised relaxation—will permit these curves to increase temporarily when subjected to shocks or jars.

How To Practice Good Posture

In seeking an erect posture, whether in standing or walking, it is important that the various segments of the body from feet to head be aligned in as straight a vertical line as possible (the fundamental structure of the body will prevent too much straightening) but at the same time be as relaxed as possible and without stiffness or tension.

The child cannot be expected to know how to assume such a posture simply upon command. He will need to be trained, just as he is trained to speak and to throw. One of the most successful methods has been to have the child stand before a mirror and then to place some object, such as a moderately heavy book, on his head. The child is then requested to push the book up higher while watching in the mirror to see that he does not stiffen and become rigid. Still holding the book in this position, he is directed to move his feet around, to swing his arms loosely backward and forward, to stretch his arms backward as though he were tired, and then to drop them relaxed to his sides. The book is removed and the child attempts to keep this straight position while moving in front of the mirror. He should be told to move his hands and arms around in order to prevent tension about the shoulders and head. Sometimes the admonition, "Ears high," accomplishes this better than suggesting that the top of the head be raised.

The child should be taught to keep a fairly straight line from the ear to the tip of the shoulder, to the center of the hip, to the center of the knee, and to the foot at the back of the ball. This straight-line test is simple and easy to learn. When the child zigzags, his standing posture is bad. In sitting the line stops at the bones upon which he sits.

The posture of the feet is also important. The most common foot defect is caused by turning the ankle inward, with a resultant flattening of the arch of the foot. This defect is usually accompanied by an eversion, or turning outward, of the feet. Look at the feet from behind. The cord running upward from the heel should be straight. This fault can usually be corrected by pointing the feet more toward the front and bending the ankles slightly outward, as though standing slightly on the outside of the feet.

If the child feels that the weight is largely borne by the heels and the large toes—on the insides of the feet—the foot position is probably wrong. Help him to experiment until he finds a foot position in which the weight is carried about equally by all the toes, and the inside of the foot (the arch) is lifted somewhat from the floor, and the lines above the heels at the back are vertical—not turned inward. If his feet are nearly parallel, the foot position is probably satisfactory.

It must not be thought that good posture is confined to standing. Sitting and walking postures are just as important. In sitting, the trunk and head should be in a relatively straight line as in standing posture. But while reading at home, a semi-recumbent posture in an easy chair, with the feet and legs elevated but the trunk and head in a straight line, is probably better than the "erect" position usually advocated. This allows gravity to draw the lymph in the legs back toward the trunk for greater comfort. The position should be slightly changed at frequent intervals to relieve pressure on the parts in contact with the chair.

As for correct walking: Studies have shown that three points characterize graceful, efficient walking in contrast to awkward, inefficient walking. First, the trunk is erect and well poised and the chest leads. (In "poor" walking the head or abdomen leads and the head tends to be inclined forward.) Second, the swing of the arms is in perfect harmony with the stride of the legs in timing and force of swing. Third, the feet push off vigorously with all the toes at the end of the stride.

PSYCHOLOGICAL ASPECTS OF POSTURE

Some of the greatest psychologists have discovered that the body and the mind practically always function together. Think for a moment of how you, as a parent, would stand and how you would feel if you were told that your child had just been awarded a ten-thousand-dollar prize for being the most perfect physical specimen in the state. Then think how you would sit or stand if you were told that you had lost your last cent. One can realize that the posture of sorrow or dejection, as well as the posture of pride or exultation, is simply harmony of body and emotions. The posture of fatigue, whether of mind or body, is the opposite of the posture of alertness, anticipation, or exhilaration. For a child to attain and maintain a desirable posture of the body, he must have a feeling of well-being and a habit of mental alertness. "Straighten up" is too frequently a brusque order that is resentfully received because it has the tone of censure and impatience. The psychology of good posture is that of

happy response. "How well you are looking!" will be more likely to effect a squaring of the shoulders and a lift of the chin than will the command to "Straighten up." Comment on the way

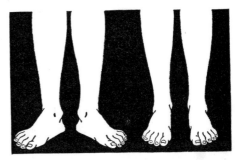

WRONG WAY RIGHT WAY

his muscles are developing, of how like a young athlete he is looking, is more conducive to involuntary straightening up than is any direct persuasion.

POSTURE AND HEALTH

Why all this emphasis on posture anyhow? Is it really related to good health? The scientific evidence concerning this relation is scanty indeed. The best evidence in support of the theory that posture affects health was obtained at Chelsea, Massachusetts, by the Children's Bureau of the United States Department of Labor. Two large groups of school children were matched as to social status, school progress, health, and other factors. For a period of a year one of these groups was given intensive instruction in how to assume good posture and was trained to assume it. What is even more important, good posture was motivated and made to seem desirable to the children. The other group devoted the same number of hours to physical education, but received none of the posture training. Such activities as games and sports were substituted for it. The group trained in posture had decidedly less sickness and, therefore, fewer absences from school throughout the year, and the teachers

Habits of faulty posture frequently result from the use of such desks as the one shown above. Unfortunately, equipment like this is all too common in many of our rural schools.

were unanimous in stating that these children improved in their application to school tasks.

Almost all the other evidence has accumulated merely from the observations of physicians and teachers—observations which are general and are not, as a rule, checked with scientific accuracy. The common arguments that posture affects health and well-being may be summarized as follows:

1. In faulty posture the chest droops and becomes more shallow from front to back, thus allowing less space for the functioning of the heart and lungs. The heart drops down a bit and tends to hang from its arteries, which leave the heart at its top. If one looks down the throat of an individual sitting in a faulty position and having a resultant flattened chest, one can see at every heartbeat a drag at the back of the throat which is the result of the heart's jerking upward. This drag disappears when the chest is not flattened, because the heart is then raised within the thorax sufficiently to take the strain away from these arteries. The more important result of proper posture, however, is that since the heart does not have to raise its weight so high at every beat it works less hard. This fact is of even greater importance to an adult with a weak heart than it is to a child, who ordinarily has a fairly large factor of safety so far as his heart is concerned.

Some lung diseases begin at the upper part of the lung, just behind the collarbones. This "digging in" of disease germs is made easier when, through faulty posture, all portions of the lung are not fully expanded but are shut off from the air. The straighter posture permits all parts of the lung to expand fully.

2. In poor posture the abdominal viscera slump downward. Put your hand on the lower abdomen and raise the chest; then lower it. When the chest is raised the lower abdomen becomes smaller, and when it is lowered the abdomen rounds out. This is be-

cause the chest, upon being raised, pulls these internal organs upward and relieves the pressure in the lower part of the trunk. When these viscera drop downward into the pelvis they exert a pressure upon the pelvic organs which is most undesirable and which, according to many experts, encourages the development of later pelvic disorders. These disturbances of the normal relationships of the abdominal organs may be associated with constipation and digestive disorders.

3. The third type of argument is associated with the mental and emotional results of poor posture. Many psychologists contend that emotions are the result of posture rather than that posture is the result of emotions. In other words, we tend to feel well, alert, and interested when we straighten up and assume the posture of alertness and interest. The psychological arguments on each side of the question are too technical to discuss here. The important thing to remember, so far as children are concerned, is that habitual poor posture is nearly always associated with emotional habits that are as undesirable and unlovely as is the poor posture.

Every mother knows of a young girl's desire to be beautiful. A poor posture is decidedly unattractive and, generally speaking, girls are motivated to improve their posture by a desire to be beautiful rather than by concern for their health. Similarly, nearly all boys want to look manly and athletic. Those who do not look robust often attempt to compensate by wearing clothing that conceals their defects. The right kind of suggestion on the part of the parent should encourage these natural urges and desires and should at all times avoid the tone of rebuke.

Need for Change of Position

No one posture should be maintained for a long period of time—a fact which is frequently overlooked by teachers and others. The body craves change. Try the following experiment: Place your thumb upon the back of the other hand, hold it there a few moments and then remove it. In the place where the thumb rested there will be found a blanched area. The blood has been pressed out and the tissue upon which pressure was exerted is temporarily somewhat distressed. When a child sits on a hard chair for half an hour or more without shifting around the whole physiological function of the skin and muscles upon which he has rested is disturbed. He should change his position, sliding forward and backward, moving a bit to one side and then to the other, in order to give all parts of the body a chance to renew their blood supply and be rejuvenated.

Scientific study has demonstrated that the kind of sleep wherein one "sleeps like a log" is not restful sleep. One awakes feeling tired. The most restful sleep is that in which the individual changes his position about every ten minutes. One should *not* always sleep on his right side. He should sleep on first one side and then the other, on his face and on his back, moving arms and legs and trunk and head into any restful, relaxed position.

Similarly, the child should not stand in one position but should shift his weight around, with first one foot a little ahead and then the other, moving his shoulders and his body. Change is restful. Good posture calls for relaxation rather than rigidity.

DIFFERENCES IN THE BONY STRUCTURE

Many attempts have been made to provide standards by which the posture of the individual child may be judged. A number of charts are in current use, but the studies in this field cast doubt upon their value. Individuals are not constructed after the same pattern any more than houses are. The architecture suitable for a bungalow is obviously not the same as that for a cathedral. Likewise, the bony skeleton of one child is quite different from that of another.

One of the admonitions most commonly heard is, "Throw back your shoulders." As a matter of fact, some shoulders throw back more easily than others. If you will place your fingers on the two bones just to the right and left of the lower part of your neck you will notice that they run from the top of the chest out to the shoulders. These bones are relatively longer and relatively more curved in some individuals than in others. As a result, some persons can swing their shoulders backward farther and much more easily than can others. The important thing is to have the shoulders poised in such a way that the weight of the arms is thrown on the side of the chest and upon the spine rather than upon the front of the chest, where gravity pulls the weight downward and pulls the chest with it.

X-ray studies of the spine show that its bony structure grows differently in different people. A casual glance will show that some persons have wider heads than others and some have heads that are longer from the ears up. Some people are broad and thick and squat, others are tall and slender. Similarly, the bones of the body differ in shape among various individuals, so that frequently the curves of the spine in one person are greater than those in another. In addition to these general differences that are present at birth, the bones sometimes grow unevenly, one side of the bone growing more rapidly than the other and producing undesirable effects on the posture. There is nothing the parent can do about such a condition except to take the child to a specialist. Fortunately, most of the peculiarities of growth are of relatively little importance because the body easily compensates for them.

Similar differences of bone structure are found in the pelvis, or that part of the body between the hips. Scientific studies have shown that in some cases the bony part of the pelvis which supports the spine (the sacrum) is located almost in the center of the pelvis and is relatively high and almost level on top, so that the spine in the small of the back goes almost straight upward. In other individuals this supporting bone is well back of the center, usually low down between the edges, the top slanting sharply downward and forward so that the spine of the small of the back makes a sweeping curve forward and upward, causing such a spine to be designated as sway-backed. There are many variations of pelvic architecture between these two extremes. Careful studies of a number of children indicate that in many cases these differences in the curve of the lower part of the spine are simply attempts of nature to balance the trunk upon the legs and need no interference.

For many years health literature has stressed the importance of keeping the feet in a parallel position when walking. Children, especially boys, have been told to "walk like an Indian." Studies of the bones of the legs and feet, however, show that these bones are not alike in all individuals. The twist of the bones of the legs varies over a range of one hundred degrees, and to force an individual whose legs normally turn outward thirty degrees to walk with his feet parallel is simply to transfer the maladjustment from the feet to the hips.

Similar natural differences occur in the heights of the arches of the feet. Not all high arches are strong and comfortable, and not all low arches are undesirable. Hence, elements other than the height of the arches alone must be taken into consideration in deciding what to do about foot posture. In doubtful cases the feet should be X-rayed, for it has been found that painful feet are sometimes normal in every respect except for the displacement of two small (sessamoid) bones, that should be beneath the large joint of the great toe. This displacement can be checked with the X-ray. In young children, however, these bones cannot be

seen with X-ray; but a physician can determine their probable displacement experimentally.

From the above facts, the parent or teacher can see that all children cannot conform in either posture or carriage to

Photo: American Seating Company

PROPER POSTURE IN SCHOOL

This type of seat is comfortable and helps the child to assume the correct posture. The adjustable table top keeps the work at the proper height and distance from the child's eyes.

a fixed standard. This is as absurd as to insist that all boys should wear size six shoes. Just as the shoe should be chosen to fit the foot, so the posture should be chosen to fit the individual.

Is INTERFERENCE SAFE?

At this point the average parent may begin to consider it dangerous to interfere with his child's posture. Not at all, if the interference is intelligent. The sensible procedure is to make conditions such that the child can correct his posture but not to expect him to be exactly like a number of other children. For example, a child who is getting insufficient sleep or inadequate diet (which usually results in lowered vitality and poor muscular tone) should have these hygienic details attended to. Improper seating equipment or inadequate lighting often causes a poor sitting posture. It is ironical for the physical-education division of a board of education to attempt to *correct* the posture defects caused by improperly constructed seats that were purchased by another department of the same board of education!

In the child's home all too frequently all the chairs are adult chairs, none of which is adapted to a small body. Frequently the lighting is poor or it comes from the wrong direction at the place where the child studies or reads. The child's clothing and shoes should be of a kind to encourage proper posture and foot movement. Clothing that is too tight across the shoulders, or that binds at the waist, and shoes that are too tight or too short may entirely neutralize all effort to improve posture. The child's eyes and ears should be tested. Much bad posture, particularly in reading, is due to nearsightedness. Some children twist the head and move it forward because of poor hearing. The parent and the teacher should notice these conditions. Finally, the parent should be sure that the child is not chronically fatigued.

Well-spaced rest periods are frequently the most important factor in the proper body control of young children.

Sometimes a child's muscles are too weak to withstand the fatigue of a whole day's activities. If this is the case, he should have more general exercise through play, interspersed with rest periods, or he should be given some special training for his condition. Some excellent exercises can be found in the publications listed in the Reading References at the end of this article.

Another method for improving posture is to provide the proper motivation. The child not infrequently maintains a poor posture in imitation of someone he admires. If this is true, try to replace this hero with another. Find out what characters in history, fiction, motion pictures, or from among the boys and girls with whom he plays appeal the most and then attempt to get the child to imitate the good posture of some one of these characters.

How can a parent know when a child is in need of expert advice on his posture problems? If the child constantly maintains a poor posture, a specialist should be consulted. If there is nothing serious the matter, the parent is reassured. If surgery or corrective treatment is indicated, the parent will be so advised. It is more important and far easier to correct poor posture when it first shows itself than to cure it after it has become habitual.

SUMMARY

The best type of posture is not a rigid, soldierly, standing-at-attention position, but a position of poise, of happiness and alertness, and of freedom and balance.

It is as important that the posture of sitting and of walking be erect and balanced as it is that the child should stand well. The carriage of the feet is also essential to a good posture. This means that the feet should assume a position of strength, with the ankles in a vertical line and the toes in such a position as enables them to grip the ground firmly.

The psychological aspect of good posture is as important as the physical aspect. The erect posture is one of mental and emotional strength and control; the poor posture is that of defeat and discouragement. Posture—good or bad—indicates a way of life and is part of one's philosophy of living. The body, the mind, and the emotions are not three separate entities but are merely different functioning aspects of the same individual. The posture of the body is perhaps the most conspicuous manifestation of the whole psychophysical unit. As such it should be considered not only as a sign of the present attitude of the body and of the emotions but also as a symbol of what is yet to develop. Hence the cultivation of a satisfactory posture is a task that involves the reshaping of parts of the whole personality.

QUESTIONS

1. How would you describe a good standing posture to a child of four years of age, emphasizing only its physical aspects? Emphasizing its emotional aspects?

2. What is meant by balance in sitting posture? In standing posture? In walking posture?

3. Describe for a six-year-old child a good foot posture.

4. Why does poor posture frequently affect the health, both physical and mental?

5. One frequently tells a child not to be so fidgety. Why is he fidgety when sitting on a hard chair?

6. Make a list of all the things that might have a bad effect on a child's posture. Make a parallel list of the steps you would take to overcome each of these influences.

READING REFERENCES

BOOKS

Bancroft, Jessie H., *Posture of School Children* (Macmillan).

Lane, Janet, *Your Carriage, Madam!* (Wiley).

Meek, Lois H., *Your Child's Development and Guidance Told in Pictures* (Lippincott).

White House Conference on Child Health and Protection, *Body Mechanics: Education and Practice* (Appleton-Century).

PAMPHLETS

Brockway, Alvia, *Stand Up Straight* (American Medical Association).

Klein, Armin, and Thomas, Leah C., *Posture and Physical Fitness* (Publication No. 205); and *Posture Exercises* (Publication No. 165, U. S. Department of Labor, Children's Bureau).

Schwartz, Louis, Britten, Rollo H., and Thompson, Lewis R., *Studies in Physical Development and Posture* (U. S. Treasury Department, Public Health Bulletin No. 179). Part One, "The Effect of Exercise on the Physical Condition and Development of Adolescent Boys"; Part Two, "Bodily Growth with Age"; Part Three, "Physical Fitness as Reflected in Tests of Muscular Strength."

U. S. Department of Labor, Children's Bureau, *Good Posture in the Little Child* (Publication No. 219).

CLOTHING

Clarice L. Scott

In this age of standardization and ready-made garments it would seem that the selection of children's clothing should present no serious problems. There are certain features of design, however, which add so greatly to the comfort, convenience, and wearing qualities of a garment that every mother should take these features into consideration when making or buying children's clothes. In this article these features are discussed and illustrated with attractive photographs. The author is in charge of clothing in the Division of Textiles and Clothing, Bureau of Home Economics, United States Department of Agriculture.

WHEN a baby is old enough to move around by himself, the time has come to put aside infant dresses. In their place he will need

Photo: U. S. Bureau of Home Economics

CLOTHES SHOULD SUIT THE CHILD

The toddler needs clothes adapted to his new activities—creeping, pulling up, and learning to walk.

clothes that are suited to his new activities—creeping, pulling up, and learning to walk. Such exercise is tiring work for one so young, but a mother can make this work easier by providing properly designed clothes that allow absolute comfort and freedom.

DRESSING THE TODDLER
SIX MONTHS TO TWO YEARS

The first point to decide when considering a toddler's clothes is how much protection he needs. To be healthfully comfortable—that is, neither too warm nor too cold—a baby's clothes have to be suited to his own vitality, the climate, and the heating system in the home. Knowing these factors, it is easy to decide how much clothing is needed and also what style of garments and what materials are most suitable. A child who is not sturdy or one who lives in a house where there are drafts will need warmer underwear and possibly long sleeves.

UNDERWEAR

Underwear for a six-months-old baby is usually limited to two pieces—a diaper and a shirt. Those that have been used during the first six months will be suitable for a while unless a change of season demands either lighter- or heavier-weight shirts. It is wise to plan ahead and get coat shirts which have extra buttons at the sides for holding up the training panties that the child will wear later.

Coat shirts are suggested because they are easy to put on and take off—a point to consider when selecting any type of garment for babies. There is, however, a special point in regard to quality that should be kept in mind when buying coat shirts—the buttonholes should be very firm and well made so that they will not break, ravel, or lose their shape. Otherwise there will be trouble in keeping them fastened after a certain amount of wear. So far as comfort is concerned, there are no objections to pull-on shirts of good quality, but they are not as easy to put on and take off as the coat shirt. If, however, a buttonless garment is preferred, choose materials that have exceptional elasticity.

In choosing any style of shirt, insist on knit materials that will give without losing their shape. If the material is "stretchy," the shirt will get large and baggy, hampering the baby quite as much as an oversize garment would. The elasticity of underwear material may be tested by stretching it between the hands and then releasing it, watching to see if it springs back into shape. While making this test, notice also the evenness of knit and make sure that there are no thin spots, which soon break into holes.

The fit of a baby's shirt can be judged only by trying it on. To be comfortable the proportion has to be right, with ample width through the body, good length, a neckline that sets well, and easy-fitting armholes and sleeves. In low-priced goods, particularly, examine these features carefully, because some

manufacturers "skimp" the cut in order to keep production costs low. Undergarments that are "skimped" wear out more quickly than those that are full-cut.

Good construction also helps to make a baby's underwear comfortable and lasting. Look at the seams and make sure that they all are flat, smooth, and durable; then examine the plackets and the finishes of front openings, neck, and armholes. These finishes should be durable and perfectly smooth, with no rough facings or stitching, which might irritate the baby's skin.

At their best, diapers are no help to a baby learning to creep and walk, but since they are inevitable during this period they should be comfortable in size and highly absorbent, yet as light in weight and free from bulkiness as possible. The best type of diaper, so far as the baby's comfort is concerned, is shaped to fit and has extra thicknesses only through the crotch. The square, folded diaper has too much bulk swathed around the hips. Unfortunately, shaped diapers are expensive and are not so easy to launder as the square type. Some mothers like the knit diapers, but they do not absorb as well as the old favorite, bird's-eye. They are a good compromise, however, between the bulky, folded type and the cut-to-fit styles that are not so practical for laundering. Knit diapers fit snugly to the hips and yet give easily; they are therefore comfortable and well suited to the characteristic activities of the toddler.

About the end of the first year diapers can be replaced with training panties,

Rompers are the most suitable type of outer garment for the toddler. These three designs are recommended because of certain desirable features, such as the plain neckline, the inverted plaits, the loose-fitting sleeves, the convenient openings, and the absence of unnecessary frills.

which are intended for that in-between period when toilet habits are being learned. The first panties should be made of very soft and highly absorbent knit cotton, with extra thicknesses at both front and back. Later on, panties that have extra material only at the back and through the crotch will be more suitable. Panties that have a plain waistband at the front (to be buttoned on to a shirt) and a band of easy-giving elastic at the back are more easily kept in place than are the other styles. These garments have none of the annoyances and discomforts of the earlier type of panties, which were made with tight elastic all around the waist. Another valuable feature in training panties is a fitted leg opening that gives readily but does not lose its shape.

ROMPERS

For the unsteady ways of a toddler, rompers of good design are the best type of outer garment. They allow the baby freedom to creep, to pull himself up, and to travel about as he pleases. He does not waste energy in struggling against dragging dress tails, which tire

and annoy babies by getting in the way. Rompers are more hygienic than dresses because they protect the underwear from soil and also because they collect less dirt than other types of garments.

Whether the baby's rompers are ready-made or homemade, choose styles that allow the greatest amount of comfort and convenience. Select only very simple designs—designs that combine attractiveness, comfort, and convenience, such as the rompers illustrated here. All are cut on comfortably loose lines about the body, and in each design there are definitely planned helpful features. In the two tailored suits there are little plaits at the hip level that spread and give the extra length needed at the lower back. At the shoulders there are inverted plaits which spread open in response to the baby's reach. Loose-fitting cap sleeves also provide shoulder and arm freedom. Unlike so many of the rompers that babies wear, those illustrated stay up over the knees where they belong and do not bunch in the crotch. This is because the leg openings are actually cut to fit; they are round, as the leg is, and are curved high at the front. Another feature that makes these rompers unique is that they have no collars, cuffs, and belts—the absence of which makes for greater neatness and comfort.

Full-length openings are planned so that dressing can be done with the least possible handling of the baby and so that diapers can be changed with very little trouble. Instead of the usual back or crotch openings—always troublesome and unpleasant to manage—these rompers are designed so that an extension of the back pulls up between the legs and buttons over the front. With this arrangement you can dress a baby or change his diaper without even turning him over.

The third romper illustrated has more softness than the others and is cut on the bias, thereby giving in any direction and making little plaits and extra fullness unnecessary. In dressing and ironing, this garment can be laid perfectly flat. The neck opening is wide, as is the lower edge. By bunching the neck and lower edge together the romper can be slipped on without the annoyance commonly associated with slipover styles of clothing. The drawstring at the neck is then pulled up and tied at the back, where it is out of the baby's reach. Like the tailored rompers, this style also has a neatly designed diaper closing that buttons well up over the front. Still another helpful feature is the fact that the buttons can be moved down for added length as the baby grows.

Materials and designs for rompers can hardly be planned separately because each is dependent on the other for a really satisfactory garment. For example, tailored designs require tailored materials, such as broadcloth or gingham; while lawn and nainsook are better suited to soft, delicate designs.

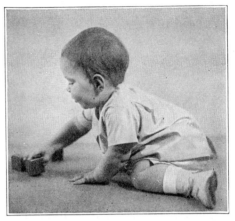

Properly designed rompers allow a baby freedom to creep and to travel about as he pleases.

The proper material frequently adds to the desirability of certain features in a design, while material that is poorly suited may detract from these features.

Without exception, cotton materials are the most practical for a baby's rompers. Choose fabrics that are smooth, firm, and durable; they stand up under hard wear, and dirt does not get ground into them as it does into loosely woven and napped materials. Soft, pliable textures are most comfortable next to a baby's skin; stiff, scratchy materials are irritating and tend to hinder a baby's play movements.

Many fabrics are colorfast, but do not take this quality for granted; look for labels that give definite information or a guarantee about the color. Some materials are colorfast to both sun and washing; others, to washing only. Rompers should be made of materials that will withstand frequent laundering.

There are a few other points to remember in regard to colors. In choosing the baby's first colored garments, take time to decide what colors will be most becoming. Choose tints rather than strong colors because they are better suited to a baby's delicate complexion.

Almost as important as fast colors, particularly in ready-made rompers, is preshrinkage. This feature may add a few cents to the cost of the garment but it guarantees that the rompers will fit just as well after washing as before. When buying preshrunk garments, therefore, one can be absolutely sure about the size and will not need to make any allowance for shrinking. One should take no chances on the matter of correct size, for risks like these are expensive, and babies need well-fitting garments at all times.

Good construction also plays a part

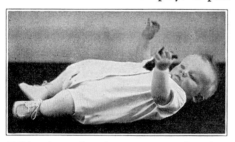

Full-length openings in rompers are planned so that dressing can be done with the least possible handling of the baby.

in the comfort, durability, and appearance of rompers. Whether the rompers are ready-made or homemade, be sure that all seams are narrow, smoothly finished, and strong. Usually French or flat felled seams are best, the choice depending on the style and material of the romper. At points of strain—such as under buttons and around neck and leg openings—see that there are good reinforcements. A bit of narrow tape or double stitching can do wonders in preserving these little clothes that get such hard wear.

WRAPS

A baby of toddler age will need a warm winter outfit to wear when he goes for daily airings. Most practical, as well as comfortable, are the knitted two-piece suits that consist of a hip-length coat and leggings. Select an outfit in which the leggings are supported from the shoulders by a suspender arrangement rather than held up by elastic or cord at the waist.

The two-piece outfit is practical because it allows for diaper changes and for going to the toilet without removing the entire suit. Furthermore, if the lower part is soiled it may be washed separately. Knit rather than woven material is particularly suited to very young children because knit fabrics fit closely and yet give easily with body movements. A knit cap or beret is suitable to wear with any type of outdoor suit. Either a cap or beret fits snugly to the child's head and can be pulled down or rolled up as needed to give the right protection.

SHOES

Shoes and stockings first make their appearance about the time that the baby is creeping and before he begins to walk. From the very beginning he should wear healthful shoes so that his feet will develop in the normal way. Both good taste and fashion now demand sensible shoes for growing children. The fragile little patent leathers, with their rosettes and other fussy trimmings, are not built to develop healthy feet. What is more, they neither wear well nor look well.

Foot specialists, who know what types of shoes are best for children, recommend moccasin styles, which allow lots of room for the toes. Laced rather than buttoned shoes are also recommended because they may be adjusted to either stout or slender legs. The leather in a baby's first shoes must be soft, yet firm enough to give the needed support. The shoes sometimes have tiny perforations across the vamps to admit air. The soles should be light-weight, yet firm and flexible. Flexibility is an especially good feature because, when learning to walk, babies should have their feet as unhampered as possible. When buying these shoes get a size that extends about three-fourths of an inch beyond the toes when the child stands, so as to provide for growth and to give ample toe room.

Socks, like shoes, should be longer than the foot. One inch is none too much, for with hosiery shrinkage and foot growth this space is soon needed. Whether one chooses socks or stockings depends upon the season. A baby has more freedom in short socks than in stockings, which are pinned to the diaper and tend to pull it down. Fur-thermore, stockings absorb moisture from the diaper and cause chafing. Either socks or stockings should be knit so as to stretch easily. This flexibility

Flat, stitched-down neck finishes are the most comfortable and convenient for children.

makes them comfortable as well as easy to put on. Before allowing a child to wear new hose, clip any ends of thread that may have been left dangling.

THE PRESCHOOL AGE

(Two to Six Years)

Clothes suitable for a child between two and six years of age are somewhat different from those suggested for a toddler. By the age of two the skill in walking has been perfected and practically the entire day is spent in romping and playing. In addition, a child about two years old has fairly reliable toilet habits and is ready to wear comfortable, convenient underwear instead of bulky diapers or training suits.

At this age, for the first time, the child shows an interest in dressing. Up until now every piece of clothing has been planned for the convenience of the mother in dressing the baby. Now it is time for the mother to be merely a helper in the business of dressing—the baby must learn to put on and take off his clothes himself.

To encourage the growing sense of independence which comes to a child of preschool age, parents should select clothes with the child's convenience definitely in mind. In this way underwear, dresses, suits, and wraps—in fact, every garment that a child wears—can be used to teach certain important habits in addition to furnishing protection and adding to the attractiveness of appearance.

UNDERWEAR

Whether or not a child is comfortably and conveniently dressed depends first of all upon his underwear. If wisely chosen, it will strengthen any good features in his outer garments, but if carelessly chosen, it may destroy the value of these features. Remember that underwear is the foundation for an entire outfit, which can be perfect only when it is carefully planned in every detail.

Union suits are the most practical style of underwear for children whose toilet habits are reliable. Since boys and girls wear practically the same styles of underwear, the same principles of selection will apply for both. The choice of material and certain features of style will depend on the individual child and the temperature conditions in his home and in the nursery school. Physicians emphasize the advantage to health in wearing only as much clothing as weather and the climate demand. There is as much danger in wearing too much clothing as in wearing too little. The aim should be to keep a child feeling comfortable but not burdened.

The best materials are porous, absorbent, and ventilating, with textures so soft and smooth that they cannot irritate even the most tender skin. Children are extremely sensitive to the "feel" of their clothes. The fabrics should be so knit that they give readily without losing their shape. Avoid bulky, heavy materials, as they are burdensome and hampering to play, thus causing a little child to tire quickly. Heaviness of material is no guarantee of warmth. Some of the warmest fabrics are very light in weight.

Underwear fits best when it is just loose enough to permit free exercise of the entire body. When buying the suits, however, one should make a slight allowance for both growth and shrinkage, but these allowances are scarcely noticeable in suits made of flexible materials. The child should try on underwear so as to insure proper fit. See that the neckline is cut fairly low, sets well to the shoulders and chest, and requires no drawstring to keep it in shape. Notice also the fit of the shoulders, the size of the armholes, and the finish of the sleeves. If the sleeves are short, they can well be finished with a ribbed cuff that clings neatly and without pressure to the arm. If the lower part of the undersuit is in French pantie style it will allow the room needed for stooping and bending and yet will require few seams. Leg openings that fit to the legs are comfortable.

A child who is old enough and who is anxious to learn how to put on and fasten his clothes will want the openings designed for self-help. Step-in styles are probably the most practical and convenient to put on, but for the sake of comfort the shoulders should be high cut and made so as to stay in place. For toilet convenience, a buttonless drop back finished with easy-giving elastic durably lockstitched to the material is simple to manage. See that the lower back can really be pulled down easily as well as far enough for convenience at the toilet. All the construction should be well reinforced, with the pull of the garment on the shoulders.

DRESSES FOR LITTLE GIRLS

For a little girl between two and six years old, choose only very simple styles —dresses that will be comfortable, convenient, serviceable, and becoming. These are recommended not only because they are the most practical but also because they are fashionable and indicate good taste. The styles that hang straight from the shoulders, loose and unbelted, are the most comfortable and becoming for a very little girl because her figure is still short and round.

Special features of design that will make a little girl's dresses both comfortable and practical are shown in the accompanying illustrations. For example, the fullness needed for free play is set in across the back and chest but held down over the shoulders and about the

face. On one dress there are rows of shirring; on the other, stitched-down plaits. These features hold the fullness comfortably flat about the face and also set the dresses to the shoulders, thus pre-

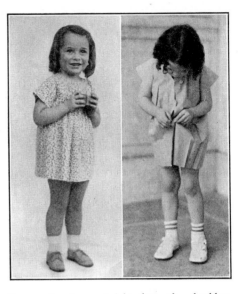

Dresses that hang straight from the shoulders, loose and unbelted, are the best styles for little girls between two and six. Front openings and fasteners that can be managed easily and quickly encourage self-help.

venting the slipping and sliding about which characterize loose, unbelted dresses when these features are overlooked. The necklines in these dresses are cut comfortably low, and though they might be pulled back a little in play, they will not be restricting about the throat nor will they become too tight as the child grows.

Each dress is collarless, because a child's indoor clothes are more comfortable and easier for dressing when there are no unnecessary extras. Wraps can then be pulled on without taking the time or trouble to tuck the dress collar inside. In addition, these dresses are easier to make and to launder than those that have separate collars. If you should

Sun-suit ensembles are ideal summer outfits, as they can be quickly adjusted to suit the occasion or the temperature. The little dress (left) covers the sun suit (right) on cool days.

prefer the becoming effect of a collar, however, you can have it—and still not spoil the practical advantage of flatness—by making a stitched-down, simulated collar. This may be cut in any desired shape and put on like an outside facing.

The sleeves, as the illustration shows, are made in the raglan style. They are short and have no cuffs. This type is preferred to others because it allows more freedom and is also more adaptable to growth.

As an encouragement to self-help the dresses open in the front and have easy fastenings. Either of the styles illustrated is simple for a very little girl because there is nothing to confuse her or to require much time.

These dresses were made of preshrunk materials, the colors of which had been tested and were fast to both sun and washing. Gaily printed lawn was used for the shirred dress with its soft lines. The pattern is small, in proportion to a little girl's size. The other dress was made of firmly woven plain-colored gingham, in keeping with the tailored style of the garment. In each case the material was chosen to carry out the plan of the dress design.

Children give their clothes hard wear and that, together with frequent washing, means that every part of a garment —from seams to finishes—must be well made and durable. In addition, all construction needs to be smooth and without bulk. Rough, scratchy seams irritate the sensitive skin of a child.

Very simple trimming was used as a finishing touch for each of the dresses. On the print, a flat, couching stitch covers the rows of shirring and accents the color. A contrasting blanket stitch, overhanded with the color of the dress, edges the neck and front of the tailored dress. This durable stitchery is attractive and also strengthens the edges that are likely to be pulled and strained in dressing.

Simple French-style panties in matching material, with a fitted band in front and elastic at the back, may be worn with either of these dresses. In summer, however, a double-duty combination, which can serve either as a cool undergarment or as a sun suit, may be preferred. The lower part of this suit is made of material to match the dress, but the upper part is of strong curtain marquisette. On hot days, when few clothes are needed, the suit is pleasantly cool.

BOYS' SUITS

Small boys are somewhat limited in the styles of their clothes, but fortunately that puts no ban on their comfort. Simplicity should be the distinguishing characteristic of boys' clothes.

Avoid all superfluous touches, such as ruffles, fancy embroideries, large floppy collars, and ties. These details only get in a child's way and spoil his play. Select simply designed suits with becoming lines, individual color, and neat tailoring. Clothes of this type indicate good taste and are always in style.

Two styles of suits—one-piece and two-piece—are popular for boys under the age of six. The first type is easy for dressing, but it has disadvantages in that it cannot be lengthened through the body and it is usually difficult to manage in ironing. The one disadvantage in the two-piece suit is that many buttons are required.

In either style, however, there are certain details pertaining to cut, style, and finish that should be kept in mind in order to insure comfort, convenience, and pleasing appearance. First of all, the suits should be cut full and should fit loosely, so as to give the freedom that is needed and also to look well. In the suits illustrated here, the blouses fit easily, with looseness across the back and chest. Necklines are cut low and are

collarless. Even with stooping and squatting in play there is no uncomfortable pulling and choking. Short, open sleeves may be cut in raglan style or they may be tailored, with short caps

A little boy needs full-cut suits so that he will have ample freedom for active play.

and large armholes. From the standpoint of comfort, sewing, and laundering, raglan sleeves are the better of the two, but either style allows ample arm and shoulder freedom. In the summer sleeves may well be omitted. Sleeveless blouses are much more comfortable in hot weather because clothes tend to cling to the body when they are damp with perspiration.

A boy's trousers, like his blouses, need to be full-cut. A good way to test their fit is to have the child bend over and squat as he would in play. To judge the fit of a suit by the way it looks when a boy stands straight and still is unfair, because a child spends very little time in such a dignified pose. What a boy needs in his clothes is roominess,

A suit should be cut full enough so that even stooping and squatting cause no uncomfortable pulling and choking.

so that he can play as he likes without restriction. Properly fitted suits wear well because they get little of the strain that breaks seams and pulls off buttons.

Conveniently placed plackets and simple fastenings that encourage self-help in dressing are other desirable features in the suits illustrated here. Each blouse opens at the center front; the plackets in the trousers lap in the logical (rather than the traditional) way; and the buttons, which are all alike, are of a size that is easy to handle. When the

buttons are all of the same size and style the child can dress himself much more easily than when his suits have buttons of one kind for the trousers and another kind for the blouse, as well as a few snaps and a belt buckle. Notice how effectively the simulated belts can be substituted for the usual separate belts, with their troublesome little supports and buckles. The simulated belts have the additional advantage of being permanently attached and fastened with buttons. Conveniences such as these are of practical value in teaching a boy self-reliance.

The materials in these suits are appropriate for the tailored designs and give a pleasing appearance. Firm, sturdy weaves that wear well and keep their shape and soft, pliable textures that adapt themselves to body movements and feel comfortable next to the skin should be chosen. Such fabrics as poplin, linen, chambray, and soft, crash-like cottons are highly suitable for boys' suits.

One should insist on preshrunk materials, because they do away with misfits and much needless waste. Oftentimes in buying a little boy's suit a mother allows (by guesswork) for shrinkage and growth. Later, when the material shrinks more than was anticipated, the fit is all wrong. The suits are then worn in spite of their poor fit or else they are discarded for new ones. Mistakes like these are unnecessary, since both suits and yard goods can be bought preshrunk.

Fast colors are also important in boys' suits, which have to be washed fre-

quently. Look for labels that give definite information and do not be satisfied
with materials that are merely tub-fast.
Fabrics that are fast to both sun and
washing are the best and the most economical.

Good construction is another point
about which to be particular when
choosing a boy's suits. Examine the
seams inside and out, the plackets, finishes, and the places where fastenings
are attached. All these details should
show strong, smooth workmanship.
There should be reinforcements wherever there is likely to be strain. Double
stitching, stay buttons, or a bit of tape
will often save tears that would ruin a
suit or at least cause troublesome mending.

CLOTHES FOR OUTDOOR FUN

For outdoor play in winter a small
child needs a protective play suit—one
that is warm enough to make up for the
difference between indoor and outdoor
temperatures. This suit should be as
lightweight and as non-restricting as possible. The choice will, of course, be influenced by the climate. In places where
the winters are severe, a child usually
needs a warm, windproof outfit—one
that conserves body heat and keeps out
snow and cold. In climates that are wet
and only moderately cold the best type
of suit is one that sheds moisture but
admits air. All such suits, however,
have certain features and qualities in
common.

First of all, they should be made of
material that is washable or that can be
cleaned easily and inexpensively. Out-

door play is rough-and-tumble, and in
winter especially, when there is so much
snow and mud, clothing gets very dirty.

AN ATTRACTIVE DESIGN FOR A LITTLE BOY'S SUIT

A hot-weather outfit for little boys is practical
when it can be quickly transformed from a sun
suit to a jacket suit for practically any occasion.

This is to be expected, and if practical,
easily cleaned play suits are chosen, a
child can be turned loose to play as he
likes.

As a second requirement, the material
should have a comfortable texture and
"feel." Harsh, scratchy, inferior wools
are frequently used in the manufacture
of play suits, and these fabrics rub and
prickle in a way that is irritating. Such
discomfort naturally spoils much of the
joy of playing outdoors. Before buying
a suit, rub its fabric against your throat
or the inside of the arm to test the
smoothness and softness of texture.

Play-suit material needs also to be pliable and adaptable to a child's movements. Pliability can be tested by crunching some of the material in your hand. When the suit is tried on, see that the fabric does not buckle but folds

A one-piece play suit, with a long front opening, adds to the enjoyment of winter play.

with every bend that the child makes.

Durability is a fourth quality needed in play suits and may be judged by examining the weave of the material. If the fabric is napped, look at the underside. In a garment that is made to wear well and keep its shape the weave is firm and even and the yarn is strong and twisted. These qualities are necessary because a child gives his outdoor play clothes exceptionally hard wear.

If the climate requires a showerproof play suit, be sure to choose a fabric that permits ventilation. Rubberized material causes a child to perspire and is likely to do more harm than good. Inquire about ways to clean the material. Some showerproof materials can be washed, and for children they are the most practical.

One-piece play suits are preferable to two-piece suits. With a long front opening that reaches from the neck to the crotch, a suit of this type can be opened wide and put on or taken off by the child with little or no help. Another advantage of a one-piece suit is its uniform protection—there are no cold gaps about the waist. There is no need of tight elastic about the waist to support the leggings; the entire suit is supported from the shoulders. There are so many one-piece suits on the market that one will need to give considerable thought to making a wise selection. Those with looseness through the body and blousiness in the sleeves and legs are good because they allow for comfortable bending and for growth. The lower back of a child's play suit should have the extra length and width needed for the most extreme bending, stooping, and squatting. If "skimped"—as many suits are, in order to save material— play movements cause the legs of the suit to pull up and the neckline to draw back against the throat. Suits which are definitely adapted to activity are not only the best for the child but the most economical for the mother.

Play suits designed with looseness always need some style device for fitting the suit closely at the ankles and wrists. The purpose of such a device is to keep out cold air and prevent floppiness, which hampers play. In a cold-weather suit, knit anklets and wristlets serve very well. These must have an easy give, however, so that hands in mittens and feet in shoes and galoshes can enter and withdraw without strain. A shower suit may have, instead of knit bands, collapsible godets and loose-fitting ankle bands made of the same material as the suit. Such an opening spreads wide to admit the foot and is then folded over and fastened. Elastic loops and buttons grooved on the underside for easy grasp are convenient and secure fastenings.

A play suit always needs a soft, warm finish about the neck. Avoid collars with an extreme roll, for they stand up stiffly at the back and restrict head and neck movements, sometimes causing bad posture. Choose, instead, a low, evenly rolled collar that fills in above the loose-fitting neckline and keeps out the cold. This style is both comfortable and non-restricting.

Look for ample, conveniently placed pockets. A play suit is hardly complete without some place to carry a few choice treasures and a handkerchief. These pockets must be large enough so that a clenched hand can enter and withdraw without strain. If placed at hand level they will wear well and the child will not bear down in them and tear the corners.

Gay rather than dull colors are most appropriate for play suits and children enjoy them. Contrary to the general opinion that gay colors are not as practical as dark ones, shades of red, blue, and green seldom show lint and soil as quickly as do navy blues, browns, and grays. Gay colors are also protective. Motorists can quickly see a bright spot of color, whereas dark blue or brown blends into the background and is hardly noticeable.

A showerproof suit is practical for outdoor play in a mild, wet climate.

A beret, stocking cap, or helmet is suitable for wear with a winter play suit. As with the suit, the choice of a head covering should be determined by the climate. In places where it is mild, a beret is all that is needed, but for extreme cold and snow the warmer stocking cap or helmet is better. In any of these different types of headwear look for light weight and an easy fit. Small children are easily irritated by head coverings that cramp their ears, rub, or ride around and block their vision.

SHOES

In order to give a young child's feet a chance to grow and develop properly, choose moccasin-style laced shoes—the kind that foot specialists recommend. These shoes are scientifically built and follow the natural shape of the feet. Unlike many other styles of shoes, those built for health are very light in weight, flexible, and neat looking. They allow lots of room for the toes, the heels are close-fitting, and the soles are not slippery. Furthermore, the leather is soft, pliable, and often washable. Buy a child's shoes in a size that is three-fourths of an inch longer and one-fourth of an inch wider than the foot itself when in a standing position, so that the shoes will not be outgrown before they have had reasonable wear.

Socks or stockings for little children should also be purchased in a size longer than the foot. Three-fourths of an inch or an inch is none too much to allow, because both growth and shrinkage must be considered. Only hose of very elastic weave are comfortable or suitable for a growing child. They are also the easiest for a child to learn to put on. Hose, at best, are a bit difficult for little folks to put on straight without help; therefore they should have a definite mark to indicate the center front.

In bad weather a child needs rubbers or overshoes to keep his feet dry and protect his shoes when he goes out of doors. A one-fastener style that opens wide, for slipping on, and then folds over and fastens at the ankle is probably the easiest to put on. These overshoes give complete protection. They are light in weight and have none of the clumsiness or heaviness common in many types of overshoes. The spread of the collapsible top allows a child to squat comfortably at play without the restriction and numbness often caused by inflexible, buckled overshoes.

CLOTHES FOR EARLY SCHOOL DAYS
(Six to Ten Years)

When girls and boys are old enough to go to school, several changes will be necessary in the type of clothes they wear. As soon as these youngsters get well started in the first grade, what "the others" wear becomes the measuring stick of rightness. This desire to imitate presents real problems at times, because not all school children are dressed according to approved standards of suitability, health, or even attractiveness. Fortunately, however, more and more parents are coming to realize that a child's clothes can be truly beautiful only when they contribute to his health and comfort. Undoubtedly a still wider appreciation of right clothing will help in solving that difficult problem presented by "the others."

Children of school age are very hard on their clothes. This is not a cause for worry, however, if you make up your mind to get only practical, simple clothes of good quality. Children like sturdy garments that they can forget about,

READY FOR OUTDOOR PLAY

A low, soft collar, a zipper opening, ample pockets, and ample fullness where needed are features that make this type of play suit ideal for the child from two to six years old.

and they detest delicate clothes that are forever getting ripped and torn. Some mothers do not understand that a shredded blouse or torn-out sleeves are more frequently due to poor judgment in choosing materials than to rough play. Clothes should be made strong enough to withstand the rough-and-tumble play that all children enjoy. Usually a few garments are wrecked before these mothers realize that they have to get right down to facts about wearing qualities if they expect to keep their children in clothes.

During school years children frequently have a flair for little accessories. Suddenly a hair bow, a belt, or a tie becomes very important. These are harmless little extras but are rarely any real contribution so far as appearance is concerned. Such an accessory may destroy the smartness of an otherwise perfectly planned outfit but, even so, it is wise to let the child wear it, for children get a great deal of pleasure from these accessories and trinkets. Besides, none of these flairs lasts for long.

UNDERWEAR

Good, comfortable underwear is the first requirement for being well dressed for school. The choice of material and some features of the style will be based on the prevailing climate and the temperature of the schoolroom. Keep in mind, however, that children of school age are extremely active and even when playing outdoors in very cold weather they seldom need as warm underwear as parents imagine. Too much clothing can be as unhealthful as too little, because good energy is wasted in trying to keep comfortable. To err in either way, though, is inexcusable, because children of school age are old enough to tell you when they need lighter or warmer underwear. The main point is for parents not to be too set in their own ideas but to pay attention to signs and expressions of comfort or discomfort on the part of the child.

Regardless of whether underwear is for warm or cold weather, be sure to get materials that will be comfortable—that is, soft, smooth, elastic, and light in weight. Manufacturers have worked out special combinations of fibers and new ways of knitting so that some of the warmest fabrics are as light in weight as those made for summer. There are comfortable textures that will not stiffen in washing and that are knit so as to give without becoming saggy. Underwear that stretches out of shape is just as uncomfortable and hampering as that which is too large or badly cut.

One can hardly tell whether or not a garment is properly fashioned or the right size unless the child tries it on. Children grow differently and underwear sizes vary in different makes. Then, too, certain manufacturers make long, narrow garments; others, short wide ones. The only way to be sure of the proper size is to fit the garment. Guesswork often results in buying misfits that will not wear well because they have not been made in proper relation to the body.

In general, look for the following features of design and cut: (1) easy width through the body; (2) a well-rounded neckline, cut fairly low in front and finished so as to set to the chest without rippling or need of a drawstring; (3) shoulders that fit and are strengthened so that they will not stretch with wear and washing; (4) leg and arm openings finished to fit snugly; (5) plenty of length and width in the lower back so that the material does not pull tight or bunch in the crotch; and (6) a convenient arrangement for getting in and out of the suit and for toilet needs.

Lasting construction is another important consideration in underwear for school children. Unless suits are well made they will not stand up under the hard wear they are certain to get. The seams must be flat, smooth on both sides, and durable; at the same time they must be elastic enough to give with the material. Avoid tight stitching because it breaks and sometimes tears the material.

Plackets should also be examined carefully, for they get hard wear. They must be durably finished, yet with soft materials rather than the cheap, scratchy ones sometimes used. If there are buttonholes in the underwear examine them closely. Those that are stitched closely and firmly wear well and keep their shape; others, finished with a loose stitch that ravels, wear out long before the suit does and this causes trouble in keeping the buttons fastened.

DRESSES FOR SCHOOL WEAR

When a little girl is between six and ten years old her dresses may be more varied in style than during her preschool days. She has grown taller, and certain designs that were unbecoming to a babyish figure are now becoming. Furthermore, she can now easily manage clothes that were too difficult before.

In general, the styles suitable for this age are all designed along loose lines. That does not necessarily mean full-gathered dresses, but easy-fitting ones that have a graceful looseness about them. Such designs are good because they allow for both free play and reasonable growth.

In any dress design there are certain features that are always desirable, such as necklines that are cut fairly low in front, large, roomy armholes, and wide sleeves cut as short as are comfortable for the season. It is well to have some fullness, such as plaits or gathers, below well-fitted shoulders. When carried into the skirt this fullness gives plenty of spread at the lower edge.

Little girls usually dress in a hurry and should not be bothered with tricky plackets or tedious fastenings. Dresses should have openings in front, where they are easy to reach, and the fastenings should be of a convenient type that holds securely.

Up to this age children may have expressed only a color preference in their clothes, but from now on they will begin to notice the style as well. Little girls differ, of course, in the amount of clothes interest they show, but whenever possible they should be allowed to select, from an approved lot, the styles and colors they like best. The mother must take special care to be up-to-date about what little girls are wearing in order to win her own daughter's confidence in her ability as a helper. She can then explain the advantages and disadvantages of each dress, including cost, because children cannot begin too early

to learn how to choose clothes wisely.

Styles for children of this age do not change greatly from season to season

One-piece wash dresses, either belted or unbelted, are practical for the schoolgirl.

except in slight details. The mother can decide on the type of outfits that best suit the family budget.

One-piece wash dresses made of color-fast, preshrunk cottons, either printed or plain, are good stand-bys for school days. On a little girl who is not very tall for her age the unbelted styles, with gathered or plaited fullness swinging loose from a shoulder yoke, are suitable; a taller child can wear a belt, which holds in the fullness that may be hampering and in the way.

One-piece wash dresses are most comfortable when they have short, open sleeves. These sleeves can be finished off effectively with contrasting trim to match the collars, which, in a youthful, round shape, can also be varied in many ways so as to make them becoming.

The jumper dress, made of tailored cotton or wool, makes a practical and attractive school dress for the girl from six to ten years old.

Some mothers vary the designs of this type of collar, and then by using materials of different colors they can economize and use the same pattern for all the school dresses. When wool materials are used for one-piece dresses, it is practical to have detachable collars that can be washed separately. Usually a pleasing variety of buttoned-on collars makes

a few dresses seem like many. Oftentimes it is not necessary to buy new material for these collars, as small pieces of goods left over from other garments may be used.

Not very different in appearance from the one-piece dresses are the two-piece jumper dresses. Made of tailored cottons or wools, these are about as practical and youthful school outfits as a little girl can have. If there is need for economy, jumpers can be made successfully from several different types of old garments or from odd pieces of material. One must not be tempted to use just any materials on hand, however; suitability of material and color must still be considered. Otherwise the dress will have that "made-over" appearance which makes children feel queer and unhappy in their clothes. Made-overs are economies only when they are so skillfully constructed that no one suspects their true origin. Careless use of materials is what marks made-overs as such.

Another advantage of jumper dresses is that they may be worn with a variety of washable blouses, thus providing, with little expense, the change that children like. Blouses, also, need not be made of new material; they can be cut from the good parts of men's old broadcloth shirts. If the jumper is cut high, like the one illustrated here, the blouse may even be pieced.

Other practical outfits that little girls like for school wear are plaited skirts with sweaters or skirts with blouses and jackets. Here again it is possible to economize by making the skirts and jackets from left-over materials. One should first make sure of a satisfactory color combination for such an ensemble. Should sweater colors be limited, the skirt material may be dyed to match. When buying a sweater, get the best quality you can afford. Avoid fussy styles with collars, ties, and worked designs, for good quality of material and construction is frequently sacrificed for these novelties. The best all-around values are found in the simple styles with hand-sewn seams that give with motion.

"STORE" CLOTHES FOR BOYS

A six-year-old boy is, in his own opinion, too grown-up to be wearing what are commonly called wash suits. He wants trousers—either trunks or knickers—and blouses. His choice is wise for reasons other than good appearance. These outfits are sturdy and well suited for the kind of play that a boy of this age enjoys.

The wise mother buys a schoolboy's suits ready-made unless she is unusually skillful at tailoring. Little boys are conventional creatures and early in life feel the blight of homemade trousers and blouses. Not long after starting to school they insist on "store" clothes which are apparently stamped with an unnamable something that satisfies a sprouting sense of manliness. Rather than make a boy miserable with homemades—which, considering the accepted styles, are difficult for the average home sewer—a mother should reconcile herself to the child's ideas and determine, from the beginning, to do the best possible job of buying ready-mades.

Boys' clothes, like men's, are standardized to such an extent that very good qualities can usually be found at reasonable prices. Even so, there is still

Trousers—either trunks or knickers—and blouses are both popular and practical when a boy has reached school age.

enough variety and difference in quality to justify a few suggestions.

The best type of blouses for schoolboys are made in the collarless cardigan style or with rolling collars. Boys usually have a preference which should not be disregarded, but of the two styles the collarless one is really the better; it is comfortable, easy to launder, and does not muss under wraps. Rolling collars wrinkle; they are difficult to adjust inside a coat and a bit troublesome to launder. Blouses can be purchased, however, with stitched-down rather than loose collar facings, and this feature makes laundering far more simple.

It pays to get blouses of the best quality because they are made of material that is durable, fast in color, and pre-shrunk. They are also full-cut, which means that they were not "skimped" in size to save material. The construction is neat and durable, with flat felled seams that are double-stitched and reinforced wherever they are likely to be strained. These qualities will be appreciated more and more as a boy grows older. Boys are not usually careful of their clothes, and the amount saved by buying bargain blouses will soon be spent in repeat purchases.

Knickers and shorts, like blouses, are serviceable and comfortable when they are of good quality and are full-cut. The child should try them on to be sure that they set right and do not rely on a belt to be kept in place. There should be roominess at the hips, and, in knickers, looseness about the knees. Knickers with knit leg bands are preferable to those with woven leg bands that have to be buckled. The former are more comfortable because they give, and there is not the bother of fastening them. In addition, the knit leg bands stay in place and are trim and neat in appearance, while the others often slip down or come unbuckled.

Only washable materials are suitable for pants for a boy of this age. He gets his clothes so dirty that nothing else is either hygienic or practical. Tweed-like materials are suggested for winter wear and strong wash cottons or linens for summer. The linens are more expensive, but they have the advantage of being easier to wash and iron than cotton materials used for pants.

WRAPS FOR BOYS AND GIRLS

Schoolgirls prefer coats for winter wear. According to a six-year-old's way of thinking, play suits are too babyish, even though this type of garment gives better protection and undoubtedly much more comfort than a coat. A garment very similar to the play suit—called a ski suit—is worn by girls of all ages for winter sports. Ski suits are warm, smart, and very practical.

The coats commonly known as sports or polo coats are the most appropriate for school youngsters. Although all these coats are similar in style and cut, certain desirable features that provide comfort and serviceability should be kept in mind when making a selection. If the coat is made of napped fabric, look at the underside to see if the yarn is good and the weave firm enough to give reasonable wear. Two years is about as long as a coat may be expected to fit a growing child comfortably, so there is no need to buy the finest quality of material, such as an adult might wish for wear over a long period. Material that is durable enough to last well for two years will be satisfactory. The fabric should be soft and pliable in texture because many coats (especially those made of inferior wool) are so matted and stiff that to raise an arm pulls the entire coat. These cheap materials also scratch and irritate the neck and wrists.

Raglan rather than set-in sleeves are practical in these coats, as this style is particularly suited to growing figures.

Whether shoulders are wide or narrow, the raglan sleeve fits because there are no definite armhole lines that have to set at a certain place on the figure. Since they are wider than other styles, raglan sleeves allow plenty of shoulder and arm freedom, which is very essential in children's clothes. Sleeves that are cut wide for their entire length and strapped loosely at the wrist keep out cold and still allow plenty of arm freedom. Another desirable feature about these sleeves is that they can extend slightly over the hands without making the coat seem too large. This extra material is most welcome as the child's arms grow longer.

There will, of course, have to be pockets on a coat of this style, so one should make sure of good tailoring that leaves no weak corners to tear and thus spoil a brand new coat. Children give their pockets hard wear by stuffing things into them, so careful construction of a coat is essential to wear as well as to good appearance.

The type of lining will depend on the climate, but whether wool or silk, it should be hemmed separately so that the coat will always hang right. It is well to select a coat with a generous hem allowance so that the garment can be lengthened if necessary. Sometimes the corners inside the front facings are clipped away, thus complicating the work of altering or letting out a hem later.

There are sport coats for boys much like those described for girls, with certain differences in cut and tailoring, however, which label them as masculine.

Long coats are not as popular with boys as are the short leather coats and blazers. For general use these jacket and lumberjack styles are very suitable. There is little need of the extra protection of a full-length coat, especially for a boy who is healthy and active. Even short coats are too warm at times.

A boy can hardly get along without a sweater or two. He usually prefers pull-over styles, and these are excellent for wear under a coat when the weather is unusually cold, when the schoolroom is chilly, and in spring and autumn when a coat may be too heavy. When buying a sweater for a boy it is well to let him choose the style and the color. Parents sometimes unknowingly select the very color that is, according to his notion, "sissy." No amount of reasoning and justification for the choice will do any good if the child thinks the sweater will not look just right in the eyes of his playfellows. If the boy disapproves of the selection it is better to exchange the sweater at once. A disliked garment invariably wears out sooner than one that meets with approval, because children, like adults, take good care of clothes they like. A tear or a hole in a garment which a child dislikes may be welcome and even helped along in the mischievous way of children.

The best type of headwear for both boys and girls is always the simplest type. Berets for girls and small lightweight caps for boys are suitable in moderate weather. On cold, windy days, knit stocking-caps are warmer, yet scarcely any heavier, than the berets.

Some boys like leather helmets, and these are all right provided they do not cramp the ears or fit too closely. Head-wear that is snug-fitting makes hearing difficult.

Gloves that are easy to put on are better than mittens, since they leave the fingers free for an easy grasp. Many children, however, dislike to wear any kind of hand covering.

SHOES

Both boys and girls should continue to wear health shoes just as they did in nursery and kindergarten days. Growing feet can ill afford to be cramped. An improperly built shoe can cause no end of trouble, which sometimes persists throughout life.

Moccasin styles are the most comfortable shoes even at this age, because they are made of soft, pliable leather, they are roomy, and they have a straight inner-line sole and lace fastenings. The leathers range in color from light to dark, so that the same style can be worn the year around. Another practical feature about shoes of this type is that they can be cleaned either by polishing or by washing. Other leathers usually stiffen when washed.

To protect the shoes and to keep the

feet dry in wet and snowy weather overshoes are indispensable. They should be light in weight and not too bulky. The one-fastener style of over-shoe that opens wide for putting on and then folds over and fastens at the instep is a practical type. It is made entirely of rubber on the outside and can be washed very easily. Another advantage of these overshoes is that children can manage them so easily and quickly that they do not mind wearing them. The overshoes are therefore not so likely to be lost, forgotten, or left at school.

Hosiery must be chosen to suit the temperature. In warm weather, when the legs need no protection, anklets are best. They are cool, particularly in mesh knit, they require no garters, and they are the easiest type of hosiery to put on. In cool weather three-quar-ter or seven-eighths hose are warmer, but flat garters have to be worn under the cuffs of these hose as a support. Long stockings should be worn when children are exposed to severe cold and have no other protection over the knees.

Children's hose should be fashioned to allow ample toe room and should give easily. To take care of shrinkage and growth it is well to get a size that is about an inch longer than the foot.

SUMMARY

When selecting any article of clothing for a child, consider comfort, convenience, encouragement to self-help, suitability of fabrics, and pleasing appearance.

To be comfortable, clothing must be right for the temperature, light in weight, ample in size, and so cut and fitted that no normal body movement is restricted.

For little children not yet old enough to dress themselves, clothes should be planned so that the mother can put them on and take them off quickly with very little disturbance to the baby. Older children want clothes that they themselves can manage without help. To encourage self-help, choose loose-fitting garments with plackets in front and fastenings that are easy to manipulate.

Fabrics should suit the purpose of the different garments, but whether for play dresses or snow suits they should be sturdy, soft, and pliable in texture, light in weight, preshrunk, fast to sun and washing, easy to wash and iron, and gay in color.

Select designs and colors that are becoming and pleasing. Little children, like adults, have definite likes and dislikes which need to be considered for greatest enjoyment.

QUESTIONS

1. Why should special kinds of clothing be worn at different periods of childhood?

2. What are the advantages and disadvantages—from the standpoint of health and comfort—in the styles popular for children?

3. Is it better to choose oversize garments or those with features adapted to growth?

4. Why is the weight of a child's clothing important?

5. Of what value is clothing that has features conducive to self-help?

6. What qualities characterize materials suitable for children's wear?

7. What is the purpose of allowing children to help in selecting their own wearing apparel?

8. What are the advantages of quality clothes over price-saving bargains?

9. How can parents help to bring about improved types of garments for children?

10. What points should be considered in selecting proper shoes for children?

READING REFERENCES

BOOKS

Key, Cora B., and others, *Process of Learning to Dress among Nursery-School Children* (Journal Press, Provincetown, Mass.).

Young, Florence E., *Clothing the Child* (McGraw).

PAMPHLETS

Scott, Clarice L., *Dresses for Little Girls* (U. S. Department of Agriculture, Bureau of Home Economics, Leaflet No. 80); *Ensembles for Sunny Days* (Leaflet No. 63); *Rompers* (Leaflet No. 79); and *Suits for the Small Boy* (Leaflet No. 52).

Scott, Clarice L., and Smith, Margaret, *Fabrics and Designs for Children's Clothes* (U. S. Department of Agriculture, Bulletin No. 1778).

COLOR HARMONY AND TASTE IN DRESS

Edith M. Leonard

AND

Lillian E. Miles

At an early age children show their delight in colors, and this delight can be trained into an appreciation of color harmonies through the selection of suitable and tasteful clothing. The authors have both had experience in teaching primary students and they know what children can absorb if properly guided. Miss Leonard is Director of Early Childhood Education at the State College, Santa Barbara, California; her collaborator, Mrs. Miles, is a member of the Board of Education at San Bernardino, California.

THE mother who begins at an early age to teach her children how to select their clothes wisely is giving them one important key to success in the society of which they are a part. This is particularly necessary with boys. Girls, with their heritage from Eve, become more and more clothes-conscious as they grow older. The young male, however, growing in stature and self-importance, often feels that any special attention to clothes is "sissy." He demands apparel that will proclaim his masculinity, and usually he wants trousers, shirts, and sweaters "like Bill and the other fellows are wearing." By all means let him run with the pack, but that need not prevent him from choosing colors in trousers, shirts, sweaters, socks, and ties that accentuate his good instead of his bad points.

Early training in selection of clothing should seem to the child casual and incidental. "Let's choose a dress for Betty from these lovely colors. Which would be best for her? Perhaps the scarlet or the emerald because her hair and eyes are a dark, rich brown and her skin is fair. As for Johnny—don't you think this blue suit would look nice on him, with his blue

Photo: U. S. Bureau of Home Economics

READY FOR PLAY

Knit stocking caps are warm, soft over the ears, and easy to put on without help. Simplicity, suitability, and good wearing quality are all part of what is known as "good taste in dress."

164

eyes?" Such remarks, repeated with variations, sink into the child's consciousness, and the idea is born in him that he must not wear unbecoming colors. Discovering those which are most flattering, however, is an individual problem, and solving it continues through life.

Dressing Homemade Paper Dolls

One way to help children select suitable colors for themselves is through their play. All young children enjoy playing with dolls. They dress and undress them, pretend to feed them, punish them, put them through every experience they themselves have had. Even paper dolls seem real to them. This make-believe parenthood fascinates small boys as well as girls. Boys of preschool age, or even of kindergarten and first-grade levels, enjoy dolls as much as girls do. One clever mother, trading on this love of dolls, developed a unique idea. She posed her children in their undergarments as if they were paper dolls and took pictures of them. (Paper dolls, of course, stand with their hands spread at their sides so that they are easily dressed.) She had a photographer enlarge and color these snapshots so that they showed the children in their natural coloring. She pasted each colored enlargement on a heavy piece of tag board and, after the paste was thoroughly dry, cut out the figure with a sharply pointed knife. The children then made wardrobes for their own paper images. Each season for a number of years she made new pictures, and the children's interest in the activity was heightened and prolonged because they were "dressing them-

selves." They worked out their own clothes problems surprisingly well.

Studying the Appearance

Children should be encouraged to study their faces in a mirror, placed to catch the strong north light, not from vanity but to discover their good points in personal appearance as well as their poor ones. The next problem is for each to find how his good points may be emphasized and his bad ones covered up or attention diverted from them. Help children to see that a good posture is essential to their best appearance as well as to their good health.

Some may feel that so much attention to appearance and clothes will make the child a vain, self-conscious little prig; but the right kind of training will not. Instead, it will be an important factor in developing an attractive personality.

First, the child whose clothes are well chosen and suited to the occasion will gain in poise. Many shy and backward children are acutely conscious of unsuitable clothing, and this contributes to a growing and harmful inferiority complex. A large number of adults, when asked to recall their most humiliating experience, will tell of being forced to wear some garment which they felt was bizarre. Second, an appreciation of color harmony in dress is no more out of place than is an appreciation of a gorgeous sunset, the multicolored flowers of spring, or the flaming tints of autumn.

Economy Limits Choice

"I have so little money to spend on my child's clothes," one mother may mourn.

This fact offers her and her child a challenge. A first principle of suitable dress is to keep within one's budget, and training in economy and careful buying is vitally important to the child. Furthermore, it is a real accomplishment to be

Photo: Lawrence Thornton-Loder

Children should be taught at an early age not only how to choose their own clothes but how to take care of them.

able to make a little money go a long way. It requires more time and patience to select clothing or materials according to a matched and planned color scheme, but no more money.

Another mother may ruefully exclaim, "My children are dressed largely from the secondhand garments of their elders!" This is unfortunate, as one of the joys of childhood is having something "brand-new." However, even this discouraging fact need not wholly defeat

the ingenious mother, for there are the dye pots. Good dyes may be procured cheaply and minute directions come with each package. Made-over clothing can also be touched up with different and colorful accessories.

No matter how the mother must scheme and skimp to clothe her children attractively, let them share the experience with her. For them it will mean knowledge, the awakening of ingenuity, and a growing sense of values.

STUDYING COLOR AND ITS VALUE

"I know so little about colors myself," objects another. Such a mother, then, has new and delightful experiences awaiting her. One of her first steps should be either to secure or to make a color wheel, and she should let each of the children make one with her. Use a glass prism and cast a spectrum on a white wall or white cardboard pinned against the wall. The glass prisms hanging on old candelabras make splendid spectrums. Tiny ones can be thrown from the facets of a diamond or any clearly cut stone in a ring. Watch the rainbows whenever they appear; tell the children how they are caused and discuss the lovely colors. Get the children to help find the colors in the spectrum. Explain how the colors on the upper half of the spectrum—red-violet, red, red-yellow, and yellow—represent warmth and light because they are associated with the sun. Those on the lower half of the spectrum—green, blue-green, blue, and blue-violet—are cool colors and are associated with air, sky, and water. Feel with the children how warm colors seem to advance or move forward, and how cool colors seem to recede or move back. Discuss why warm colors are worn in winter, cool colors in summer. Look for colors in the landscape, in rooms, in pictures, in other people's clothes. Older children will be interested in knowing that light waves from the sun vibrate at different speeds and produce different sensations in the eye, causing what is known as color. These light waves strike different objects which absorb all the rays except the one which they reflect back; for example, a green leaf absorbs all color waves except green, which is then reflected back. Color waves combine to produce the in-between colors like red-yellow, yellow-green, green-blue, blue-violet, and violet-red. After the children and the mother have decided the order of the colors, they can then make their color wheels together.

The local paint stores frequently have color wheels, which they will gladly give away.

THE PROPERTIES OF COLOR

Color has the three properties of hue, value, and intensity. Hue means *color*. A dress has a red hue, or blue, or green, but the adjective does not indicate *how* red, or *how* blue, or *how* green.

The amount of light or dark added to any color determines its *value*.

The *intensity* of a color is determined by its quality, that is, the purity of the light-wave producing the color. An intense color is seen more quickly than one less intense. That is the reason for red danger signals and stop lights.

WAYS OF ACHIEVING COLOR HARMONY

Colors that adjoin on the color wheel are known as neighboring, related, or analogous colors. For example, yellow-green, green, and blue-green. Such colors go well together and result in a related color scheme because there is one common or "related" color in the group —in the above instance green.

Opposing or unrelated colors lie opposite each other on the color wheel. Red opposes blue-green; yellow opposes blue-violet; green opposes red-violet; blue opposes red-yellow. A dress of one of these colors is often more attractive if a touch of the opposing color is added in trim or accessories. Here is an interesting experiment with color which children will enjoy. Stare at a red light for about thirty seconds and then look quickly at a white wall or a white piece of paper. Presently a blue-green spot of color will appear. Stare at an intense blue object; then look at white, and a red-yellow spot will appear. With any one of the colors the complementary color appears as an afterimage.

If a number of brilliant colors are to be used in a dress or accessories, they may be used on either a black or white background. The colors are harmonized in this way.

Also a number of colors may be used together if each color has had a single color, as yellow, added to it. This is called harmony by *saturation*.

Harmony in dress may also be achieved by a one-color or monochromatic scheme. Here the wearer uses one color in varying values or intensities. For example, a boy might wear a light blue suit, navy blue socks, and a tie of medium blue. It would be well, though, to remember that all the shades should lean toward "warm" blue rather than "cold" blue—that is, they should all have a light trace of violet in them rather than green or yellow.

INDIVIDUAL CHOICE OF COLOR

As has been suggested, the wise choice of color is an individual matter, since no two persons are exactly alike. The mother should study her child critically and impersonally to decide what colors are most becoming. It is important, also, that the child co-operate in the choosing of colors. A little girl who looked lovely in brown and orange tones complained bitterly because she always had to wear them. One day her mother took her to the city department store and with the aid of a large mirror and many different colored materials showed her how browns brought out the golden lights in her hair and accentuated her creamy skin; also how much more ordinary she appeared in certain other colors. However, to her own surprise, the mother found that her child looked equally well in emerald green and scarlet. After this experience the little girl was eager to wear colors that became her.

In general, make the color of the skin, the hair, and the eyes a part of the value scheme of the clothing and play up to the child's most striking feature. This can be done either by matching color, repeating it in lighter or darker tones, or by using a contrasting color. Vivid types can wear vivid colors; pale or delicately complexioned children are obliterated by wearing too vivid colors.

The following colors will help to emphasize the color of the eyes:

BLUE EYES: periwinkle, sapphire, powder blue, and certain shades of orchid and rose.
BROWN EYES: browns, burnt orange, rose-beige, emerald, and scarlet.
BLACK EYES: orange, certain shades of yellow and gold, jade green, and black.
GRAY EYES: old rose, mauve, heather, and gray.
HAZEL EYES: certain shades of green, brown, peach, flame, and coral.
GREEN EYES: various shades of green, turquoise or other shades of blue-green, and copper.

The following colors emphasize the color of the hair:

ASH BLONDE: gray, certain shades of green, mauves, and pinks.
GOLDEN BLONDE: white, certain shades of green, yellow, amber, certain shades of blue, and black.
LIGHT RED HAIR: black, deep browns, lavender, gold, blues (sparingly), and soft blue-greens.
FLAMING RED HAIR: black, golden browns, turquoise, certain shades of gray, and reds that deepen the tone of the hair.
DARK RED HAIR: black, certain shades of bright blue, yellow, green, and, if the hair is dark enough in tone, dark red.
RICH BROWN HAIR: hennas and yellows, browns slightly darker than the hair in tone, scarlet, and bright greens.
BLACK HAIR: varying shades of red, gold, certain yellows, and some shades of green.

One important thing to remember in choosing colors is to have one color predominating. Do not have a dress half red and half blue. Rather have a blue dress with touches of red. A large dark area is "pointed up" by a touch of light; the effectiveness of a light costume is heightened by the contrast of dark. Closely related colors are less conspicuous than those which contrast sharply.

FRILLS VERSUS PLAIN CLOTHES

There are other factors besides color which should have consideration in planning a child's wardrobe. A moment's thought will show that there are different types of children. Some little girls can wear frills and ruffles and bows. They are romantic types—picturebook children who look well in organdies and large hats.

Robust, rangy children are potentially the athletic type and look better in sports clothes. Vivid, unusual-appearing children look best in "different" clothing which accentuates their type.

A dark-eyed, dark-haired, broad-faced child can be dressed in colorful peasant smocks; or the oriental-slant of eyes can be emphasized by oriental colors and styles. This dressing to suit the type is called "dramatizing the personality."

Boys, generally, prefer sports clothing; but for formal occasions there are those who look well in straight-cut, well-fitted clothes which are characterized as manly.

DRESSING THE DIFFERENT CHILD

Provided colors are well chosen, the average child may wear many different styles of clothing and look well in them all. The stout child and the tall, thin child each present a problem to the thoughtful mother.

THE STOUT CHILD

In dressing the stout child it is well to remember that heavy materials, shiny, or light-colored fabrics make one look larger. There is a rule for decorating rooms which holds for human beings: To make a room look larger, paint it in a light color. Accordingly, to avoid making the child appear larger, do not dress him in light colors. Also a sweater, knitted suit, or any material or style that has lines that go round and round should be avoided like the plague. Choose instead vertical stripes, and long seams and lines. If using prints, select small all-over patterns that blur and mingle. They will reduce the child's silhouette, while large, bold prints serve only to widen it. Never put a broad, big hat on a fat child. To do so gives a mushroom effect. Use trimmings above the waistline and make skirts slightly

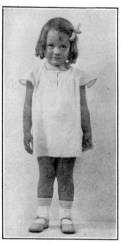

Photo: U. S. Bureau of Home Economics

Little girls enjoy Sunday dresses that are simple and cannot be hurt by the soil of play. Note the straight-from-the-neck style, the harmonious touches in the hair bow, the socks, and the shoes.

longer than are generally worn. Avoid complete belts and favor a raised waistline rather than a lowered one. Avoid skirts that are too full and waists of one color with skirts of another, for light and dark tones break the lines and make the figure appear shorter. Avoid frills and ruffles about the neck. The fat child often has a plump, attractive neck, and so can wear necklines that display it to advantage. Socks the color of the dress, or darker colored, are better than light ones.

For the fat boy choose sweaters and shirts with vertical rather than horizontal lines. Let shirts and trousers be almost the same color. The color contrast should be with hair or eyes rather than in the garment itself.

THE TALL, THIN CHILD

For the tall, thin child the reverse of what has been said concerning the fat child applies. Remembering that tucks, seams, rows of buttons, stripes, and plaits accentuate the direction in which they travel, keep to horizontal lines and trimmings as much as possible. If prints are used, select clearly defined patterns. Generally speaking, large prints are not considered suitable for children, although the matter of current style governs all matters of dress to some extent.

Skirts may have contrasting color running horizontally, and the height may be broken by blouses of one color and skirts of another. The waistline may be low, and discreet flounces and ruffles make the child appear less skinny. Contrasting socks and accessories add to the tall child's attractiveness.

SUMMARY

The choice of clothing is closely related to the study of practical art—color-harmony and design—and to the art of sewing. Parents should study all these arts as one, not as individual subjects.

The wise parent must realize, too, that personal appearance is of vital importance in the social world, and that the boy or girl who early learns to make the most of his or her looks through wearing becoming clothes has found an invaluable asset for successful living.

Therefore, children should be taught at an early age to choose their own clothes. They should learn, too, which are the most becoming colors to them; and they should know how to study their own types so that they can choose clothes which suit them best. This means knowing which are their best points and how to bring them out; and knowing, too, their poor points, and how to conceal or divert attention from them by the proper type of dress. Finally, suitability of dress includes learning to buy economically and wisely. Children should know how to choose durable, long-wearing clothes as well as stylish ones.

QUESTIONS

1. Name the principles which should govern the choice of children's clothing.
2. Assuming that you have a limited budget, list the essential clothes for a boy or a girl.
3. Mention four ways in which one may prolong the life of children's clothing.
4. Name several different types of fabrics and discuss suitability for children's clothing.
5. Name four rules for dressing a fat child.
6. Name four for dressing a tall, thin child.

7. Write the names of the color families. Then name as many members of each family as you can. (Example: RED—maroon, crimson, henna, and so on.)
8. List the most popular colors of the season under the color families to which they belong.
9. For each of the colors which your child can wear successfully plan monochromatic color harmony; complementary color harmony; adjacent color harmony.

READING REFERENCES

Buttrick, Helen G., *Principles of Clothing Selection* (Macmillan).

Cades, Hazel Rawson, *Any Girl Can Be Good-Looking; Handsome Is as Handsome Does;* and *How to Make Your Daughter Better Looking* (Appleton-Century).

Dooley, W. H., *Clothing and Style* (Heath).

Foster, Constance J., *The Attractive Child* (Messner).

Giles, Nell, *Susan, Be Smooth!* (Hale).

Goldstein, Harriet I. and Vetta, *Art in Everyday Life* (Macmillan). Read Chapters XII, XIII, XIV, XVI.

Hawes, Elizabeth, *Fashion Is Spinach* (Random House).

Hempstead, Laurene, *Color and Line in Dress* (Prentice-Hall).

Hunter, Lucretia P., *The Girl Today, the Woman Tomorrow* (Allyn & Bacon).

Kettunen, Marietta, *Fundamentals of Dress* (McGraw).

Picken, Mary B., *Secrets of Distinctive Dress* (McKay).

Ryan, Mildred G., *Your Clothes and Personality* (Appleton-Century).

Story, Margaret, *Individuality and Clothes* (Funk).

Weinberg, Louis, *Color in Everyday Life* (Dodd).

Winterburn, Florence M., *Principles of Correct Dress* (Harper).

SAFETY IN THE HOME

Florence Nelson

Accidents on the street and highways are dramatic and have, therefore, been given great publicity. Accidents in the home are less spectacular and hence less publicized, but they are almost as numerous as traffic accidents. By providing simple safety devices and by training children in safety practices parents may do a great deal to prevent accidents in the home. The author, formerly Executive Secretary of the Education Division of the National Safety Council and Editor of *Safety Education* magazine, has written two textbooks on safety and is a special writer in this field. In this article she gives suggestions that have been tested and approved by authorities in safety education.

THE child of today enters a world greatly enriched by the benefits of modern science and invention. Automobiles, airplanes, electrical devices for the home, and many other marvels of a mechanical age have contributed lavishly to the well-being and pleasure of all. But if life today is more interesting and decidedly more comfortable than it was twenty years ago, it is also in many respects more dangerous. For example, nothing is of greater benefit than the automobile, yet nothing has proved so serious an instrument of death and injury.

Modern education recognizes the need for special training if children are successfully to meet the hazards of modern life. The schools are now quite generally teaching

Photo: National Safety Council

From infancy the child should be protected against physical dangers in the home surroundings and should be trained in safe habits.

safety and the results of this instruction have been remarkable. Child accidents have been decreasing in recent years, both in the home and on the streets, while accidents to adults have been increasing. Children adjust themselves more quickly to unfamiliar conditions than do adults, and their response to safety instruction has amazed even the most enthusiastic supporters of this type of education.

Particularly interesting is the following observation of a mother who lives in a community where a good deal of attention has been given to safety: "As I drive about the neighborhood I notice that the children no longer play in the middle of the street and that adults are much less observant of traffic regulations than are the children."

Long before a child goes to school, however, he is exposed to the possibility of accidents. From early infancy he should be protected against physical dangers in his surroundings and trained in safe habits which will stand him in good stead in later years.

Education has proved that accidents are for the most part unnecessary; some of them are due to ignorance, but usually they are the result of carelessness or thoughtlessness, in other words, the deliberate refusal to take simple precautions or to use common sense. Accidents are expensive. They waste time, money, and human life. They cost the nation annually 100,000 lives of which 14,400 are children under fifteen years of age. The economic cost of these accidents is $3,600,000. Incredible as it may seem, almost as many persons are killed in home accidents each year as in accidents on streets and highways.

There are three important considerations in properly safeguarding a child during his early years: (1) a well-ordered home, free from accident hazards; (2) intelligent guidance as the child learns how to do things safely, not only in the home but in the world outside; and (3) provision for emergencies which call for quick thinking and acting if a serious accident is to be avoided.

Planning the Safe Home

The safe home is also the comfortable and happy home. Proper order and arrangement not only reduce the possibility of accident but considerably lighten the daily housekeeping tasks and help to create a harmonious atmosphere.

Many devoted and conscientious parents will be surprised and perhaps humiliated, when they really go into the matter, to find the kinds of dangers to which they have unconsciously exposed their children. Since any accident in the family may affect the welfare of the children, consider, in the order of their importance the most common types of accidents in the home.

FALLS

Falls, which are first on the list, include those caused by slippery floors, small rugs, and objects left in unexpected places, as well as the falls from steps and stairs, ladders, windows, and porches. These causes of accidents seem so unimportant that it is hard to believe them responsible for the death or serious injury of thousands of persons every year.

In planning the safe home, then, eliminate the highly polished waxed floor, which, though beautiful, is exceedingly dangerous. Small rugs which rumple easily and slide under the foot can be made accident-proof by placing pads under them or by coating them on the underside with a harmless substance which makes them adhere to the floor. Small rugs should never be placed at the top or bottom of a flight of stairs. Wet linoleum is another thing to be avoided, as are splintered or uneven floors.

More falls occur on stairs than anywhere else in the home. It is therefore important to see that the treads are in good repair and that a strong bannister guards those using the steps. Safety gates, which prevent tiny children from crawling up or tumbling down flights of stairs, can be obtained at small cost from any hardware store. Stairs should also be properly lighted. Electric switches at both top and bottom insure convenience and safety.

Falls in bathtubs are frequent, but they may be avoided by placing handholds on the wall. Soap is best kept in a con-

Photo: National Safety Council

Small rugs which rumple easily and slide under foot can be made accident-proof by placing pads under them.

venient container, not in the tub, and shower apparatus and other fixtures must be securely fastened.

Window screens should be provided with strong catches which cannot be unfastened by small fingers. Stout bars protecting the lower section of the window are often necessary when children become large enough to climb about.

The old maxim about a place for everything and everything in its place is a good one to follow in safe housekeeping. Toys left strewn about the floor, objects placed on stairs, and brooms, mops, pails, and other cleaning equipment out of place cause many a stumble and often a serious accident. The rocking chair

used as a stepladder is another menace to home safety. So many good, inexpensive ladders are on the market today that there is little excuse for not having one conveniently at hand. If it is of the collapsible type, inspect the catches frequently to make sure that they are in good repair.

BURNS AND EXPLOSIONS

Burns, scalds, and explosions are next in importance to falls on the home-accident list. In fact, for children under five years of age, burns are the chief cause of accidental death and injury. Care and intelligence are especially needed in handling the many electrical devices which are now found in most homes and which have eliminated much of the drudgery of housekeeping. Reputable manufacturers of such equipment have spent considerable time and money in making it safe for home use. Electric irons, toasters, washing machines, heating pads, and so on are equipped with regulators and other devices which make them accident-proof when ordinary care is used. Trying to put such electrical equipment to some use for which it is not intended, however, usually results seriously, as in the case of two women who put gasoline in an electric washing machine to do some dry cleaning. When the current was turned on a terrific explosion occurred and both women were killed.

Appliances equipped with safety devices, even though they cost a little more, are the most economical in the long run. Purchase only those appliances made by reliable manufacturers and then follow carefully the instructions for their use. All wiring should be done by competent electricians. Both for safety and convenience, wall or floor outlets should be installed if electric appliances are to be used. Lamp sockets are not designed to withstand the strain of connection cords. A frayed cord or one from which the insulation is worn is dangerous and should be replaced by a new one.

Electric fuses are the safety valves of the wiring system and constitute the most important safeguards on the home circuits. Any substitute for a fuse is extremely dangerous. The main-line fuses are installed at the point where the service wires enter the building, usually near the meter. In modern houses there are generally several branch circuits for different parts of the building, each of which has its own fuse. These should be of smaller rating than the main-line fuse. The size of all fuses should be determined by a competent electrician or representative of the electric company. Fuses blow (burn off or melt) when an emergency, such as a short circuit or a damaged appliance, develops on the line. The cause should be located and corrected before a new fuse is installed.

Gas appliances also require frequent inspection and careful use. In selecting equipment it is wise to ask the advice of the gas company, as unsafe appliances are not ordinarily recognized by the purchaser, who must depend largely upon the manufacturer and the dealer for his assurance of safety. Flexible tubing

should never be purchased if a metal pipe connection can be used. Valves and cocks should be adjusted to turn smoothly but *not* easily.

Complete and safe combustion of gas

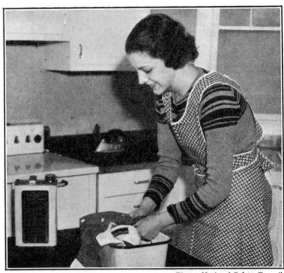

Photo: National Safety Council

PREVENTION IS THE BEST POLICY

When cleaning garments indoors, it is always wisest to use nonflammable cleaning fluids. Then all danger of burns from explosions is avoided.

requires that burners be kept clean, which can easily be done by washing them in boiling water and soda once a month. Burners should be thoroughly dried before using.

Under ordinary conditions, with proper ventilation and proper flue connections, no harm will result from the burning of gas in a room. When much gas is burned in a tightly closed place, however, too much oxygen is taken from the air, it becomes stuffy, and breathing is difficult. Such symptoms as headache, dizziness, nausea, extreme drowsiness, hurried breathing, and rapid heart action may indicate approaching asphyxiation. The person affected should be treated at once and the gas equipment investigated. The public-service company is ready at all times to inspect gas appliances, and it is

"A frayed cord or one from which the insulation is worn is dangerous and should be replaced by a new one."

wise to take advantage of this opportunity frequently.

Any odor of unburned gas, however slight, should receive immediate attention. Rooms in which the odor is particularly strong should not be entered except to remove someone who has been overcome. Never look for a gas leak with a match, candle, or open flame; use only an electric torch when searching in dark places for leaking gas.

The careless use of matches and cigarettes, the careless burning of refuse, and defective stoves and chimneys are the chief causes of home fires. It is advisable for the housekeeper to make periodic inspections of every part of the house to make sure that heating equipment is in good condition; that proper metal containers are supplied for matches, refuse, ashes, and the like; and that open fires are protected by screens.

It is a wise practice to destroy all cloths used in cleaning with oil or wax and not to allow rubbish to accumulate. Spontaneous combustion frequently takes place in heaps of rags, wool, and cotton which have become saturated with oil and in piles of damp hay, straw, and leaves.

Cleaning with gasoline and other flammable liquids is highly dangerous. *Gasoline has no place in the home.* It is the most dangerous commodity in everyday use because its vapor has an explosive quality more dangerous than dynamite. Gasoline itself, though highly flammable, is not explosive. Gasoline vapor, however, may linger for a long time in a container or in the air after the fluid is gone. Nonflammable cleaning fluids, such as carbon tetrachloride, are easy to obtain and there is no need for buying the flammable variety.

ASPHYXIATION AND POISONING

Accidents due to asphyxiation, suffocation, and poisoning can be prevented with ordinary care and forethought. Small children should be kept away from a gas range until they are old enough to understand the danger of turning the cocks without applying a match. Adults, especially women wearing loose sleeves, frequently turn on gas cocks unknowingly. Food that is cooking is sometimes allowed to boil over and extinguish the flame while the gas flows unchecked.

Accidental poisoning usually results from the confusing of bottles. Medicinal poisons, such as iodine, rubbing alcohol, and liniments for external use, should always be isolated. Under no circumstances should they be left standing on shelves, washstands, or bureaus.

Even in the medicine cabinet bottles of poisons should be safeguarded by a double precaution. They should be placed on a certain shelf of the cabinet restricted to poisons and barricaded behind a wire screen, a hinged strip of light wood, or some other obstacle which can easily be made. This barrier need not be difficult to remove; its function is merely to cause anyone groping in the dark to stop and think before getting the wrong bottle.

In addition to warning labels which can easily be seen, all bottles containing poison should have some other signal which will operate in the dark. There are poison labels made with tiny bells attached which serve this purpose. A pin stuck in the cork (point buried) will also act as a warning.

Household disinfectants and cleaning powders should be carefully labeled and kept on high shelves.

The Questions at the end of this article provide a practical and efficient check on whether or not one's house is in order from the standpoint of safety. If you can answer all the questions in the affirmative, the safety of your home will become only a matter of reasonable thought and care each day.

SAFEGUARDING AND TRAINING THE CHILD

When a child is a baby, keeping him safe means keeping him away from dangerous things and dangerous places. As soon as he can understand simple explanations, the reasons for certain safety practices should be given him and his conscious training should begin.

It is unnecessary to describe to the parent how easily a tiny child can get into trouble unless he is constantly watched and protected. Play pens for the house as well as for the porch and yard are a necessity. Placed in one of these, the child can play safely and happily with his toys while his mother goes

Photo: National Safety Council

To avoid shocks caused by grounding electrical current, replace all metal chains in bathroom and kitchen fixtures with cotton or linen cord.

about her activities. In selecting a child's playthings, care should be taken to avoid those which have sharp points or edges, paint which will rub off, or small parts which may be swallowed. As a matter of fact, most toys recommended by responsible dealers are safe, for they have been carefully designed and tested for safety before being put on the market.

As children begin to reason and understand, it is important to encourage them to rely upon themselves. Otherwise they will be defenseless when they encounter new situations. In this connection Margaret Mead, Assistant Curator of Ethnology at the American Museum of Natural

At an early age children should be given lessons in crossing the street safely.

History, has made some interesting observations. Dr. Mead spent six months on the island of Manus, a South Sea community untouched by foreign influence, where she studied the way in which the lagoon dwellers prepare their children for life.

"It is reasonable to ask," writes Dr. Mead, "how these savage people train their children to such a high degree of physical self-sufficiency, for we know that the child of savages is born as unequipped to meet the dangers of the surrounding world as is the child born to the luxury and care of the modern nursery.

"In a village of lagoon dwellers I watched the parents of the Manus tribe train their small children to meet light-heartedly and efficiently the continual challenge of their precarious water existence. And there was much in the education of these lithe, brown savages, in G

string or grass skirt, which could be transplanted with profit into our educational systems.

"In the first place, the parents considered that the physical training of their children was a serious matter, not one to be left to chance nor the casual ministrations of other children—the primitive equivalent of ignorant nursemaids. The baby's first step, its first experience in the water, its first attempt to handle a paddle or a punt, all were carefully supervised by a patient, attentive parent. There was a strong feeling that a good start was all-important—that sure-footedness on land and ease in the water could best be secured if the child learned to make the proper adjustment in the beginning. A child was never encouraged to attempt a new feat too soon, for to have done so would have defeated the parents' aim, that each new skill should be learned correctly from the start. . . .

"The Manus are interested in the child's making the maximum physical adjustment of which he is capable; they have delighted praise and vociferous applause for the baby's first step, cold indifference for the baby who falls down and refuses to take another step. The only way in which the child can recapture the delighted admiration of his elders is to stifle his cries, struggle earnestly to his little bruised legs, and try again. An older child who falls down or makes some other awkward mistake is likely to be actually punished; so that the Manus child doesn't look about to see if mother is near enough to make it worth while to cry, but rather looks about in devout hope that no one has seen his stupid blunder. We, on the other hand, are too anxious to console the stumbler, to surround him with warm arms, kind words, and the promise of a piece of candy and a ride in the car.

"The Manus are exceedingly careful not to frighten their children, either purposely or accidentally. This is one of the reasons that the care of very little children is kept in the parents' hands. The child is not made conscious of continual supervision; no hailstorm of 'don'ts,' 'be-carefuls,' rains upon his playground; he is trained to use his own judgment as much as possible, but he is not allowed to get bad frights when his two-year-old judgment fails.

"The results of this system of training are truly amazing. Children of three are perfectly at home amid the perils of their water world. They can swim as well as they can walk. They can climb up and down the slippery housepiles; they can tread their way sure-footed and quick-footed over the treacherous muddy shallows of the lagoon at low tide. They can be trusted to carry father a glowing cinder to light his pipe without fear that they will fall down and set the light, thatched house afire.

"At about two or two and a half their fathers make them small canoes of their own, tiny craft, four or five feet long, simply shallow wooden shells hollowed out of tree trunks. In these little canoes the children race and play about the lagoon, learning to paddle accurately and to judge distances correctly. . . . About the same time their parents begin training them in handling larger canoes, and it is no uncommon sight to see a child of three or four slowly punting along a twelve-foot canoe, while father sits patiently cross-legged upon the platform.

"When the whole aim of parental training is to make children feel at home in the world, feel self-reliant, easily resourceful, surely confident, they do not try to deter a child by the sayings which are so often upon adults' lips among ourselves: 'Don't do that, you are too little.' 'Your legs aren't long enough.' 'Your hands aren't strong enough.' "

We have quoted at length from this article of Dr. Mead's in *Safety Education* magazine because it expresses so well the cardinal principles of safety education. Caution and timidity are by no means the same thing. To be afraid of getting

Photo: Cleveland Public Schools

Teach children to watch for cars coming out of driveways, especially when they are on roller skates or bicycles or playing with other wheeled toys.

hurt is a bad thing to instill in the child's mind. The inevitable bumps, bruises, and scratches of childhood bring their own lessons.

The desire to safeguard others and to save the people who love him from anxiety should be encouraged in the child. If there are younger brothers and sisters, the task of training him in safe habits is made easier because he will want to be trusted to take care of them and not lead them into dangerous practices. The child's affection and thoughtfulness for others may be appealed to in nearly every

FLAMMABLE- **NON-FLAMMABLE**
EXPLOSIVE VAPOR   **-SAFE**

Gasoline should never be used in the home, but such nonflammable cleaning fluids as carbon tetrachloride may be easily obtained and used with absolute safety.

instance. Many serious falls may be avoided, and, incidentally, children may be trained to a sense of order by showing them how easily they may hurt some other member of the family if they leave their things around or move furniture out of its accustomed place and do not put it back again.

A good deal of patience and kindly guidance is demanded of a mother in teaching lessons of safety without inhibiting curiosity and the sense of adventure. Unless children are in actual danger, let them investigate things for themselves, answering their questions and explaining carefully why they must not play with such fascinating objects as shining, nickel-plated stoves, gaily colored kitchen utensils which may contain hot or harmful

liquids, knives, electric cords, lamps, and the many other objects about the home which naturally arouse their interest.

As children grow older and begin to explore the world outside they will need to develop a whole new set of habits to protect them from the greatest single cause of accidents to young and old— the automobile. This hazard is by no means confined to the city; in fact, country roads, where traffic is not regulated and cars travel at high speed, may be even more dangerous.

A good way to teach children safe conduct on the street is to go with them to the corner and let them stand there for a while watching the traffic signals and the policeman. Show them that automobiles and other vehicles keep to the right, so that in crossing the street people must look first to the left and then to the right to see what is coming. Let them talk to the policeman, their friend and protector.

When they get home ask them what they have noticed. The next time they are playing with other children suggest that they play a traffic game. One child may be a policeman; others, the automobiles and trucks; and others, the pedestrians. The automobiles run down the room to the edge of the rug, which is the curb, where they must stop at the traffic light or policeman's signal. The pedestrians, too, must put on their brakes at the curb and wait until it is safe for them to cross. Explain that it is easier for the children to stop quickly than for an automobile, which must travel at least its own length before stopping.

One of the most dangerous of children's habits is that of suddenly darting

A LESSON IN STREET SAFETY

As part of the work in safety education, many schools carry on demonstrations and drill in safety procedures, especially in regard to the everyday problem of crossing the street.

into the street, chasing a ball or running after each other, or merely crossing to the other side. Show them how hard it is for an automobile driver to avoid them when they do this. Another way to teach children about traffic is to let them build with blocks a model of a street crossing, putting in the traffic lights, the car lines, and all the other things they notice when out walking. A model like this may be used to illustrate many street hazards, including the dangerous right and left turns and the danger of darting out from behind or in front of a parked car. Country children should be taught to walk on the left side of the highway, facing oncoming traffic.

In this kind of training it is wiser first to find out the hazards your children are likely to meet rather than to inhibit them with general prohibitions. If a railroad runs through your neighborhood or if there is a river, a dangerous stream, a quarry, or some exciting place which inevitably attracts children, visit the spot with them and explain why it is not a safe place to play.

Mothers and fathers who have devoted considerable time and thought to training children in safe habits are sometimes upset by the realization that another serious problem in safety training remains to be solved. The realization comes, for example, when two-year-old daughter, having learned that as a matter of safety she should put her toys away in a box, discovers that mother has herself endangered life and limb by putting a pile of things on the stairs "to take up when she goes." Or it may be that father, who has given careful lessons in street safety, is detected dodging recklessly across the street with complete disregard of corners and signals. Plausible excuses are usu-

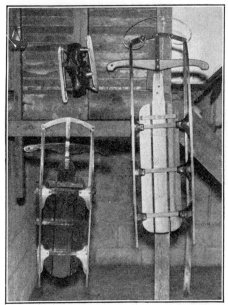

Photo: Cleveland Public Schools

Sleds and skates should be hung where they will not cause falls or injuries.

ally in order on such occasions, but mother and father, if they are honest with themselves, must admit that the good results of many hours of patient training are undone by a single instance of their own carelessness and that "it is unwise to be heedless ourselves when we are giving advice to others."

WHAT TO DO IN AN EMERGENCY

A knowledge of what to do in case of accident will often prevent a bad situation from becoming worse and may be the means of saving a life. It is therefore important that each member of the family be familiar with simple first-aid treatment and know how to secure help as quickly as possible in the case of serious injuries.

Scratches and Abrasions (skin broken). Do not wash a scratch or abrasion with soap and water. If the wound is visibly dirty, use rubbing alcohol for cleansing. Using clean gauze, begin at the edge of the wound and wash away from it, never toward it. When it is dry, paint it with iodine. Let the iodine dry and then apply a sterile dressing and bandage so that it remains firmly in place. Adhesive tape may be used to prevent the dressing from slipping, but never put adhesive tape directly on a wound.

If the scratch or abrasion is apparently clean, paint it with iodine and apply the dressing as above. Tincture of iodine as purchased from the drugstore is stronger than necessary. Have the druggist dilute it to half strength (3½ per cent) or dilute it at home by adding an equal amount of rubbing alcohol. The bottle containing iodine should have a glass or rubber stopper and should be kept tightly closed at all times when not in actual use, otherwise the alcohol evaporates and the iodine becomes too strong. Do not use iodine near the eyes or body cavities.

Bumps and Bruises (skin not broken). Apply cold wet compresses of gauze.

Cuts. If the cut is shallow and apparently clean, dry the edges lightly with sterile gauze, apply iodine, allow the cut to dry, and bandage it lightly, just to keep it covered.

If the cut is visibly dirty, cleanse it gently with gauze or cotton soaked with rubbing alcohol. Be careful never to touch the wound with the fingers or to touch the surface of the cotton or gauze or bandage that is to be next to the wound. Cover the cut with sterile gauze compresses and bandage. It is best to have all but the most superficial wounds examined by a doctor.

Splinters. Small splinters may be re- moved by "teasing" them out with a needle that has been held a moment in a flame and then cooled. Paint with iodine the spot where the splinter was imbedded. Do not attempt to remove a splinter that is deeply imbedded. See a doctor.

Strains and Sprains. Apply cold, wet compresses and rest the injured part.

Foreign Body in the Eye. Do not rub. Close the eye. Grasp the lashes of the upper lid and pull it out and down over the lower lid. This gives the tears a better chance to wash the foreign body to the inside corner of the eye, where it can easily be lifted out with the corner of a sterile bandage or handkerchief. Hold the upper lid in this position for several seconds and repeat the operation if necessary. Wash the eye, using an eye- cup, with boric acid solution (teaspoon- ful of boric acid powder in a glass of warm water). Never attempt to remove an imbedded body, but consult a doctor at once.

Foreign Body in the Ear. In all cases consult a doctor.

Blisters. Apply a small amount of iodine to the point at the edge of the blister where it is to be opened. Steri- lize a needle in an open flame. Be care- ful not to touch the end of the needle after it is sterilized. Puncture the blister at its edge and apply gentle pressure to its outside margins, gently pressing out the water or blood. Apply a sterile dressing.

If the blister is very extensive, or if there is evidence of inflammation or in- fection, a doctor should be consulted.

Choking, or Object in Nasal Passage. Do not try to remove an object from the throat by reaching for it unless a portion of it still remains in the mouth. Marbles, candy, and other small objects frequently lodge at the entrance to the windpipe. These are out of reach of everything ex- cept expert hands. A sharp blow on the back may dislodge the object. Small chil-

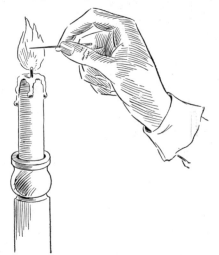

"Small splinters may be removed by 'teasing' them out with a needle that has been held a moment in a flame and then cooled."

dren are often relieved by holding them by the feet, head down, and shaking them vigorously.

If an object becomes lodged in the nasal passage, close the free passage with the fingers and blow in the mouth. If this does not dislodge the object consult a doctor at once. Do not probe for the object, as severe complications may result from this practice.

Burns and Scalds. Burns are classified according to the degree or depth to which the body tissues are injured. This classification should be remembered, as the treatment depends upon the degree of the burn: first degree—skin reddened; second degree—skin blistered; third degree —deeper destruction of tissue, as charring or cooking.

For first-degree burns (skin reddened) apply baking soda (in water) or any good burn ointment. Cover the burned area with sterile gauze. Tannic acid is now used extensively in the treatment of burns. It may be obtained in the form of a jelly, which should be spread on sterile gauze and applied.

Bottles of poison in the medicine cabinet should be well marked so as to avoid the tragedies that all too frequently result from groping in the dark and getting the wrong bottle.

If the skin is broken, take every precaution, as the danger of infection is great. Place the patient in a physician's hands as soon as possible. Do not try to remove clothing that adheres to the skin. Cut around it and leave the part that adheres for the doctor to remove. If there is delay in getting a doctor to treat second- and third-degree burns, a dressing may be made by using either one tablespoonful of baking soda or about two tablespoonfuls of Epsom salts to a pint of warm water—preferably water that has been boiled. *The dressings should be kept moist and warm until medical aid is obtained.* Tannic acid jelly spread on sterile gauze may also be applied.

Never apply iodine to a burn nor use absorbent cotton next to a burn. Large blisters should be opened by a doctor.

Burns caused by an acid, alkali, or any other chemical *should be washed immediately and continuously with large quantities of water,* preferably not too cold, until the chemical is thoroughly washed away. Then apply an ointment dressing and consult a physician at once.

Powder burns (from exploding firecrackers, firearms, and so on) should always be examined by a physician so that he can give proper treatment to the injury and administer tetanus antitoxin.

Sunburn. Severe sunburn is dangerous. Application of olive oil, cocoa butter, a good burn ointment, or tannic acid jelly before exposure is advisable. The same remedies may be used for the treatment of sunburn. In severe cases a wet dressing of Epsom salts solution is excellent. If blistering is extensive, a dressing of sterile gauze should be used. If burns cover a considerable area, or if a fever develops, a physician should be consulted.

Nosebleed. Usually no treatment is necessary. If the bleeding continues, have the patient sit up with the head thrown slightly back, breathing through the mouth. Loosen the collar and anything that is tight around the neck.

Pressing the nostrils together firmly often stops the bleeding and gives opportunity for a clot to form. This pressure must be applied for at least four or five minutes to be effective. Apply cold, wet compresses over the nose and over the back of the neck. The patient should avoid blowing his nose for a few hours. If these measures do not stop the bleeding in a few minutes, a physician is needed.

Dislocations and Fractures. Great care must be taken to avoid creating a compound fracture (bone piercing the skin) in cases of simple fracture (skin not pierced). Do not move a person who seems to have suffered a fracture or dislocation. Keep him warm and as comfortable as possible until the doctor arrives or until a first-aid expert can apply the proper splint. *This is most important,* as minor injuries often develop into serious ones because of improper treatment.

A compound fracture results when the broken bone pierces the skin. A simple fracture is one in which the skin is not pierced. Great care must be taken to avoid creating a compound fracture in cases of simple fractures. Do not try to move the injured person, but make him as comfortable as possible until the doctor arrives.

Shock and Fainting. Some degree of shock is present in almost all injuries. It is characterized by paleness, rapid pulse, sweating, thirst, shallow breathing, and low blood pressure. Send for a doctor at once, but do not wait for him to arrive before beginning treatment. Use hot-water bottles and blankets to keep the patient warm. A light hot-water bottle lying over the heart acts as a special stimulant to that organ. If possible, place the patient's head lower than his body. If he is able to swallow, give him half a teaspoonful of aromatic spirits of ammonia in half a glass of water (preferably hot water), repeating the dose in half an hour. Hot coffee, hot tea, and hot milk may be used as stimulants.

In cases of fainting, the patient should have plenty of air, while the face and chest are sprinkled with cold water. Stimulants suggested in the case of shock may be used. Keep the patient lying on

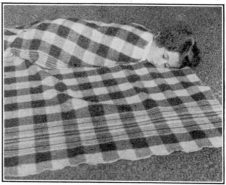

When putting out a clothing fire, wrap victim in a blanket, heavy rug, curtain, or coat. Cover neck first. Make him drop to the floor and roll over slowly.

his back with the head lower than the body.

Infected Wounds. Always consult a physician at once.

Sunstroke or Heat Exhaustion. Consult a physician at once.

Insect Bites. A paste made of baking soda or a compress moistened with ammonia water gives relief.

Animal Bites. Wash the wound to

remove the saliva of the animal. (This is the exception to the rule not to wash wounds with water.) Holding the wound under a running tap is an excellent way to wash it. Dry it with clean gauze, apply tincture of iodine, let it dry, and dress as any other wound. *Always consult a physician at once.* He will need to give the wound itself further treatment, and he will either ad-

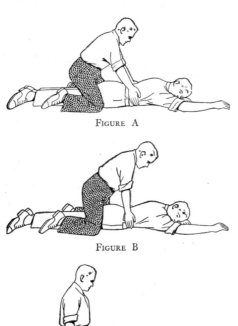

FIGURE A

FIGURE B

FIGURE C

minister the Pasteur or vaccine treatment himself or send the patient to the proper place to receive such treatment if he believes it necessary.

Poisoning. Poison cases demand immediate action. Always call a doctor at once but in the meantime give first aid. It is not necessary to remember a long list of antidotes; use the simple measures always at hand.

A poison diluted with a large amount of fluid is never absorbed as rapidly as when it is in a concentrated form. Induce vomiting repeatedly until the fluid is as clear as when swallowed. Use any of the following emetics: soapsuds (any ordinary soap), salt water, soda water (baking soda), lukewarm water, or milk (particularly in corrosive poisons).

When the stomach is well washed out the antidote may be given if it is known and on hand, but do not waste time getting an antidote before washing out the stomach.

The treatment for food poisoning, popularly called ptomaine poisoning, is the same as for drug poisoning.

Asphyxiation; Drowning; Electric Shock. See *Artificial Respiration.*

Escape from a Burning Building. Speed and clear thinking are absolutely necessary. Cover the nose and mouth with a wet cloth or handkerchief, as this keeps out some of the irritating fumes and lessens the danger of inhaling flames. The danger of carbon monoxide gas poisoning is present at every fire. Crawl to the nearest exit, keeping as close to the floor as possible. If caught on the upper floor of a burning building be very careful about opening doors into hallways or stairways. Superheated air may have collected there, and one breath may cause death. Furthermore, opening doors and windows makes a draft and increases the danger. Feel the door with your hand and if it is hot go to an open window immediately. If you can get out safely, do so. If not, call for help and wait. Jump from a window only as a last resort. A rope made from sheets and blankets securely tied at one end may be used to slide to safety, but this should not be attempted unless absolutely necessary.

Putting Out a Clothing Fire. Never run or remain standing. Wrap a blanket, heavy rug, curtain, or coat about the body (around the neck first), drop to the floor, and roll over slowly. Try not to inhale any of the flames. Put the left hand on the right shoulder and the right hand on the left shoulder and pull the arms against the face for protection. If there is water near at hand, douse yourself with it and roll in the spilled water on the floor. If a blanket or similar material is not available, lie down, roll over slowly, and use the hands to beat out the flames. If the clothing of another person takes fire, use similar measures.

Artificial Respiration. The prone pressure method of artificial respiration described should be used in cases of suspended respiration from all causes— drowning, electric shock, carbon monoxide poisoning, injuries, and so on. Delay of even one minute in the application of the method may lose a life. Follow the instructions * even if the patient appears dead. Continue the artificial respiration until natural breathing is restored or until a physician declares that *rigor mortis* (stiffening of the body) has set in. Success has come even after three and one-half hours of effort!

1. Lay the patient on his belly, one arm extended directly overhead, the other arm bent at the elbow, and with the face turned outward and resting on the hand or forearm so that the nose and mouth are free for breathing. (See Figure A.)

2. Kneel, straddling the patient's thighs with your knees placed at such a distance from the hip bones as will allow you to assume the position shown in Figure A. Place the palms of the hands on the small of the back with the fingers resting on the ribs, the little finger just touching the lowest rib, with the thumb and fingers in a natural position, and the tips of the fingers just out of sight. (See Figure A.)

3. With the arms held straight, swing forward slowly so that the weight of your body is gradually brought to bear upon the patient. The shoulder should be directly over the heel of the hand at the end of the forward swing. (See Figure B.) Do not bend your elbows. This operation should take about two seconds.

4. Now immediately swing backward so as to remove the pressure completely, thus returning to the position in Figure C.

5. After two seconds, swing forward again. Thus repeat deliberately, twelve to fifteen times a minute, the double movement of compression and release, a complete respiration in four or five seconds.

6. Continue the artificial respiration without interruption until natural breathing is restored (if necessary, four hours or longer) or until a physician declares the patient is dead or until definite *rigor mortis* (stiffening of the body) sets in.

7. As soon as this artificial respiration

* Agreed upon by a special committee of national organizations and persons appointed by the United States Public Health Service.

has been started and while it is being continued, an assistant should loosen any tight clothing about the patient's neck, chest, or waist. Keep the patient warm. Do not give any liquids whatever by mouth until the patient is fully conscious.

8. To avoid strain on the heart when the patient revives, he should be kept lying down and not allowed to stand or sit up. If the doctor has not arrived by the time the patient has revived, he should be given some stimulant, such as one teaspoonful of aromatic spirits of ammonia in a small glass of water or a drink of hot coffee or tea. The patient should be kept warm.

9. Resuscitation should be carried on at the nearest possible point to where the patient received his injuries. This means removing the patient from the dangerous position by breaking the contact with live electrical equipment (if a case of electric shock) or from the gaseous atmosphere (if asphyxiation). In breaking contacts with live electrical equipment, protect yourself by shutting off the power or, in removing the victim, use a dry piece of wood or other nonconductor. He should not be moved again until he is breathing normally of his own volition and then moved only in a lying position. Should it be necessary, due to extreme weather conditions or other factors, to move the patient before he is breathing normally, resuscitation should be carried on during the time he is being moved, if practicable.

10. A brief return of natural respiration is not a certain indication for stopping the resuscitation. Not infrequently the patient, after a temporary recovery of respiration, stops breathing again. The patient must be watched and, if natural breathing stops, artificial respiration should be resumed at once.

11. In carrying out resuscitation it may be necessary to change the operator. This change must be made without losing the rhythm of respiration. By this procedure no confusion results at the time of change of operator and a regular rhythm is kept up.

CONTENTS OF HOUSEHOLD FIRST-AID KIT

It is a good plan to have a first-aid kit in or near the medicine cabinet. The kit should be arranged in a neat and orderly fashion and the packages of supplies should be small rather than large. For example, it is wiser to purchase twelve one-inch compresses on adhesive than a one-yard roll of one-inch bandage; and three-inch gauze squares of bandage are better than rolls of three-inch bandage. A roll of adhesive tape is advisable. The kit should also contain tincture of iodine (cut to half strength with alcohol), aromatic spirits of ammonia, vaseline or any good burn ointment, baking soda, rubbing alcohol, boric acid, absorbent cotton, scissors, and toothpicks or applicators.

QUESTIONS

Check up on the safety of your home by asking yourself these questions:
1. Are safety matches used?
2. Are matches kept in metal containers placed well out of reach of small children?

3. Are chimneys and flues inspected and thoroughly cleaned and repaired annually?
4. Are stoves and furnaces clean and in proper repair?
5. Are ashes, oily rags, papers, and other

flammable rubbish placed in metal containers?

6. Are closets, attic, cellar, and so on inspected regularly and kept free of rubbish?

7. Have you at least one fire extinguisher? Is it charged yearly?

8. Are wall or floor outlets provided for electrical appliances?

9. Are electrical and gas appliances inspected frequently?

10. Do you know the proper fuses for use in your home wiring system and have you a supply on hand?

11. Do you prohibit the storage or use of gasoline and other flammable liquids in the house?

12. Are fire escapes and other exits unobstructed?

13. Do you know the location of the nearest fire-alarm box and how to turn in an alarm?

14. Are stair treads, bannisters, and porch railings in good repair?

15. Are stairs well lighted?

16. Are areaways, cellar entrances, and so on protected by railings to prevent falls?

17. Are pads or other devices used to prevent small rugs from slipping?

18. Is a good stepladder part of the household equipment?

19. Are barriers placed across lower sections of windows to protect small children?

20. Are screens equipped 'with safety catches?

21. Is there a handhold near the bathtub?

22. Is a special shelf in the medicine chest set aside for bottles containing poison? Are these medicines labeled plainly? Is a barrier placed in front of the shelf?

23. Are cleaning powders, lye, insecticides, and other harmful substances kept on high shelves and plainly labeled?

24. Are firearms unloaded before being brought into the house, and are they kept out of reach of children?

READING REFERENCES

For Adults

Cobb, Walter R., *Everyday First Aid* (Appleton-Century).

Delano, Jane A., *American Red Cross Textbook on Home Hygiene and Care of the Sick* (Blakiston). Fourth edition, revised and rewritten under supervision of the Public Health Nursery and Home Hygiene Service.

Dougherty, Thomas F., and Kearney, P. W., *Fire* (Putnam).

Good Housekeeping Institute, *Safety in the Home* (Good Housekeeping Institute).

Holbrook, Stewart, *Let Them Live* (Macmillan).

National Safety Council, *Safe at Home and First Aid Reminders* (National Safety Council, Chicago, Ill.).

U. S. Department of Commerce, Bureau of Standards, *Safety for the Household* (Circular No. 397).

For Children

Barbour, Ralph H., *For Safety* (Appleton-Century).

Brinkerhoff, George I., and Rowe, Celena, *Safety First Stories* (Longmans).

Bryce, Catherine T., *Safe-way Club* (Nelson).

Buckley, Horace M., and others, *Road to Safety*, Volumes One to Six (American Book).

Cannon, Fanny V., *Rehearsal for Safety* (Dutton). Plays.

Fox, Edith K., *Roller Bears and the Safe-way Tribe* (Macmillan).

Gentles, Harry W., and Betts, George H., *Habits for Safety* (Bobbs-Merrill).

Hader, Berta and Elmer, *Stop, Look, Listen* (Longmans).

Leaf, Munro, *Safety Can Be Fun* (Stokes).

Roberts, Mildred M., *Safety Town Stories* (Lyons & Carnahan).

Stack, Herbert J., and Schwartz, Esther T., *Safety Every Day* (Noble).

Waldo, Lillian M., *Safety First for Little Folks* (Scribner).

THE NURSERY SCHOOL AND THE CHILD

Christine M. Heinig

Nursery schools are among the more recent developments in primary education, but they are meeting with widespread enthusiasm on the part of parents because they fill a real need. The objectives and methods of nursery schools are clearly set forth in this article. The author is Principal, Kindergarten Training College, Melbourne, Australia.

THERE is less crying in a single morning among twenty children in a nursery school than among two or three children at home. Nursery-

Photo: H. Armstrong Roberts

It is valuable for children to be with playmates who are older and also with those who are younger than themselves.

school children are usually reluctant to leave school at noon or at three oclock, and they frequently express regret because there are no school sessions on Saturday and Sunday. A place where

purposes are carried out with interest and remembered with pleasure is certain to aid the child's development in every aspect.

The years 1919–1925 are credited with the establishment of the first nursery schools in America. Interest in scientific training for very young children was by no means new at that time, however. The nursery school as an institution organized for the care and guidance of children was the result of earlier educational developments in America and Europe.

England organized the first nursery schools in accordance with the English Educational Act of 1918, which provided for the education of children under the age of five as a part of the public-education program. America was also studying child development, and by 1920 four nursery schools had been established in this country. In the following decade there was an increase of approximately two hundred and fifty such schools.

Age of Attendance

The nursery-school program is planned for children from eighteen months to four or five years of age. The upper age limit is usually determined by the age at which the local kindergartens accept children. Where there are no kindergartens, the nursery school usually includes kindergarten activities for the older children. There is no set requirement for the admission age. The age range is usually determined by the facilities of the particular school. If there is a wide age range in the enrollment, the children are grouped into smaller units, with not more than a twenty-four-month age span in each unit. At the lower age level it is desirable to include in one group children from eighteen months to thirty months. If there are no very young children in the school, children from two to four years of age may be grouped together; children from three to five years; and so on. Homogeneous grouping according to the abilities of the children is the most desirable. Children should also have an opportunity to be with children who are older and also with those who are younger than themselves, and such experiences are provided occasionally in the day's program of the nursery school.

THE DAILY PROGRAM

Children come to the nursery school each morning at about half-past eight. A parent usually brings the child and reports to the school any physical or emotional upset which has occurred at home and which might influence the child's behavior during the school day. Before the child is admitted to the group, an examination is made by a nurse, a physician, or a qualified member of the staff, to determine whether or not the child is in good physical condition and to dis-

cover symptoms of any communicable disease. This careful inspection, followed, when necessary, by the exclusion of a child who shows any signs of illness, minimizes the danger of group infection.

After examination the child enters the play group, usually on an outdoor playground, and plays until about eleven o'clock. At this time he comes indoors, washes his hands, and rests about fifteen minutes on a mat or a bed. Dinner is served at eleven-thirty.

The noon meal is the main meal of the day, and during the winter months cod-liver oil is usually given as a part of this meal. The diet is planned by a nutritionist who works closely with parents and physicians in determining what foods are best for children of this age. In consultation with the mother, she works out a twenty-four-hour diet for each child.

During the morning play, a serving of fruit juice or tomato juice is given. Frequent opportunities to drink water are provided, and a toilet room is accessible. Children under three years of age and any others who need it are also given a mid-morning rest. Dinner occupies from thirty to forty-five minutes. The children sit at tables suited to their size, four or five children and one teacher eating together.

Afternoon naps come immediately after dinner. Sticky pudding and other traces of the meal are washed from small faces, toileting is cared for, and clothing is removed. In some nursery schools the children remove only their outer clothing; in others, they sleep in regulation night clothing. For the afternoon nap, canvas cot beds are provided. They are supplied with sheets as well as warm pads and covers when necessary. No pillows are used, since it is generally conceded by specialists that a flat surface promotes the best posture and the most complete relaxation. The children are in bed for about two hours. Upon waking and dressing, about two-thirty o'clock, those children who need it are served a light lunch of milk and graham crackers, sandwiches, or fruit. At three o'clock the children are usually called for and taken home. If they stay longer at school, they play out-of-doors or, if the weather requires it, in the playroom.

During the afternoon rest period and also when the parents call for the children, parent-teacher conferences are held. Special procedures used by the teacher in guiding the behavior of a child are explained to the mother, and together they plan for subsequent treatment. Thus the school and the home share in the child's care and training.

The program and organization in various nursery schools differ. In all schools, however, the first consideration is to arrange the daily schedule so that it best fits the physiological needs of the children. For example, if the school is in session only in the mornings, it dismisses in time to permit the children to arrive home for an early dinner. If the children stay through the afternoon, however, supper is usually served them before leaving, so that their meal may be unhurried and on time. Play activities are interfered with as little as possible, and physical and mental examinations are not allowed to interfere with routine procedures. A regular schedule for eating, resting, and toileting is established, and other activities are given secondary consideration.

The regular teachers carry on these play activities, so far as possible, so that the play periods will not be broken up by

Photo: Kirkland

DINNER HOUR IN THE CRANE NURSERY SCHOOL, CHICAGO

"Dinner occupies from thirty to forty-five minutes. The children sit at tables suited to their size, three or four children and one teacher eating together."

getting ready for special teachers at definite hours.

ACTIVITIES

The activities in a nursery school are as varied as the children's individuality and the richness of the environment will permit. In general, there is a great deal of physical activity, such as walking, running, jumping, climbing, riding on wheeled toys, swinging, balancing, hanging, sliding, and pulling.

There is manipulative play with sand, water, clay, dirt, gravel, hammer and nails, blocks, beads, fitting and sorting games, and small toys. Informal materials for a multitude of activities include empty spools, boxes, baskets, seeds, pieces of linoleum or odd lots of tiles, clothespins, and papers.

There is painting with liquid watercolor paint and large brushes; and drawing with pencils or with large, bright-colored crayons. There is doll play with dolls and miniature housekeeping equipment. There are language and literature experiences with people, picture books, and stories.

The music experiences include rhythmic expression in singing, listening to music sung or played, and the spontaneous expression of song and rhythm as an accompaniment of various activities.

The children also engage in housekeeping activities, actually carrying on some of the work of the school, such as serving each other with water or food; setting the tables; helping to prepare the food by stringing beans, using the meat grinder, and making sandwiches; clean-ing up various kinds of spills; putting away and caring for play materials; participating in the care of pets, flowers, and plants; and helping to dress and undress themselves and otherwise care for their needs.

EQUIPMENT AND ITS USE

In keeping with the results of educational research, nursery-school equipment is planned to provide children with many opportunities for physical development, social co-operation, self-help, and mental development. The furnishings are therefore scaled down to the size of the children and so far as possible all equipment is placed within their easy reach. Supply cupboards are low and have open shelves; small toilets and wash bowls are provided; and wash cloths, towels, combs, and hand brushes are hung low. All individual equipment, such as towels, combs, lockers, blankets, and chairs, is marked with name-picture tags, and each child easily learns to recognize his own. All the furnishings are decidedly attractive in design, color, and size.

Opportunities are provided for specific types of development by means of individual pieces of equipment and by the simplicity, durability, stability, and purposefulness characterizing the equipment.

Most of such equipment is as well suited to the home as to the school; and much of it can be constructed by parents or carpenters from such materials as crates, packing boxes of wood or paper board, tin cans, wooden spools of all sizes, tiles, woodcuttings, fruit hampers, baskets, wallpaper-sample books, mill ends of cloth, sand, clay, gravel, sawdust, and the like. These abound around the home or they may be obtained free, as waste materials, from stores and factories.

All nursery schools have some type of climbing apparatus, a sandbox, planks and boards, large-size packing boxes for huts or cages for pets, wagons, pedaled wheel toys, swings, doll equipment, and the usual materials furnished in schools to satisfy the literature, music, art, nature, and manipulative interests of the children. Equipment constructed for play involving the larger body muscles is made with adjustable features to allow for frequent changes in use. By change of position a climbing ladder is con-verted into a ladder for crawling or hanging. Jouncing boards are used as balance boards, seesaws, slides, walks, or gangplanks. Most of this equipment is portable, so that it may be used either indoors or outdoors and in a variety of ways. The wood used in its construction is well seasoned, tough, and non-splintering. All corners and edges are rounded for purposes of safety and wear.

The difference between regular-school and nursery-school play lies chiefly in the way in which the children use the materials rather than in the kinds of materials. Mechanical toys are conspicuously absent, and in their place are materials with which the child creates his own toys and expresses his own ideas.

Photo: Kirkland

MANIPULATIVE PLAY BY CHILDREN IN THE CRANE NURSERY SCHOOL

The activities of the nursery school include manipulative play with blocks, beads, fitting and sorting games, and many kinds of small toys.

MAKING HALLOWEEN DECORATIONS, CRANE NURSERY SCHOOL

Children in the nursery school are encouraged to express their own ideas through various types of creative activities.

The function of the teacher is: (1) to provide an environment rich in educational values, (2) to supervise the children and thus avoid possible dangers and too much fatigue, (3) to protect the group from the domination of one child, and (4) to act as friend and counsellor to both the child and his parents. The rest of the program is centered around the self-initiated activities of the children. In this well-planned environment, children are not at a loss to know what to do, but the teacher must be resourceful enough so that when necessary she can stimulate the children to awakened interest in the environment. She accomplishes this by a rearrangement of materials and equipment, by introducing a dramatic element through a verbal suggestion, by providing a nature experience, or by a short excursion.

Through their spontaneous and guided interests and activities, children gain a great deal—physical growth and vigor, intellectual interests and development, emotional stability, and the ability to know and respect each other, to play and to share with each other. Children in nursery schools are happy, busy children.

STAFF AND METHODS OF WORK

Each child enrolled in a nursery school is observed and studied by the staff, which is usually composed of specialists, including trained teachers, a nurse, and a nutritionist. When not included on the staff as full-time members, the services of a pediatrician, a psychologist, a sociologist, a psychiatrist, and a parent educator are frequently arranged for on a part-time basis. After observing individual children, each specialist contributes suggestions and recommendations regarding the child's present and future needs. The nursery-school teacher carries out the program thus jointly decided upon by the staff. Parents have the benefit of this complete study and are kept informed as to their child's needs and progress through visits to the school, consultations with the teacher or specialist, and home visits by the staff. Records are also kept by the school and by the parent and are available daily to both school and parent. Sleep, elimination, and food records are kept in every nursery school, while records for noting regularity and progress in habit formation, behavior, abilities, food intake, and capacities of various kinds are kept in many schools. The goal is for home and school together to provide a continuous and beneficial program for the child and his associates.

AIMS OF THE NURSERY SCHOOL

All normal parents want their children to have the best possible opportunities for developing to their maximum abilities. They want them to learn how to get along with other people, how to be good leaders, and how and when to be good co-operators. They want them to develop the ability to think out ways of accomplishing their goals, with a resulting sense of legitimate power and enthusiasm. An increasing number of parents desire these opportunities for their children seriously enough to take the trouble to find out how to obtain them. They realize that parenthood has become a profession. One of the fundamental purposes of the nursery school is to help parents understand the needs of their children and to guide them in recognizing their responsibility in setting patterns of behavior which their children will imitate.

FOUR GROUPS OF NURSERY SCHOOLS

Nursery schools are of four classifications, as follows:

1. Schools organized chiefly for the education of children and their parents. This group includes those schools which relieve parents who are employed outside the home and those which supplement the care provided by the home. Most of these schools are privately or philanthropically supported, although in some public-school systems nursery schools are provided.

2. Nursery schools which function as demonstration and training centers for students in teacher-training institutions; for students in home-management courses of colleges and universities; and for students majoring in special fields, such as psychology, physical growth,

and sociology. Observation classes are also provided for pupils in the upper elementary and high-school grades and for medical nurses, nursemaids, and parents. Some nursery schools embrace several of these objectives.

3. Nursery schools which provide laboratories for research study of the behavior and development of normal children. Until these laboratories were organized, information on young children was obtained only through a limited number of studies, since there was no place where groups of normal young children could be studied as they played naturally.

4. Federal Emergency Nursery Schools, which were first organized in 1933 under the auspices of the Federal Emergency Relief Administration and with the sponsorship of the United States Office of Education. The value of these schools in offering relief employment to needy teachers and other workers was only secondary to the opportunities for education, feeding, and general mental and physical health which were made available to hundreds of young children for whom the public schools heretofore have not provided. The program was also important in that it gave widespread emphasis to the value of the nursery school. This relief program was expanded in the summer and autumn of 1934 and emergency nursery schools were opened in almost every state in the Union. It was anticipated that with the aid of local support many of these schools would be maintained after relief funds had been withdrawn. Parents of the children enrolled

responded to the program with enthusiasm, and in many communities this emergency nursery-school program stimulated parents to make an effort to reopen kindergartens which had been closed.

ENROLLMENT

The average number of children enrolled per trained teacher is ten. Eight,

Photo: H. Armstrong Roberts

Neighborhood parents may organize a play group, with the group meeting each day of the week in a different yard.

however, is considered an ideal number, and it is always desirable to have a sufficient enrollment to require two teachers, so that the children are never left unsupervised. The length of the school day varies from two and one-half hours to twelve hours. One school in New York offers twenty-four-hour service, and several summer institutes enroll children on a twenty-four-hour basis. Most nursery schools are in session five

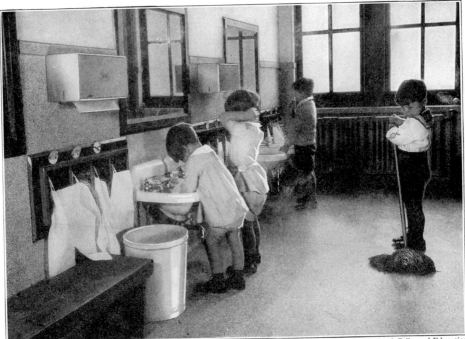

Photo: National College of Education

CLEANING UP AFTER OUTDOOR PLAY

Equipment fitted to the size of the children encourages the formation of right habits. All individual
equipment is marked with name-picture tags for ready identification.

days a week, but those housed in welfare centers may be in session six or
seven days.

It is not an exaggeration to say that
almost every nursery school maintains a
waiting list for entrance. This is especially true of emergency nursery schools,
which have no tuition charge. Many
nursery schools give guidance in child
care and training to those parents whose
children do not gain admittance.

WHAT PARENTS CAN DO WHEN NO
NURSERY SCHOOL IS AVAILABLE

If there is no nursery school in the
community, parents can provide the

educational opportunities of such a
school in various ways. First of all,
they can supplement their own understanding of children's needs and methods of guidance through individual
study or through organizing a child-
study group of neighborhood parents.
Such study is both stimulating and
helpful, and parent study groups frequently organize a nursery school in
their community. Study-group outlines,
with reading references to guide the
study, are available from several sources.
(See the Reading References at the end
of this article.) Courses in child study
are offered by the extension service of

state departments of education, by the National Council of Parent Education, the National Child Study Association, and the National Association of Parents and Teachers. Such courses include practical problems in child guidance and training. Tuition is often free or is set at a minimum fee.

Back-yard or roof play groups offer another substitute for nursery schools. Where funds are limited, such play groups are especially practicable, because the groups are small and play equipment is the major expense item. When organized and conducted by trained workers, these groups offer supervised social play for the children. If the parents take turns in assisting a trained worker, the play group also becomes a training center for parents. The neighborhood parents themselves may organize such a play group, with each family sponsoring it on their own premises for a period of time, or the group might meet each day of the week in a different yard. Through the friendship thus built up, parents will be able to co-operate in solving the many problems that arise to cause friction when goals, standards, and daily

programs vary from home to home. Supervised play groups are always more successful when conducted in conjunc-

Photo: H. Armstrong Roberts

Back-yard play groups offer another substitute for nursery schools.

tion with study groups. The situations that arise in the play group vitalize and stimulate the group study.

SUMMARY

The nursery school is a growing institution. Its program provides opportunities for young children to live wholesomely, happily, and purposefully and to form the habits conducive to such living before undesirable habits are formed.

Education in the nursery school does not call for the early acquisition of

specific skills but it does take into consideration every phase of child development—physical, mental, emotional, and social.

Education in the nursery school stresses a twenty-four-hour educational program for children in which parents and school share equally the responsibilities for the complete development of the child. It is believed that the demonstration of this wider scope for education is influencing educational procedures with all children and that the result will be a better understanding and adjustment of the individual to life and society.

The nursery school is dealing with the individual at the most formative period of life. Since social and material environment is ever changing and our concepts and understandings of it can never be complete, it is desirable that the program shall never become set, finished, or crystallized and that studies and experimentation may continue.

QUESTIONS

1. How does the nursery-school program differ from the kindergarten or primary program? How does it differ from the child's day at home?

2. Why is so much emphasis now being placed on early childhood education?

3. Of what significance is it that the nursery-school program considers the child's twenty-four-hour day?

4. Of what value to the child is play with children who are at his own stage of development?

5. In what ways does nursery-school equipment differ from the provisions for a young child at home?

6. What nursery-school ideas can be adapted to home use?

7. Why is it difficult to provide at home the advantages in social experiences which a nursery school offers?

8. What are the various advantages to the mother of sending her children to a nursery school?

9. How does a child benefit by having the teachers and the parents mutually informed regarding his program?

10. How can you interest the parents of your child's playmates in getting better educational facilities for the children of your community?

READING REFERENCES

BOOKS

Baruch, Dorothy W., *Parents and Children Go to School* (Scott).

Blatz, William E., and others, *Nursery Education; Theory and Practice* (Morrow).

De Lissa, Lillian, *Life in the Nursery School* (Longmans).

Foster, Josephine, and Mattson, Marion L., *Nursery-School Education* (Appleton-Century).

Johnson, Harriet M., *Children in the Nursery School* (Day); and *School Begins at Two* (New Republic).

Poppleton, Marjorie, and Blatz, W. E., *We Go to Nursery School* (Morrow).

BULLETINS AND PAMPHLETS

Association for Childhood Education, Washington, D. C., *What Is a Nursery School?*

National Committee on Nursery Schools, *Minimum Essentials for Nursery School Education* (National Committee on Nursery Schools, Washington, D. C.).

U. S. Department of the Interior, Office of Education, *Preparation for Teachers of Nursery Schools, Kindergarten, and Primary Grades* (City School Leaflet No. 31). The problem from the standpoint of the school.

University of Iowa, Extension Department, *Preschool Equipment* (Extension Bulletin No. 263, University of Iowa, Iowa City).

THE KINDERGARTEN AND THE CHILD

Miriam H. Brubaker

The kindergarten, like the nursery school, fills a real need in the life of the child. In communities where there are no kindergartens, parents can, through co-operative effort, provide many of the advantages of the kindergarten. The author has directed the Nursery School and instructed in Nursery School and Kindergarten Education at the National College of Education, Evanston, Illinois. In this article she discusses the growth and the purposes of the kindergarten and tells parents what they may do for the child who does not go to kindergarten.

WHAT is a kindergarten? The term means literally "child garden," a name given by Friedrich Froebel to the school for young children which he founded. The history of the kindergarten movement is interesting because the principles upon which it was built show their influence more and more in the education of today.

History of the Kindergarten

Froebel was a young German who lived a century ago. He held the idea that school practices of that time did not take into consideration the importance of the preschool years, and he urged that mothers and nurses play with the young child and give him much attention.

Froebel believed that through play and activity the child found himself. As this idea was developed, he organized a school for children from two to six years of age which was free from formal education and rigid discipline. Courtesy, helpfulness, and social living together were emphasized. He evolved play materials, called "gifts," which consisted of yarn balls and a set of blocks cut in balls, cubes, oblongs, triangles, and so on.

A Locomotive Built by Four-Year-Olds

Such crude materials as boards, boxes, and barrels offer many possibilities for construction.

Other handwork materials, called "occupations," consisted of lentils, sticks, sewing cards, and similar materials. Through the symbolic use of these gifts and occupations Froebel planned that the children might learn something of themselves and of the universe and also have an opportunity for self-expression. Songs, stories, and games were a regular part of the program, but all these contained symbolism and a certain degree of mysticism.

201

Photo: University of Chicago Laboratory Schools

A WELL-PLANNED KINDERGARTEN ROOM

A large, sunny room, with low shelves around the walls and with tables and chairs of the right size for young children, makes an ideal place for carrying on kindergarten activities.

Kindergartens very soon began to spread throughout Germany, although Prussia, for a period of ten years, forbade their existence because Froebel's ideas seemed revolutionary. Among the wealthier classes in England kindergartens began to appear, but in general the "infant schools," which were planned for children of working parents, especially in industrial centers, were more prevalent. These infant schools were modified formal schools which had little in common with the kindergarten.

France had a few kindergartens, but in the United States and Switzerland the democratic principles upon which Froe-

bel based his system of education made an appeal and the kindergarten movement spread very rapidly.

The first kindergarten in America was established in Watertown, Wisconsin, in 1855. Mrs. Carl Schurz, a pupil of Froebel's, was its founder and teacher, and she carried on the work in this German-speaking community. This kindergarten was largely for Mrs. Schurz's own children and was conducted in her own home. The first kindergarten established in an English-speaking community was in Boston in 1860. The city of St. Louis opened a public-school kindergarten in 1873 which was conducted by Susan

Blow. Many kindergartens appeared following the Centennial Exposition at Philadelphia in 1876, for at that time an exhibit of kindergarten materials created great interest and comment. In 1880 there were about four hundred kindergartens in the United States, most of them being of a philanthropic nature. Today, kindergartens are found in nearly all countries.

At first the kindergarten was not a part of the public-school systems, nor is it today considered by many school boards as an integral part of education. The kindergarten was a detached unit of education, partly because of its symbolism, idealism, and mysticism. There was no connection between the kindergarten curriculum and the program of the primary grades. Kindergarten teachers themselves held aloof and considered that they were different from other teachers. There was a need for a change in principles before the kindergarten could be considered the first round of the educational ladder. Realistic experiences had to take the place of symbolism.

With a continued study of the child and a greater understanding of his nature there came a modification of kindergarten procedure. G. Stanley Hall, Francis W. Parker, John Dewey, and Patty Smith Hill were the educators who were influential in bringing about these changes. Their methods were based on sound psychological principles. The theory of the informal program, the idea of learning through doing, and the realization that there must be opportunity for activity of body as well as of mind have all helped to make changes in the

program of the primary grades in thousands of public schools today. By a sympathetic understanding of both fields and by basing the education of young children on scientific studies, there has

A SUMMER PLAYHOUSE

This playhouse was made by four- and five-year-old children in their back yard.

come about a closer relationship between the kindergarten and the first grade.

COMPARISON OF OLD-TIME AND MODERN KINDERGARTENS

The kindergarten of twenty years ago and that of a progressive modern school provide an interesting comparative study. The play materials in the old kindergarten were small and were supposed to be used in logical sequence. Blocks were an inch square or were cut in various forms from an inch cube. Pegs, made to fit into small pegboards, were an inch in length and smaller than an ordinary match in thickness. There were small beads to string, cards with outlines to be sewed with yarn, paper mats to weave in intricate designs. The use of fine muscles, which made for strain and tension, was evident in practically all the children's activities. Songs were long and often sentimental and included a great deal of story element. The stories told had obvious morals, which were supposed to influence character. Games were complicated and formal, requiring teacher direction. Symbolism was present in all activities.

The rooms in which the kindergarten was housed were often dark and also inadequate as to floor space. Equipment was meager and the groups were large. Children were herded together in utter disregard of the principles of hygiene.

The teachers were not adequately trained, for there was not then the wealth of scientific information that is available today. "A love for children," perhaps a smattering of kindergarten practice, and a brief study of philosophy were the requirements for kindergarten teaching. Teachers were often women of culture and fine background, who carried on a noble work, giving generously of their time and money. These women also acted as social workers in their neighborhoods. Some work with parents was carried on, but this was incidental and usually in regard to discipline.

Compare the above situation with the modern kindergarten. The teacher must have not only a love for children but she must meet certain requirements as regards culture and education. Personality, adaptability, and emotional balance, as well as a knowledge and scientific understanding of children, must be part of the kindergarten teacher's equipment.

In modern schools the largest and sunniest room usually is given over to the kindergarten. Proper and adequate toilet facilities are accessible and well-planned outdoor space is available. All equipment and materials are selected with the child's all-round development in mind. Play materials are large, thus avoiding muscle strain and fatigue. They are selected for the purpose of promoting social growth and social consciousness as well as for individual development. Some materials assist mental growth, others promote physical activity and a gain in muscular control. Creative effort and independent thinking and learning are encouraged.

The modern kindergarten teacher fits the program—which is flexible—to the needs of the children. She is not bound by a time schedule. If the children need vigorous activity, she provides for it. In the event of a sudden interest, such as a passing balloon man, a fire truck, or the arrival of a pet, discussion ensues—the children are not asked to wait until the "language period" to talk about something that interests them. There is definite planning for balance between quiet and active pursuits, between individual and group enterprises, and between indoor and outdoor play. The atmosphere is one of harmonious living; each day is rich and full and sufficient, not merely preparation for a stage that is to come. Studies show that kindergarten training lays a foundation for the school experience that follows; its greatest value, however, lies in what it does for the child in its own special sphere.

The kindergarten of today no longer plans its curriculum weeks in advance nor does it try to cover every subject within the possible range of a child's interest, for, as John Dewey says, "this means danger of the mental habit of jumping rapidly from one thing to another." The new procedure provides the child with simple experiences and affords him, whenever possible, firsthand contacts. Scheduled periods are avoided. Hundreds of individual projects are carried on, but frequently units of work which interest several children and sometimes the entire group are in progress. These activities are often suggested by the children, but may be initiated by the teacher through environmental settings and suggestions, thus bringing about new interests.

Records of the child's growth are kept so that the teacher can make a scientific and thorough study of the child—physically, mentally, emotionally, and socially —and so that she, in turn, can help the parent to a better understanding of the child through these records. The child himself thus benefits immeasurably, since both parent and teacher can work more intelligently for his good by studying and making use of the concrete data gathered.

These records serve as a point of contact for parent education, for conferences, parent meetings, and for child-study classes. The modern kindergarten urges parents to visit the school, which is a different attitude from that held some years ago when mother and father came to school only in case of "trouble."

The aims of the progressive type of kindergarten may be briefly stated as follows:

1. To provide an environment where the setup, materials, and companions are suited to the child's needs.

2. To provide expert guidance—a factor not found in unsupervised neighborhood play.

3. To help the child to develop individually to the best of his ability without losing sight of the fact that he is a member of a social group where he must at times subordinate self for the good of the whole group.

4. To provide for the child a happy day full of worth-while experiences.

WHAT THE HOME CAN DO FOR THE PRESCHOOL CHILD

One of the chief values of kindergarten experience is the social living together and regularity of schedule which such a school affords. Many executives and school boards are not aware of the advantages of this phase of education, and until the preschool child is given as much consideration as the grade-school child, the home must supplement and enrich the child's life.

SOCIAL OPPORTUNITIES

Children of three, four, and five are gregarious little creatures and long for companionship. Adults may offer a fair substitute for younger playmates, but it is human nature for grownups to make allowances for the child and let him have the advantage of the situation.

His whims, his personality, his lack of experience, the fact that he is so young, or even his tears or tantrums may sway adults to his way of thinking or doing. This is not good for him, for he does not learn sportsmanship nor does he learn to take defeat and disappointment manfully, which is fundamental in the building of strong character.

Adults do not have the time, the same interests, or the same sort of play spirit and imagination that children have. Often the adults have developed inhibitions. Mother becomes self-conscious and makes excuses when four-year-old Jack wants her to be the bear at the zoo, so that he can throw peanuts to her. She does not feel comfortable pretending to be the "ticket taker" on the improvised train while son is the stalwart engineer or the conductor shouting, "All aboard!"

Children *need* children for their play, and it behooves most mothers to make the effort to have children of the same age get together for play every day or a few times a week. While constant supervision by the mother is not necessary or even desirable, the children should feel that there is an interested, sympathetic person to whom they can

Photo: Marshall Field School for Children, Chicago

A KINDERGARTEN GROUP ABSORBED IN PICTURE BOOKS

Children of the kindergarten age like to look at picture books, and this activity is encouraged in every way, since it is one of the preliminary stages of learning to read.

go with their joys as well as their problems.

The mother must take the place of the kindergarten teacher in acting as friend, adviser, or counsellor of the group. Social groups need rules in order that individual as well as group rights may be recognized. If children feel that they have a voice in creating their own rules as occasion demands, they are more likely to abide by the rules.

Sometimes a "council" may be held to decide what punishment shall be meted out to an offender, but only the mother is competent to settle, finally, any questions of discipline. Children are quite likely to be drastic and sometimes cruel in their ideas of how others should be disciplined. Problems are bound to arise, but if they are handled justly, so that the child realizes that he has brought the discipline upon himself, he will learn to think before he acts.

The mother in whose home the group is playing must learn to view her child objectively. This is difficult for most mothers, but if the child is to receive the greatest benefits from his association with others and learn to stand on his own feet, he must be "one of the crowd" and must not rely on mother to shield him and fight his battles. An impartial attitude must be maintained, for the members of the group will not tolerate favoritism. Even very young children are quick to resent unfair tactics and discrimination.

THE AGE RANGE

A wide age range always makes for trouble, and that is why, in progressive schools, the kindergarten is divided—the four-year-olds in one group and the five-year-olds in another. Five-year-olds are ready for more complex organization in work than are children a year younger. Their play is of a co-operative nature as they plan who will be the grandmother, the storekeeper, or the passenger on the airplane. Interest is more sustained, play is more complicated, imagination more vivid, and details are decidedly on a higher plane than at the four-year level. Four-year-olds can be great nuisances to their older companions. Their interest is shorter in span and their attention is usually diverted more easily. Their lack of experience gives them less background to see the possibilities in the use of materials, and because they are not socialized they want to be the important persons in any play activity—a situation which usually makes for friction.

Above all, the four-year-old child needs almost unlimited space and opportunity for vigorous activity. He is often an awkward, impulsive, strenuous little person who offers many problems. He has grown out of the highly individualistic stage of babyhood and yet has had so little experience in dealing with others that he has not become socially adjusted. As one kindergarten teacher has said, "Four-year-olds belong in a ten-acre field with a ten-foot fence—then turn them loose." It is an intensely interesting age, but unless the mother has understanding it is a perplexing time.

While it is not possible for the neighborhood group to be divided exactly as in a modern school, it is advisable to keep the range within two or, at the

KINDERGARTEN CHILDREN PLAYING FIREMAN

Fire engines and the activities of firemen are intensely interesting to young children. They often build a fire engine and dramatize the firemen's activities with the seriousness of reality.

most, three years. The seven- or eight-year-old who joins the group will tend to dominate and spoil the fun. The child below four will not only be in the way but will be overstimulated and show ill effects from the contacts.

CHILDREN'S PLAY
THE PLACE TO PLAY

Just as in a good progressive school discipline problems are at a minimum when children are occupied, so in the home plans must be made to keep children busy at worth-while pursuits. This necessitates the provision of space which the children may consider their territory. If they feel that their rights will not be infringed upon as long as they stay in the space allotted them, there will be greater happiness for everyone in the household.

Children should learn early in life that adults have certain privileges and that in every home there are rooms or places that are not for the children to play in. Why should the grand piano be used as a workbench, the kitchen table as a setting for a block village, or the living-room rug as a yard for railroad tracks? Some persons interpret this freedom as self-expression on the part of the child instead of making him realize that all the world is not his to play in as he pleases and when he pleases. The result of such liberty in the home is license rather than freedom, for human beings are free only within limits. The child should be taught consideration of others. If the dining-room or a bed-room is to be the play place, have an understanding with the children from the beginning that this one room is theirs and that materials and activities may not be scattered over the entire house. A cluttered house is a poor object lesson for children and will not make for good social habits or an orderly mind. The child's physical environment has a distinct influence on social and mental traits. Ample shelf space and a designated place to play should be the right of every child.

One interested mother who lived in an apartment, in considering how little time was spent in the dining-room of her home, decided that it would be wise to convert it into a playroom while her children were going through the pre-school years. Meals for the family were enjoyed in a sunny corner in the kitchen. When guests were present dinner was served from a large, attractive gate-leg table in the living-room.

If the house or apartment is small, the dining table may be kept against one wall so that the children may have floor space in which to build. Little children naturally demand space, and if denied it they may develop surly dispositions and "jangled" nerves.

Thought must be given to out-of-door play places as well, for just as the modern kindergarten plans a program of balanced indoor and outdoor play, so should the mother think of outdoor activity. Crude materials, such as boards, boxes, a barrel, a stepladder, or a swing made out of an old automobile tire offer worlds of play possibilities. (See "Indoor and Outdoor Games," in Volume Eleven.)

Expensive playground equipment is not necessary and does not offer the creative type of play that flexible waste materials suggest. What child does not love an old piano box playhouse that he can paper and paint? It is far more interesting to him than a ready-made playhouse. A good wagon or two, a tricycle, a scooter, roller skates, durable spades for digging—all add fun to the day. An improvised sandbox, made of four planks held by stakes at the corners, will be an incentive for building castles and tunnels. Many parents make the mistake of filling a sandbox almost to the top and then complain because the sand is scattered about. A box made of planks ten inches in depth and five or six feet in length, with sand half way to the top, is satisfactory.

Old boards and boxes that can be used for manual work—the building of a shack, a train, or a wagon—are desirable. Such equipment is a fine outlet for excess energy and has value from the standpoint of co-operative planning. Flimsy tools are neither safe, usable, nor economical. Remember that this type of activity is the kind that the modern teacher of young children values greatly, for it teaches sound social principles, requires clear thinking, involves problem solving, and puts the *whole* child to work.

Handwork in the kindergarten formerly required fine muscle adjustment and often caused strain and tension. The

Photo: National College of Education

A CO-OPERATIVE VENTURE IN SHIPBUILDING

Boats of any kind are fascinating to young children. This kindergarten group has co-operated in constructing an ocean liner which provides a motive for many hours of dramatic play.

creative activity and effort that go into handwork rather than a well-finished product that is pleasing to adult standards are the goal today. Interest, effort, and a growing sense of doing the job better today than yesterday give evidence of development. In the old type of kin-dergarten the highlight of the day was when the child went home with some bit of flimsy paper construction—a basket, perhaps, which the teacher had planned, directed, and often "touched up" to make Robert's efforts look more nearly perfect. That type of thing was of little value. Robert did not plan and often was not interested in the task; and of what use was the basket when it was finished? It was too fragile to play with, and, as a result, it furnished him with an excuse for tearing it up.

THE MATERIALS TO USE

Materials for indoor play should be carefully selected, for they are the tools the child will use to develop mental habits, attitudes, tastes, and skills. How can a child be expected to become dexterous with his hands if he has no materials to work with? Of course, he goes through a period of experimenting—merely handling and manipulating—but he should pass from this stage into one in which he is no longer merely pulling, pushing, and carrying his toys but is actually using them in a constructive or a dramatic way. With art materials —paints, crayons, paste, paper, and clay —he evolves from the manipulative into a symbolic stage, where his achievement may not be discernible to the adult, but if it has meaning for him it is an outlet for the expression of his ideas. (See "Art," in Volume Nine.) From this he progresses to the realistic stage, where he tries to make his pictures, his clay objects, his block building, and so on as true to life as he can. Blocks are quite essential to the happiness and growth of the preschool child. Any local carpenter can saw two-by-fours into various lengths which will make satisfactory blocks for home use. Sheets of cardboard or parts of corrugated boxes make good roofs.

Durable steel trucks, especially those with mechanical features, such as dump trucks and cranes, suggest dramatic play. This type of toy has possibilities for many years and is an excellent investment. Wooden animals found in the toy shops will add to the fun of farm play or circus play. (See "Dramatic Play," in Volume Eleven.)

Dolls and housekeeping toys, such as dishes, doll clothes, furniture, a' stove, an egg beater, or a telephone, will encourage play of domestic activities, and at this level boys are almost as interested in this type of thing as are girls. Parents should not tease or shame boys who enjoy playing house.

Any child is challenged by a scarcity of material, so it is well to keep in mind that a few carefully selected toys are better than a mass of materials. Give the child plenty of castoffs—boxes, bags, bits of string, empty spools, jar tops, and illustrated magazines. Encourage him and his playmates to make things out of these waste materials and then praise his attempts, making suggestions from time to time to show him how he can improve his product or see new possibilities in it.

If the following principles are kept in mind in selecting toys or materials the result will be happier and more purposeful children:

1. Toys and materials should have a "do-with" feature and should be usable in a variety of ways in order to encourage creative activity.

2. They should not merely amuse but should promote activity on the part of the child and lead to further activity.

3. They should be durable (wheels and pedals that will not come off; dolls'

heads that are not too easily broken).

4. They should be appealing to the child (attractive in color and form).

5. They should be simple and should promote the use of large muscles.

6. They should stimulate sociability as well as individual play.

7. They should be sanitary and easily cleaned.

Photo: Institute of Child Development, Teachers College, Columbia University

ART MATERIALS OFFER A MEANS OF SELF-EXPRESSION

Large sheets of paper tacked to the fence allow great freedom in art expression.

8. They should require little or no help from the adult in their use. Materials needing adult supervision or help are beyond the child's level of ability.

NATURE EXPERIENCES

The mother whose home becomes the play center for neighborhood children will greatly enrich the children's lives by bringing nature materials to their attention. The children of nursery-school and kindergarten age are eternal question marks. They are eager to explore and learn about the world they live in. A canary, fish, turtles, guinea pigs, rabbits, moths, butterflies, caterpillars, birds' nests, insects, gardening on a simple scale, water play, and soap-bubble blowing are phases of nature education well within the scope of young children's interests. Understanding one's environment makes for security, and if the little child can develop an interest in, and appreciation of, nature, his fears will be fewer and life will be of greater interest to him. (Volume Ten is devoted to nature experiences that are suitable for children.)

EXCURSIONS

If only the busy mother will take time from her daily round of tasks to take the group on an excursion now and then she will feel well repaid. Visiting a farm, a store, a zoo, a dairy, an airport, going to the woods or to the beach, or going on a picnic will stimulate thinking and enlarge the child's horizon. A previous discussion as to how one conducts oneself on an excursion will insure the greatest enjoyment.

SONGS, STORIES, AND POETRY

Songs, stories, and poetry should be a part of every child's day. The artistic, the creative, and the imaginative phases of his nature are satisfied and developed through these channels. A few simple songs that are really good music (not sentimental trash as are many of the songs for little children), a repertoire of realistic and imaginative stories, a few of the old folk tales, and well-selected poems make a good foundation for musical and literary tastes. (See Volumes One to Six of Childcraft for an excellent selection of stories and poems.)

If only adults could appreciate the satisfaction that comes from creating one's own songs and stories, they would be more serious about the child's feeble attempts at singing his ideas or telling stories. An interested, sympathetic listener might develop in a child a greater

Suitable Handwork for the Kindergarten Age

Handwork that calls into play the large muscles of the body is far more suitable for young children than the old-time activities which required fine muscle adjustment.

freedom of language ability, clear thinking, increased vocabulary, and joy in being able to create. The world needs more people like Hughes Mearns and Satis Coleman to understand and encourage children's own creations in music and poetry. (See "Creative Verse" in Volume Two.)

When children are learning to sing they go through much the same stages of voice experimentation as they did when learning to talk. They may not, and in many cases will not, sing on the key. Let them sing anyway, for only through singing will they care to sing and learn to sing. Spontaneous performance and not skill is the important thing in a child's early years. Too many adults never resort to singing as an emotional outlet, because at some time in their childhood or youth a teacher made them self-conscious about their voices.

A mother with just a little ingenuity can help children to make simple instruments, such as oatmeal box drums, rattles of various kinds (pebbles in a cardboard carton or gourds, in which the seeds have dried). A cheesebox or a chopping bowl with a drum skin (or even linen) stretched tautly and then shellacked makes an excellent drum. (See "Music," in Volume Nine.)

COOKING EXPERIENCES

Can you recall the days when mother let you have a wad of dough as she was baking bread or cookies? Do you remember that dingy little piece of piecrust you so carefully rolled out? It was fun, wasn't it? The modern mother does not let children have enough of this kind of experience, and so the modern kindergarten plans for simple cooking experiences in its curriculum.

The first thing might be a lump of cooky dough already mixed, for it is the rolling, patting, playing with it, and finally cutting it that provide the fun. Later on the children may share in putting the ingredients together, but at first this is too long-drawn-out a process to be of vital interest. The making of simple sugar cookies decorated with small cinnamon "red hots," the making of gingerbread boys, with candies or currants for features and buttons, and the washing and cutting up of apples for applesauce are all possibilities in introducing the child to culinary arts. Making grape jelly or cranberry sauce, preparing sandwiches of various kinds, shelling peas, and breaking up string beans are also fun and are simple chores to manage. As a special treat, uncooked fondant—with nuts, cherries, or dates to decorate the pieces—will keep children busy for a long time. Through cooking experiences they gain an understanding of how things are made. Sometimes a child may become interested in a certain food (for which he has previously expressed a dislike) through helping to prepare it—cutting up the spinach with scissors, beating the eggs, stirring the pudding, or cutting pineapple, grapefruit, or oranges with scissors. (See "Cooking and Sewing," in Volume Eleven.)

HABITS TO BE DEVELOPED

In all dealings with young children it should be kept in mind that they are in the formative period and that guidance in building habits that will be an asset in adult life is important. (See "Children and Their Habits," in Volume Eight.) Habits of orderliness are essential. Children will have more pleasure in play materials when the mother teaches care and orderliness.

In a progressive kindergarten the teacher guides and helps the children in putting away their playthings until they learn where things belong. As the children learn the care and proper use of materials and tools, more responsibility is placed upon them. Paper scraps, sticky paste brushes, spilled sand, and used cooking utensils are theirs to care for.

Do not overload the playroom or play corner with too much, however, or the task will be so great that the child's sense of responsibility will be discouraged. Rotate the play materials and hold in reserve for rainy days such experiences as blowing soap bubbles, cooking, or water play in the bathtub or washtub. There are times when it is advisable to leave block constructions to carry over to another day. If interest is high and possibilities have not been exhausted, the chances are that the children will go back to their play with fresh interest.

Other desirable habits to develop at this level include the following:

Physical Habits. Caring for wraps; proper use of the toilet and washing of hands after going to the toilet and before eating; proper use of the handkerchief, especially in covering coughs and sneezes; wiping rubbers and galoshes before entering the house; and regularity of schedule as regards eating, rest, and elimination.

Social Habits. Learning to say "Please" and "Thank you" without adult nagging; answering when spoken to; picking up one's own materials; helping others in any way possible; settling difficulties without using force; and gaining in frankness and honesty but always with a spirit of kindness.

Emotional Habits. Controlling tears and temper outbursts; taking bumps and other minor injuries without undue fuss; letting mother leave the house without making a scene; accepting criticism when due without upheaval; developing a sense of humor; and overcoming fears. (Fears are overcome by wise guidance on the part of the adult. Removal of support, sudden motion, and loud sounds are the only inherited fears; all others come to the child through unpleasant experiences.)

Mental Habits. Trying to solve one's own problems (unless the solution is far too hard), asking help only when really needed; and gaining in powers of observation, concentration, self-reliance, adaptability, initiative, effort, and persistence.

WHEN MOTHER NEEDS TO STEP IN

Just as the skillful, artistic teacher knows when to take a hand and use her influence with the group, so should a mother study play situations and find her place. The following suggestions may indicate when she is needed:

1. When emotional pitch is high and a quarrel is about to ensue.

2. When an individual or the group are discouraged with something they are trying to make or do.

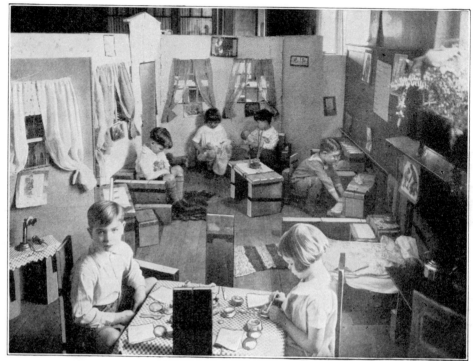

PLAYING HOUSE

At the kindergarten age boys are almost as interested in playing house as girls are. These kindergarten children have furnished one corner of their room as a house and are carrying on many kinds of domestic activities.

3. When the technique or way of doing things is beyond the child's ability.

4. When materials are unsuitable or inadequate.

5. When too many children are trying to work on one thing or when work is being carried on in too limited a space.

6. When the repetition of an activity ceases to be valuable.

7. When a child can find nothing to do that is of value to him or to the group.

8. When the play is of a detrimental nature (as in playing war or robbers).

9. When they need help in organization.

10. When physical welfare or moral well-being is at stake.

11. When habits need redirection.

The mother needs to be in the background but she should never dominate the play. When she feels that the time is right for her to make suggestions she should do so, but a true test of whether or not she has gone too far is seen when she slips out again. If the group carries on without her she may compliment herself on her success. If the activity goes to pieces it may mean that she has given too much direction and that the children were not ready for her contributions. Sometimes the group is ready for a change of activity and no matter what subtle or worth-while suggestions may be made the children will not respond. There, again, is the adult's obligation to change the type of activity in which the children are engaged. A romp out-of-doors or a restful stretching out on the floor may be the next step.

SAFEGUARDING CHILDREN'S HEALTH

If children are gathered together in any group, be it in nursery school, kindergarten, Sunday school, play clubs, neighborhood groups, or parties in the home, the teachers or parents in charge must be on the alert for any signs of sickness, even symptoms of a common cold. Many diseases of childhood begin with running noses, watery eyes, and fever. A child with any of these symptoms should be excluded from the group. Some parents think the modern school is unduly fussy for carrying out such a policy, but the protection offered to every child is usually appreciated in the end. This is the only way to keep contagion at a minimum.

PLAY GROUPS VERSUS KINDERGARTENS

Though play groups under the guidance of a wise mother are desirable where public education does not offer opportunities to children of four and five years, it is to be remembered these groups are *not* kindergartens. The space, the development of materials to meet growing needs, the development of the curriculum in order to insure the best possible growth of the individual as well as of the group, and the study and correction of behavior problems can be offered only in a well-organized, well-equipped, and well-staffed kindergarten. Recent studies and statistics have shown the value of kindergarten training, not only as a foundation for later school life but for enriching the child's life today. The kindergarten builds patterns of behavior and develops character traits in the child that will enrich his life and make him valuable to society. Kindergarten training for every child should be devised by every community, but until that wish is realized, a conscientious and interested mother can herself help to make the preschool years rich and full for her children and for other children in the neighborhood.

SUMMARY

A kindergarten is made up of a group of four- or five-year-old children, who, under the guidance of a well-trained teacher, are working and living together in an environment planned especially for them and their needs. The room, the materials and equipment, the program, and the curriculum are selected with the child's best growth in mind. Close cooperation between the home and the school is an important phase of kindergarten education.

All children do not have the advantage of going to kindergarten and therefore mothers need to make special effort to provide companions, materials, and experiences that will make for rich, wholesome living at this level.

Just what part the mother must take in guiding the play of children is worthy of serious consideration. The play materials she is to provide should be selected with care and thought, so that her child may have the greatest possible opportunity for developing his mental capacities, his muscular skills, his social needs, and sound emotional balance. Songs, stories, and poetry enrich his life and lead to a wise use of leisure later on; just as working with art materials, wood work, and scrap materials may lead to worth-while hobbies.

The home should plan for simple excursions that will broaden the child's horizon and help him to see new possibilities in his playthings or help him to find interesting things to do. This kind of excursion, which interests and enlightens but does not fatigue or overstimulate, leads to worth-while pursuits and tends to lessen the desire for motion pictures and other less desirable experiences for young children.

The home must ever be on the alert for safeguarding the child's health, although *all* people dealing with groups of young children should be alert to the importance of healthful surroundings and activities. Health habits, as well as those involving wholesome mental hygiene, habits that make for better social living and those that make for clear thinking and character building should be of great concern. Early childhood is the formative period when habits, attitudes, and appreciations are taking root.

Although attendance at kindergarten makes for an easier adjustment to school life and provides a foundation for school activities, its greatest value lies in the fact that it makes for the child's happiness by providing satisfactory outlets for his emotions and his desire for social contacts.

The kindergarten is, in the fullest sense, a challenge to the child's mind and body.

QUESTIONS

1. In what respects did the early kindergarten differ from the modern kindergarten? Why is the program of the kindergarten today so different from that of early kindergartens?

2. How has the kindergarten of today influenced the procedure in the primary grades?

3. What fundamental principles of hygiene are involved in the planning of the modern kindergarten?

4. Of what value are records of individual children?

5. What are the advantages of the kindergarten over an unsupervised play group?

6. What are the chief benefits of kindergarten attendance?

7. Why are child companions necessary to children?

8. In what respects do four- and five-year-old children differ? What are the advantages of keeping a play group within an age range of two or three years?

9. What type of outdoor play material is most desirable?

READING REFERENCES

Forest, Ilse, *School for the Child from Two to Eight* (Ginn).

Foster, Josephine, and Headley, N. E., *Education in the Kindergarten* (American Book).

Garrison, Charlotte G., Sheehy, E. D., and

Dalgliesh, Alice, *Horace Mann Kindergarten for Five-Year-Old Children* (Teachers College, Columbia University).

Minor, Ruby, *Early Childhood Education* (Appleton-Century).